Concepts in Particle Physics

A Concise Introduction to the Standard Model

Concepts in Particle Physics

A Concise Introduction to the Standard Model

V Parameswaran Nair

City College of the City University of New York, USA

World Scientific

NEW JERSEY · LONDON · SINGAPORE · BEIJING · SHANGHAI · HONG KONG · TAIPEI · CHENNAI · TOKYO

Published by

World Scientific Publishing Co. Pte. Ltd.

5 Toh Tuck Link, Singapore 596224

USA office: 27 Warren Street, Suite 401-402, Hackensack, NJ 07601

UK office: 57 Shelton Street, Covent Garden, London WC2H 9HE

Library of Congress Cataloging-in-Publication Data

Names: Nair, V. P., author.

Title: Concepts in particle physics : a concise introduction to the Standard Model /
  V. Parameswaran Nair (City College of New York, USA).

Description: Singapore ; Hackensack, NJ : World Scientific, [2017]

Identifiers: LCCN 2017029780| ISBN 9789813227552 (hardcover ; alk. paper) |
  ISBN 9813227559 (hardcover ; alk. paper)

Subjects: LCSH: Standard model (Nuclear physics) | Particles (Nuclear physics)

Classification: LCC QC794.6.S75 N35 2017 | DDC 539.7/2--dc23

LC record available at https://lccn.loc.gov/2017029780

British Library Cataloguing-in-Publication Data

A catalogue record for this book is available from the British Library.

Typeset by Stallion Press

Email: enquiries@stallionpress.com

To
Dimitra Karabali

Preface

In 2013, when the Higgs buzz was in the air, a number of undergraduate students requested our department for a special topics course on Particle Physics. This is a subject seldom taught at the undergraduate level as a regular course, most of the books available are at the graduate level. After talking with the students, I realized that their interests in such a course are quite varied. A small number of students wanted to know the technical details, many were interested in the concepts and a bit of the history to appreciate where we stand today, some wondered about what the challenges and the unknowns are to see how the subject might evolve. Some of the students were planning to go on to do research in particle physics, but many students wanted to get a general feel for the subject, and why we should feel excited about something like the discovery of the Higgs particle. So the question was, could one put the key concepts together in an appealing way and yet give enough extra tidbits for the students seriously contemplating graduate studies in particle physics? This book is my attempt at designing such a course.

The plan is to give an introduction, primarily based on concepts, to the Standard Model of Particle Physics. But some technical details are necessary (and important), so there is definitely mathematical work involved. This is not a popular science book, neither is this a comprehensive textbook. It is meant for interested students at the senior undergraduate level or starting graduate level.

The book is presented in a somewhat informal lecture style with the topics unfolding in the sequence followed in the course. It starts with some recapitulation of relativity and quantum mechanics which students learn as part of their regular coursework and then builds on it. A number of remark-sections are added to the lectures where some extra material or technical details are presented for the more interested students. There are also remark-sections on the historical development of the subject. The last lecture presents an assessment of the open questions and where the future might take us.

Thanks are due to a number of individuals whose help has been invaluable. First of all, thanks go to the students who attended the lectures, particularly Marcelo Nomura, whose enthusiasm helped to buoy up the class. Professor Dimitra Karabali of Lehman College, my wife and long-term collaborator in research, went through the entire book and made many important suggestions. My distinguished colleague Professor Daniel Greenberger also read through most of the material and made many suggestions, particularly to ensure proper emphasis on important topics. Their work has certainly made this a better book, and I express my gratitude and appreciation.

I also thank Christopher Davies, Low Lerh Feng and Rachel Seah Mei Hui of the World Scientific Publishing Co. for their help.

V. Parameswaran Nair

Contents

Chapter 1

The Standard Model

The Standard Model of particle physics is arguably the most important intellectual achievement of the human race. It describes a number of fundamental particles (fundamental to the best of our knowledge, to date) and their interactions. It is a conceptual and logical structure which is expected to have a very wide range of applicability essentially being the kernel for building up most of physics. And while many details of the phenomena which follow from it are still being worked out, there is good reason to believe that most of the observed results within its expected domain of applicability can be obtained from it. Admittedly, there is evidence for phenomena such as dark matter, which may be beyond the purview of the Standard Model. But as for *observed results* within its expected domain, we do not yet have any evidence for deviations from the Standard Model. This is both good and not so good. The range of observations we have carried out to date stretch from a microscopic distance scale of about 10^{-18} meters to cosmological scales of the order of 10^{26} meters. The Standard Model, including classical Einstein gravity (with a cosmological constant), can account for most of these observations, at least in principle. This is a remarkably good situation, when we recall that at the time of Newton, a little over three hundred years ago, all physics was essentially confined to the terrestrial scales. In fact, one of Newton's great achievements was to realize that the same physics which applies to terrestrial phenomena could also be applied to explain planetary motion and other phenomena at the scale of the solar system. However, the success of the Standard Model is far from complete because there are still many puzzles left, many features of the Standard Model are awkward and it is hard to believe that it is the final theory of the particle interactions, even apart from deeper issues such as quantum gravity and so on. For further progress, we need to push the limits of validity of the Standard Model, until we find deviations from it, so we can improve it and take it to the next level of understanding and explanation. We will talk about the inadequacies of the Standard Model towards the end of this course, but let us begin by accentuating the positive. Here is an immensely successful theory, arguably the most successful theory ever. What does it look like?

Table 1.1 gives a list of all the types of fundamental particles in the Standard Model. There are six species of leptons: the electron (e), the electron-neutrino (ν_e), the muon (μ), the mu-neutrino (ν_μ), the tau (τ) and the tau-neutrino (ν_τ). Of these, the electron is familiar as one of the particles constituting the atoms of all elements. There are also six species of quarks; the names are the up (or up-quark u), the down (or the down-quark d), charm (c), strange (s), top (t) and bottom (b). Protons and neutrons which are the basic constituents of atomic nuclei are bound states of three quarks each, the combination uud for the proton and udd for the neutron. Other combinations of quarks form other particles such as the baryons Σ, Λ, Δ, etc., and mesons. There are a large number of these, but being unstable, most of them do not make it into the matter we know from everyday experience. The quarks and leptons form the set of "matter" particles, so to speak, in the sense that all matter is primarily made of these particles. They are organized into three "generations", with (e, ν_e, u, d) forming the first generation, (μ, ν_μ, c, s) and (τ, ν_τ, t, b) being the second and third generations.

But the quarks and leptons by themselves are not sufficient to make up matter. There should be forces between these particles which help them to bind together and form protons, neutrons, nuclei and atoms. We know from the theory of relativity that nothing can travel faster than the speed of light in vacuum. This means that if we consider two particles with a certain force between them, and we move one of the particles, the other, even though it is bound to the first, cannot respond at least until the time it takes a light signal to go from the first to the second. This ultimately leads to the idea that even the forces between particles must be thought of as caused by the exchange of some particle. In other words, there must be force-carrying particles as well. Of the various force carriers listed in the table, the photon is the quantum of light or the basic quantum of the electromagnetic field. It is responsible for electromagnetic forces, including the binding of electrons to atomic nuclei to form atoms. The graviton is the force carrier for gravity, although we must keep in mind that we do not yet have a quantum theory of gravity. There are 8 types of gluons which are the force carriers for the strong nuclear force. They help to bind the quarks to form nucleons such as the protons and neutrons; they are also ultimately responsible for binding protons and neutrons into atomic nuclei. So they are a very important ingredient of matter. The graviton, the photon and the gluons are massless particles. The gluon is not seen as an isolated particle but many gluons can be bound together to form "glue balls" which are massive particles. Among the remaining force carriers, $W^{\pm}$, Z^0 are responsible for the weak nuclear force, whose most familiar manifestation is the β-decay of some of the atomic nuclei. They are massive particles as well.

Finally, we have the Higgs particle. This is somewhat special. It is responsible for giving masses to many of the other particles, including the quarks, leptons and the $W^{\pm}$, Z^0 and itself, via an effect similar to the Bose-Einstein condensation. Such a particle is necessary to construct a theory of electroweak forces consistent with the requirement of the conservation of probability to arbitrarily high energies. The detection of this particle in

Table 1.1: List of fundamental particles (antiparticles are not separately listed.)

Type	Species			Spin	Electric charge
Leptons	e	μ	τ	$\frac{1}{2}$	-1
	ν_e	ν_μ	ν_τ	$\frac{1}{2}$	0
Quarks	u	c	t	$\frac{1}{2}$	$\frac{2}{3}$
	d	s	b	$\frac{1}{2}$	$-\frac{1}{3}$
Force Carriers	γ (Photon)			1	0
	$W^{\pm}$			1	± 1
	Z^0			1	0
	g (Gluons, 8 types)			1	0
	Graviton			2	0
Condensate	H (Higgs)			0	0

2012 has brought to completion the essential ingredients of the Standard Model. We have arrived at a new watershed in the long journey of trying to understand fundamental interactions, a journey that has taken well over a hundred years. A brief glance at this history is certainly worthwhile.

A century of particle physics

The idea that matter is made of particles, in the modern scientific context, goes back to John Dalton's atomic hypothesis in 1805. (One could argue that the idea of a unit of matter goes back to Democritus in ancient Greece, Kanada in ancient India or to many others in many other ancient civilizations.) But modern particle physics essentially started with the discovery of the electron in 1897 by J.J. Thomson. It was clear (because it was produced from matter under high temperature and electric fields) that the electron is a constituent of the atom, and since it carries a negative electrical charge and atoms are neutral, one could immediately argue that there should be some entity of positive electrical charge in the atom. Experiments on scattering of α-particles by thin gold foils, carried out in Rutherford's laboratory in 1911, in conjunction with the theoretical analysis done by Rutherford himself, made it clear that the positive charge was carried by a central nucleus localized to a size much smaller than the size of the atom. The nucleus also carried most of the mass of the atom, the electron being much lighter. (The electron has a mass of approximately 0.5 MeV, while the nucleus of the lightest element Hydrogen has a mass of approximately 938 MeV.) The atom thus looked more like a miniature solar system, although the compatibility of such a picture with classical electrodynamics was a major issue. (The resolution of this difficulty was one of the key steps in the development of quantum mechanics.) The lightest of all nuclei, that of the Hydrogen atom, could be taken as the new particle of positive charge; this was the proton. The Helium nucleus had a mass approximately 4 times that of the Hydrogen nucleus, but had charge only equal to twice the charge of the proton. This suggested the existence of an additional neutral particle of approximately the same mass as the proton. Such a particle would also give a natural explanation of isotopes. The discovery of the neutron, as this particle came to be called, by J. Chadwick in 1932 confirmed this simple hypothesis.

Now we enter the saga of the mesons. Protons carry positive electrical charge, so they repel each other. How can we then bind them together to form nuclei of higher charge, from Helium with charge equal to 2 in the units of the charge of the proton, to Uranium with charge equal to 92? There had to be an attractive force strong enough to overcome the repulsive electrostatic force between protons. Yet, two faraway protons did not seem to show any evidence of this force. So the putative new force should have a very short range. This led Hideki Yukawa in 1935 to suggest that there should be a massive particle whose exchange created this force and the mass of the particle would explain why the range was short. Based on the size of the atomic nuclei, he estimated that the new particle should have a mass around 250 times that of the electron, something over 100 MeV. Thus it would be a "meson", something of mass between those of the proton and the electron. Cosmic ray experiments by C.D. Anderson and S. Neddermeyer did detect a meson in 1936. However, it turned out that this particular particle had only a very weak interaction with the proton and neutron, ruling it out as the carrier of a nuclear force which could overcome the electrostatic repulsion of the protons. This particle is what we now call the muon (μ). Yukawa's meson was eventually detected by C.F. Powell's group in 1947; it is now called the pi-meson or the pion (π). There are three types of these, with charges $+1$, -1 and 0, in units of e, the charge of the electron.

Another whole new category of particles, it became clear from the early 1930s, would be needed on theoretical grounds. These are the antiparticles for the known fermions of the day. Dirac's theory of the electron in 1928 led to the idea of the positron as an antiparticle to the usual electron. Although there was some early confusion about whether this could be the proton, it was clear by the year 1930 or so that this would be an as-yet-unseen new particle. Anderson (1932) was able to observe the pair creation of an electron-positron pair by gamma rays in cosmic ray emulsions, confirming Dirac's prediction. The antiproton was discovered in 1955 by E. Segre and O. Chamberlain. Shortly afterwards (in 1956), the antineutron was also discovered by B. Cork.

Today we know that many particles have corresponding antiparticles. This applies to the quarks and leptons, for sure. If we are willing to extend the terminology to include that the particle and the antiparticle may be the same in some cases, then we can say that all particles have antiparticles. Thus the neutral pion is its own antiparticle, while the π^- is the antiparticle to the π^+. The Higgs is its own antiparticle as well.

The 1930s also led to the prediction of neutrinos. The β-type of radioactivity had been known since the turn of the twentieth century. With the discovery of the neutron, it seemed like one could interpret this as arising from the decay of a neutron in the atomic nucleus, with the products being a proton and an electron, i.e., $n \rightarrow p + e^-$. The electron would escape from the nucleus and would be detected as β-radiation. However, this interpretation ran into trouble because energy conservation did not seem to work out: the energy carried away by the electron was less than the energy difference between the parent and daughter nuclei. This prompted Wolfgang Pauli to suggest that there was perhaps another particle among the decay products which escaped detection because it was neutral and hence did not interact significantly with the detector. Enrico Fermi very quickly included this idea in constructing a phenomenological theory for β-decay; he also named this little neutral particle as the "little neutral one" or the neutrino in Italian. Fermi's theory also showed that the neutrino would be a fermion. The decay of the neutron would thus be

$$n \rightarrow p + e^- + \bar{\nu}_e$$

where we use the benefit of hindsight to identify the extra particle as the anti-electron-neutrino. The neutrino was eventually detected by the group led by F. Reines and C. Cowan in 1956. The work by L. Lederman, M. Schwartz and J. Steinberger (1962) showed that there are at least two species of the neutrino, ν_e and ν_μ. (The third one, ν_τ came much later.)

Most of the particles we talked about so far were somehow expected, except perhaps for the electron. Once the electron was discovered, the proton was needed for the neutrality of atoms, the neutron was needed to explain isotopes, and the pion was needed for binding the neutrons and protons into nuclei. The discovery of the muon was somewhat accidental and it was certainly not clear, at least at that time, why the muon was needed from theoretical considerations. The zoo of unexpected particles, however, grew rapidly in the 1950s. The K-meson was originally detected in cosmic rays, but was eventually produced in the laboratory by particle collisions. It carried many names, such as the V-particle and the τ (not to be confused with the lepton τ) and the θ, and the discovery of parity violation (in 1956) confirmed them to be the same, now called K. (Although, in retrospect, there was no reason to think of parity as being sacrosanct, the discovery that it is not conserved was a shock to the world of physicists who had grown accustomed to thinking that nature would respect all spacetime symmetries.) Some of the properties of the K-mesons (or kaons) were understood in the 1950s. They had to have a new quantum number "strangeness" which was conserved by strong interactions but broken by weak interactions. (Eventually this was identified as the net number of strange quarks in the particle.) Soon came the ρ's, the ω, the heavier baryons Δ, Σ, Λ, etc. By the beginning of the 1960s, the number of particles was around 100; it was hard to imagine they were all "fundamental" particles. There were many attempts to classify the particles in some sensible scheme making groups of particles with similar interactions, the idea being similar to the classification of elements in the periodic table by Mendeleev. Even though there was the earlier Sakata model for this, the first successful model was the "Eightfold Way" proposed independently by Murray Gell-Mann and Yuval Ne'eman in 1961. It offered a classification scheme, and a group-theory-based method for relating masses and magnetic moments and even the interactions of many of the particles. The most notable prediction was yet another new particle, the Ω^-, predicted to have a mass of about 1675 MeV. The discovery of the Ω^- with a mass of 1672 MeV in 1964 (by the N. Samios group at Brookhaven) was a real triumph of the Eightfold Way.

With a reasonable classification scheme based on symmetry, the possibility of understanding the particles in terms of a substructure could be contemplated. The quark model for all strongly interacting particles was suggested in 1964 by Gell-Mann and independently by G. Zweig (who called them "aces", a name which did not take hold). Initially it was not really clear whether quarks should be considered real or a mathematical convenience, but by the time of the scaling violation experiments at SLAC in 1969, quarks as fundamental particles had come to stay. At that time, the understanding was that there were three types of quarks, the up, the down and the strange. In this picture,

(1) Every baryon is composed of three quarks (and every antibaryon of three antiquarks) plus a cloud of virtual quark-antiquark pairs and gluons.
(2) Every meson is composed of a quark and an antiquark, plus a cloud of virtual quark-antiquark pairs and gluons.

Quantum field theory is the framework for describing particles and their interactions in a way consistent with the principles of the quantum theory and relativity. There was a parallel development of quantum field theory during all this time. The discovery of parity violation led to the formulation of the $V - A$ theory of weak interactions, by George Sudarshan and Robert Marshak, and elaborated on by Murray Gell-Mann and Richard Feynman, and by J. Sakurai. The development of Yang-Mills theories led to the prediction about the ρ-mesons, but also, more significantly, led to the possibility of a unified electroweak theory. The Higgs mechanism came in 1964. (This mechanism was obtained in the context of superconductivity by Philip Anderson earlier; it was also independently obtained at the same time as Peter Higgs had by R. Brout and F. Englert and by G. Guralnik, C. R. Hagen and T. W. B. Kibble.) Combining the Higgs mechanism with electromagnetic and weak interactions produced a unified theory for the first time since the unification of electricity and magnetism by Maxwell in the 1850s. There were many contributors to various pieces of this theory, with the main work due to Sheldon Glashow, Steven Weinberg and Abdus Salam. The fact that strangeness-changing neutral weak processes are very small led to the prediction of the charm quark, which was detected soon after in the J/ψ particle which is a $c\bar{c}$ bound state. The Kobayashi-Maskawa matrix (elaborating on earlier work by Nicola Cabibbo) and the third generation of quarks came in the mid-1970s. CP-violation, which is a crucial feature in, and the main motivation for, the Kobayashi-Maskawa scheme, had been detected earlier in 1964 by J. Cronin and V. Fitch.

A large number of significant developments have to be omitted unless one writes a whole history of the Standard Model by itself. The renormalizability of quantum field theories, including Yang-Mills theories, the role of symmetries in field theory, understanding the pseudoscalar mesons as (pseudo) Goldstone bosons, the conserved vector current hypothesis, current algebra and nonlinear σ-models, the discovery of neutral currents, the parton model, the anomalies of quantum field theories, the renormalization group and asymptotic freedom all have played an important role in the development of the Standard Model. And, although we did mention some of the experimental work and discoveries, a lot more credit is due to the thousands of experimentalists who have contributed. From small groups of a few people in the early days, experimental groups grew to tens of physicists, to hundreds, to the thousands we find today in each experimental collaboration. Particle accelerators were constructed at great cost and effort, with accessible energies increasing steadily to the present day value of a few TeV (10^{12} eV). Experiments had to be done and redone with greater precision to sort out possibilities and cross-check against various theoretical considerations. Even the negative experiments, which aimed for new results but did not find any, were important in elucidating the theory. For example, there were many searches for free quarks, all of which failed, but led gradually to the appreciation of quark confinement.

So the Standard Model is, in the end, a joint effort by many, many people. Truly, it should be viewed as an achievement of the human race as a whole.

Remark 1.1.
A few words about particle names

Particle names, you may have noticed, are a strange and puzzling assortment. The electron was the first of the particles to be discovered. In the true classical tradition, its discoverer J.J. Thomson named it the electron, after the Greek word "elektron" for amber. After all, static electricity, obtained by rubbing amber, was the first instance of electricity to be investigated. The proton, derived from the Greek word "protos" or the first, had every claim to the name. The proton is arguably the protagonist of any theory of matter, starting with the lightest element, Hydrogen. The neutron was the neutral one, with the neutrino as the little neutral one and the positron was the elision of "positive electron". The meson is "meso" or intermediate in mass between the leptons (light ones) and baryons (the heavy ones). The meson as a name for what Yukawa suggested was fine, until the muon came along uninvited and one had to distinguish it from Yukawa's meson, and the tradition of using Greek letters for the various particles began. But there are only 24 Greek letters and even with the use of capital letters for some particles, it was soon necessary to use Latin letters. Even though the K in K-mesons could pass for the capital kappa, we will find the as and the Bs and the fs and the Ds and so on in the Particle Data Book.

But what of the up quark and the down quark and the strange? In 1932, Heisenberg had noticed the symmetry, as far as nuclear properties are concerned, among isobaric nuclei[1] and had introduced the isospin symmetry which treated the proton and the neutron as two components of a single entity, the nucleon. The theory could be written in terms of an isospin doublet

$$N = \begin{pmatrix} p \\ n \end{pmatrix}$$

allotting the up position to the proton and the down position to the neutron. Later, when the quark model described the proton and neutron as bound states of three quarks ($p = uud$ and $n = dud$ in our present day notation), the main difference between the two was in one of the quarks, so it became conventional to represent the quarks as

$$Q = \begin{pmatrix} u \\ d \end{pmatrix}$$

---

[1]These are nuclei with different charges but (almost) the same mass.

So, in effect, these two quarks got their names for a very mundane reason: The u was in the upper (up) slot and the d was in the lower (down) slot in the conventional way of writing the doublet, that is all.

"There is no excellent beauty that hath not some strangeness in the proportion", so wrote Francis Bacon in his essay *Of beauty*, and chancing upon this in his reading led Gell-Mann to name the property of K-mesons which was conserved in strong interactions but broken by the weak interactions as strangeness. This was inherited by the strange quark when the substructure of the K-mesons was understood. Gell-Mann, a man of greatly eclectic learning, named many other things as well: "quarks" came from "Three quarks for Muster Mark" from James Joyce's *Finnegan's Wake*, the eight noble truths of Buddhism led to the "Eightfold Way". The charm quark, so named by Glashow, needs no explanation. The top and bottom quarks came out of the same way of writing them as an isospin doublet as the up and down quarks. Clearly physicists were running low on new names, although "truth" and "beauty" had a short diffident existence.

The photon goes back to the same classical tradition as the electron, for "phos" is Greek for light. The gluon provides the "glue" binding the quarks into mesons and baryons. The Ws signify they mediate the weak interactions. Z was just the letter used for the field for which it is the quantum in the first set of papers which introduced it.

Remark 1.2.
What are these particles we talk about?

We have given a list of leptons, quarks and the gauge and Higgs bosons in Table 1.1. These are "fundamental" at our present level of knowledge. We mentioned a number of other particles such as the proton, neutron, pion, K-meson, Λ, etc. We also mentioned that we can understand these particles as bound states of quarks, although, for many years, before we had sufficient resolution in experiments to see into their inner structure, these were thought of as fundamental. In any case, since their names will often turn up in our discussion, it is good to have a list of some of the common ones for easy reference. This is given in the baryon and meson tables. The lists are incomplete; there are many other particles which have been detected and analyzed. We have not listed the properties of the particles beyond their masses, charges (indicated by superscripts), spin and parity. Most of these particles are unstable, so their decay modes and decay rates are important. In addition, properties such as magnetic moments are known for some of the particles. Also, for baryons, the antiparticles are not shown. An up-to-date list of particles and their properties can be found in the Particle Data Book, maintained by the Particle Data Group, http://pdg.lbl.gov. For completeness, we start with the masses of the quarks and the leptons and of the $W^{\pm}$, Z^0 and the Higgs particle H. There is a complication for the masses of the quarks because we never find isolated quarks, only bound states. One needs an estimate of the binding energies for these bound states to separate out the mass of the quark as if it were in isolation. This makes the values somewhat imprecise, especially for the low mass quarks.

Table 1.2: Masses of fundamental particles

	u	d	s	c
Quarks	$\approx$2.3	$\approx$4.8	$\approx$100	1275
Mass (MeV)	b	t		
	4650	173.5×10^3		
	e	μ	τ	ν_e
Leptons	0.511	105.66	1776.82	$<0.32\times10^{-6}$
Mass (MeV)	ν_μ	ν_τ		
	$<0.32\times10^{-6}$	$<0.32\times10^{-6}$		
	γ	Graviton	Gluon	$W^\pm$
Gauge bosons	0	0	0	80.385
Mass (GeV)	Z			
	91.1876			
Higgs	H			
Mass (GeV)	125.3			

Table 1.3: A partial list of baryons. p is the familiar proton and n is the neutron. (Spin and parity are indicated in Spin^{Parity} notation.)

	p	n	Λ	Σ^+	Σ^0	Σ^-
Baryons ($\frac{1}{2}^+$)	938.27	939.57	1115.6	1189.4	1192.6	1197.4
Mass (MeV)	Ξ^0	Ξ^-				
	1314.9	1321.3				
	Δ^{++}	Δ^+	Δ^0	Δ^-		
	$\approx$1232	$\approx$1232	$\approx$1232	$\approx$1232		
	Σ^{*+}	Σ^{*0}	Σ^{*-}			
Baryons ($\frac{3}{2}^+$)	1382.8	1383.7	1387.2			
Mass (MeV)	Ξ^{*0}	Ξ^{*-}				
	1531.8	1535				
	Ω^-					
	1672.4					

Table 1.4: A partial list of mesons (Spin and parity for some are indicated in Spin^{Parity} notation.)

Pseudoscalar Mesons (0^-) Mass (MeV)	$\pi^\pm$	π^0	$K^\pm$	K^0	$\bar{K}^0$
	139.57	134.97	493.65	497.67	497.67
	η	η'			
	547.45	957.75			

Vector Mesons (1^-) Mass (MeV)	$\rho^\pm$	ρ^0	$K^{*\pm}$	K^{*0}	$\bar{K}^{*0}$
	768.1	768.1	891.6	896.1	896.1
	ω	ϕ			
	781.95	1019.4			

Scalar Mesons (0^+) Mass (MeV)	$a_0^\pm$	a_0^0	$K_0^*(1430)$	
	982.7	982.7	1429	
	$f_0(975)$	$f_0(1400)$		
	974.1	1400		

Pseudoscalar Mesons with one c-quark (0^-) Mass (MeV)	$D^\pm$	D^0	$\bar{D}^0$	$D_s^\pm$
	1869.3	1864.5	1864.5	1968.8

Pseudoscalar Mesons with one b-quark (0^-) Mass (MeV)	$B^\pm$	B^0	$\bar{B}^0$
	5278.6	5278.7	5278.7

Charmonium Mesons ($\bar{c}c$) Spin^{Parity} Mass (MeV)	$\eta_c(1S)$	$J/\psi(1S)$	$\chi_{c0}(1P)$	$\chi_{c1}(1P)$	$\chi_{c2}(1P)$
	0^-	1^-	0^+	1^+	2^+
	2978.8	3096.9	3415.1	3510.5	3556.2

Bottom-quark Mesons ($\bar{b}b$) Spin^{Parity} Mass (MeV)		$\Upsilon(1S)$	$\chi_{b0}(1P)$	$\chi_{b1}(1P)$	$\chi_{b2}(1P)$
		1^-	0^+	1^+	2^+
		9460.3	9859.8	9891.9	9913.2

Chapter 2

Review of Special Relativity

The theoretical underpinnings for much of what we want to discuss are what are often referred to as the twin pillars of twentieth century physics: the theory of relativity and quantum mechanics. It is not too difficult to see why these are important for particle physics. Most often we deal with particles which have speeds comparable to the speed of light in vacuum so that Newtonian (nonrelativistic) physics is totally inadequate. (To dramatize this by an extreme example, recall that the protons circulating in the rings of the Large Hadron Collider (LHC) travel at 0.999999991 times the speed of light in vacuum.) Further, particle collisions can lead to the annihilation of particles and/or the creation of new particles, both of which rely on the interconversion of mass and energy via the famous Einstein relation $E = mc^2$. So relativity is central to particle physics. In addition, the scales involved in particle interactions are such that quantum effects are not negligible. Let us note that the very concept of a point particle requires the possibility of localizing it to a very small region, otherwise how do we know that it has no extent, and this can be problematic because of the uncertainty relation $\Delta x \, \Delta p \geq \hbar/2$. Thus the picture of a point particle as a little rigid ball of extremely small radius is meaningless, we have to define the concept of a particle via the observables and their algebra of commutation rules in quantum mechanics. Also, quantum fluctuations of observables (which are the hallmark of quantum mechanics) can affect the intermediate states in particle interactions and this too must be taken account of. So quantum mechanics is central to particle physics as well.

We shall review the key ideas of the theory of relativity and quantum mechanics, starting with the former for which the seminal concept is the spacetime metric, so it is appropriate to begin with its definition.

Metrics and Lorentz transformations

The metric is the measure of distance in any given physical coordinate system. In Newtonian mechanics, we are familiar with the distance between two nearby points, say ds, playing a central role in its formulation. For example, for two points which are infinitesimally close to each other, the coordinates in the Cartesian system may be taken as (x, y, z) and $(x + dx, y + dy, z + dz)$, The distance between these two points is given by the Pythagorean theorem as

$$ds^2 = dx^2 + dy^2 + dz^2 \tag{2.1}$$

We can also measure the distance in other coordinate systems by appropriate transformation of coordinates. For example, to use cylindrical coordinates, the transformation of coordinates is

$$x = r\cos\theta, \quad y = r\sin\theta, \quad z = z \tag{2.2}$$

The metric (2.1) expressed in the cylindrical coordinates becomes

$$ds^2 = dx^2 + dy^2 + dz^2 = (d(r\cos\theta))^2 + (d(r\sin\theta))^2 + dz^2$$
$$= dr^2 + r^2 d\theta^2 + dz^2 \tag{2.3}$$

In a similar way, one can introduce spherical polar coordinates by the transformation

$$x = r\sin\theta\cos\varphi, \quad y = r\sin\theta\sin\varphi, \quad z = r\cos\theta \tag{2.4}$$

with the corresponding expression for the metric

$$ds^2 = dr^2 + r^2 d\theta^2 + r^2 \sin^2\theta \, d\varphi^2 \tag{2.5}$$

In the case of a particle moving with some velocity, we may think of the coordinate changes dx, dy, dz as given by the corresponding components of the velocity multiplied by dt, the elapsed time, so that

$$ds^2 = (v_x dt)^2 + (v_y dt)^2 + (v_z dt)^2$$
$$= (v_x^2 + v_y^2 + v_z^2) dt^2 \tag{2.6}$$

The kinetic energy of a particle in mechanics can then be constructed as

$$T = \frac{m}{2}v^2 = \frac{m}{2}\left(\frac{ds}{dt}\right)^2 \tag{2.7}$$

We see that the metric is the key to the definition of the kinetic energy. Recall that the variational principle states that the true classical trajectory for particle dynamics is given by the extremum of the action

$$S = \int dt\, L = \int dt\, (T - V) \tag{2.8}$$

where V is the potential energy. We see that the metric or the distance function plays a crucial role in constructing the Lagrangian $L = T - V$.

However this formulation in terms of the metric for spatial directions alone is inadequate as we approach relativistic speeds. The basic recognition which emerged from Einstein's special theory of relativity (and which was reinforced by the general theory of relativity) is that it is the *spacetime* metric, where space and time are treated on a roughly equal footing, that is relevant for physics. The key entities of interest are "events" which take place at a given point in space at a given time. The infinitesimal distance ds between two such events is given by the *spacetime* metric

$$ds^2 = c^2 dt^2 - (dx^2 + dy^2 + dz^2) \qquad (2.9)$$

where c is the speed of light in vacuum. Notice the relative sign difference between the temporal part and the spatial parts; as a result ds^2 need not have a definite sign anymore. (The overall sign in (2.9) is a matter of convention; a different convention, which is equally acceptable, would be to choose the spatial parts positive and the temporal part negative.) We now have four coordinates (ct, x, y, z) specifying any event and therefore it is useful to develop a 4-vector notation. Just as we write $\vec{x} = (x, y, z)$ as the position vector of a point, we can use $x^\mu = (ct, x, y, z)$ in the present case. Here $x^0 = ct$ is the time-component. In a similar way, we can consider other 4-vectors (with four components), say, $A = (A^0, A^1, A^2, A^3) \equiv (A^0, \vec{A})$. If we have two such vectors A, B, their scalar product will be denoted by $A \cdot B$, given explicitly by

$$A \cdot B \equiv A^0 B^0 - (A^1 B^1 + A^2 B^2 + A^3 B^3) = A^0 B^0 - \vec{A} \cdot \vec{B} \qquad (2.10)$$

The signs are chosen to be consistent with the metric (2.9). Often, it is useful to consider the components of 4-vectors, so we write A^μ where the index μ, or other similar Greek indices such as ν, α, etc. to be used in other expressions, takes the values 0, 1, 2 and 3, corresponding to the time-component and the components along the x, y, z directions, respectively. Further, we can introduce the "metric tensor" $g_{\mu\nu}$ which is a rank-2 tensor since it has two vector-type indices; it may be conveniently displayed as a 4×4-matrix,

$$g_{\mu\nu} = \begin{pmatrix} 1 & 0 & 0 & 0 \\ 0 & -1 & 0 & 0 \\ 0 & 0 & -1 & 0 \\ 0 & 0 & 0 & -1 \end{pmatrix} \qquad (2.11)$$

The scalar product of two vectors with components A^μ, B^ν can be expressed using this tensor as

$$A \cdot B = g_{\mu\nu} A^\mu B^\nu = A^0 B^0 - \vec{A} \cdot \vec{B} \tag{2.12}$$

The spacetime metric takes the form

$$ds^2 = g_{\mu\nu} \, dx^\mu \, dx^\nu \tag{2.13}$$

where $x^\mu = (ct, x_1, x_2, x_3) = (ct, x, y, z)$ is the position 4-vector.

In writing expressions involving 4-vectors or tensors, as in (2.12), (2.13), we adopt the Einstein summation convention. In any expression, it is implied that there is summation over repeated indices. Thus $g_{\mu\nu} dx^\mu dx^\nu = \sum_{\mu,\nu=0}^{3} g_{\mu\nu} dx^\mu dx^\nu$ (because both μ and ν are repeated), $g_{\mu\nu} B^\nu = \sum_{\nu=0}^{3} g_{\mu\nu} B^\nu$ (because only ν is repeated), etc. This takes a bit of getting used to, but after a little while, it will become second nature and it helps to avoid a lot of clutter in writing the formulae.

We have seen that the metric plays an important role in Newtonian mechanics since it determines the kinetic energy as in (2.7). For the same reason, rotations are important because they are the linear transformations of coordinates $(x, y, z) \to (x', y', z')$ such that the metric (2.1) is unchanged. The scalar product derives its importance from the fact that it is unchanged under rotations, which is also traceable to its definition in terms of the metric. The metric is thus seen to be the key to setting up mechanics. The basic principle of relativity upgrades this to the spacetime metric (2.9).

Prop 2.1 (The principle of special relativity). Physics is invariant under the continuous linear transformations (with constant parameters) of the coordinates (ct, x^1, x^2, x^3) which leave the metric $ds^2 = c^2 dt^2 - (dx^1)^2 - (dx^2)^2 - (dx^3)^2$ unchanged.

The statement is approximate in the sense that gravitating bodies modify the metric (2.9). So the principle has to be suitably modified when gravity is included. But for most situations where gravitational effects are negligible, we can use the principle as stated. Also, strictly speaking, the principle only applies to continuous transformations which are continuously connected to the identity. We will comment on this later.

There are discrete symmetries of the metric (2.9) such as parity (which is $\vec{x} \to -\vec{x}$, $t \to t$) or time-reversal (which is $\vec{x} \to \vec{x}$, $t \to -t$). Physics (for example, the weak nuclear force) is not invariant under such transformations. So the restriction to continuous transformations in the statement of the principle of relativity is significant; it is not vacuous.

What are the linear transformations of interest referred to in the principle of relativity? Spatial rotations are certainly some of these since they are already transformations which leave the spatial part $dx^2 + dy^2 + dz^2$ invariant and do not affect the time-coordinate. Thus

$$ct' = ct, \qquad x'_i = R_{ij}\, x_j \qquad (2.14)$$

where R_{ij} are the elements of a 3×3 rotation matrix will give $ds^2 = c^2 dt^2 - dx^2 - dy^2 - dz^2 = c^2 dt'^2 - dx'^2 - dy'^2 - dz'^2 = ds'^2$. The angular parameters in R_{ij} should be constants, independent of the spacetime coordinates.

Lorentz transformations constitute another set of transformations which leave the metric unchanged. For example, consider a Lorentz transformation along the x-direction corresponding to

$$t' = \frac{t - v_x x/c^2}{\sqrt{1 - v_x^2/c^2}}, \qquad x' = \frac{x - v_x t}{\sqrt{1 - v_x^2/c^2}} \qquad (2.15)$$
$$y' = y, \qquad z' = z$$

where the parameter in the transformation, namely, the velocity v_x, is independent of spacetime coordinates. It is easy to check that if we use the primed variables as defined above, $ds'^2 = c^2 dt'^2 - dx'^2 - dy'^2 - dz'^2 = c^2 dt^2 - (dx^2 + dy^2 + dz^2) = ds^2$. There are similar transformations possible for the other directions (along $x_2 = y$ and $x_3 = z$) as well. In writing down these transformations, for brevity, we often use the symbol γ which is defined as

$$\gamma \equiv \frac{1}{\sqrt{1 - v^2/c^2}} \qquad (2.16)$$

The equations for the Lorentz transformation given above are thus

$$t' = \gamma \left(t - \frac{v}{c^2} x \right), \qquad x' = \gamma(x - vt) \qquad (2.17)$$
$$y' = y, \qquad z' = z$$

for choice $\vec{v} = (v_x, 0, 0)$.

The set of all rotations and Lorentz transformations constitute the full set of continuous linear homogeneous transformations of coordinates which leave the metric (2.9) unchanged. (Since the composition of two Lorentz transformations along two different directions will also involve a purely spatial rotation, it is important to consider rotations and Lorentz transformations together. They constitute the Lorentz group. Because all elements of the Lorentz group can generally be referred to as Lorentz transformations, one often specifies the ones involving changes of velocity as Lorentz boosts to distinguish them from purely spatial rotations.) To these, we can also add the constant shifts or translations of coordinates ($x'^{\mu} = x^{\mu} + a^{\mu}$, for constant a^{μ}). These two sets of transformations, namely all the Lorentz transformations (including rotations) and the translations, together form the full set of metric-preserving transformations of the coordinates (which are also continuously connected to the identity). All these transformations together form the Poincaré group.

We introduced coordinates which can be used to characterize the position of a particle. But there are other vectors of interest as well, other than the position vector. For a particle, the next most important vector is the momentum $\vec{p}$. Including the time-component, we must consider the momentum 4-vector given as

$$p^{\mu} = (p^0, p^1, p^2, p^3) \tag{2.18}$$

The square of this vector $g_{\mu\nu}p^{\mu}p^{\nu}$ is invariant under Lorentz transformations and rotations. For a free particle, we can set it equal to some constant which is characteristic of the particle. Thus

$$p^2 = p \cdot p = g_{\mu\nu}p^{\mu}p^{\nu} = (p_0)^2 - \vec{p} \cdot \vec{p} = m^2 c^2 \tag{2.19}$$

The parameter m is identified as the mass of the particle. (This is the so-called rest mass; when we refer to the mass, it will always mean the rest mass.) In the special theory of relativity, we may take this equation (2.19) as the definition of mass, the notion of mass as inertia (or how a body responds to force) being a derived concept. Since p^2 is the same in all frames of reference, we can evaluate it in the rest frame of the particle for which we expect $\vec{p} = 0$. Thus, from (2.19), $p^0 = mc$ in the rest frame. We take the positive sign as we will shortly identify p^0 with the energy. In a frame in which the particle is moving, we can use the inverse of the transformations (2.15)[1] to get

$$p_0 = \gamma(p_0' + vp_1') = mc\gamma$$
$$p_1 = \gamma(p_1' + (v/c)p_0') = mv\gamma \tag{2.20}$$

Here $\vec{v}$ is the velocity of the particle as it is the parameter connecting the frame in which the particle is at rest to the one in which it is moving. So the transformation (2.20) gives the general formulae

$$p_0 = \frac{mc}{\sqrt{1 - v^2/c^2}}, \qquad \vec{p} = \frac{m\vec{v}}{\sqrt{1 - v^2/c^2}} \tag{2.21}$$

---

[1] The transformations (2.15) correspond to the frame of reference moving with velocity v, so that the velocity of the particle viewed in that frame is diminished. To describe the particle with velocity v, we should view the primed coordinates as corresponding to the rest frame.

What is the meaning of p^0, $\vec{p}$? From (2.21) we find $\vec{p} \approx m\vec{v}$ if $v^2 \ll c^2$. Thus we may regard $\vec{p}$ in (2.21) as the fully relativistic generalization of momentum. Since momentum generates translations in space via canonical transformations (or via the quantum mechanical rule $\vec{p}\psi = -i\hbar\nabla\psi$) and since $i\hbar\frac{\partial\psi}{\partial t} = H\psi$ where H is the Hamiltonian (whose eigenvalues are possible energy values) we expect the time-component of the momentum to be related to the energy. We make this more specific identifying

$$p^0 = E/c, \quad \text{or} \quad E = cp^0 = \frac{mc^2}{\sqrt{1 - v^2/c^2}} \tag{2.22}$$

Going back to (2.19), we can also write the energy directly in terms of the momentum as

$$E^2 = c^2\vec{p} \cdot \vec{p} + m^2c^4 \tag{2.23}$$

Massless particles

We know of at least a few types of massless particles, the photon being the best known example. Formulae (2.19) or (2.23) show how this can be realized. Setting m equal to zero, we find $E^2 = c^2\vec{p} \cdot \vec{p}$. In this case, it is not meaningful to use the formulae (2.21) in terms of the velocities. From the relation $speed = \partial E/\partial|\vec{p}|$ (which may be considered as one of the canonical equations in classical mechanics), we see that the speed of propagation of a massless particle is c. Such a particle cannot be brought to rest by Lorentz transformations and so the argument which led to (2.21) does not apply. We cannot characterize the state of a massless particle by its velocity or speed; rather we must specify its momentum $\vec{p}$ with energy given by $E = c|\vec{p}|$.

The photon in terms of frequency

Recall that the electric field of a classical electromagnetic wave has the form

$$\vec{E} = \mathcal{E}_0\,\vec{\epsilon}\,e^{-i\omega t + i\vec{k}\cdot\vec{x} + i\varphi} + \text{complex conjugate} \tag{2.24}$$

where $\vec{\epsilon}$ is the polarization vector, ω is the (circular) frequency and $\vec{k}$ is the wave vector. The direction of $\vec{k}$ gives the direction of propagation of the wave and

$$|\vec{k}| = \frac{2\pi}{\lambda} \tag{2.25}$$

where λ is the wavelength. Further $\omega = c|\vec{k}|$.

In the quantum theory, electromagnetic radiation is described in terms of photons. We attribute an energy $\hbar\omega$ to a photon of frequency ω and a momentum $\hbar\vec{k}$,

$$E = \hbar\omega, \quad \vec{p} = \hbar\vec{k}, \quad E = \hbar\omega = \hbar c |\vec{k}| = c |\vec{p}| \tag{2.26}$$

The relation between the frequency and the wave vector leads to the relation $E = c|\vec{p}|$, which is consistent with the photon being a massless particle. We must also have two independent types of photons corresponding to the two independent polarizations in (2.24). This is something we shall consider in more detail later.

Compton Scattering

Thomson scattering is the scattering of electromagnetic waves by a charged particle as given by classical electrodynamics; it shows no shift in frequency between the incident and scattered electromagnetic waves. Compton scattering refers to the scattering of photons by charged particles. The quantum treatment of light as composed of photons shows that a frequency shift is possible. The discovery of Compton scattering in 1923, with a frequency shift (which agreed with the kinematics of using the particle idea for light), was thus a significant step in confirming the idea of the photon. What we have reviewed of relativity is sufficient to give a simple and neat calculation of the frequency shift, so here it goes.

A photon has momentum, energy and zero mass. This means that for the photon we have the relation

$$p_0^2 - \vec{p} \cdot \vec{p} = m^2 c^2 = 0 \tag{2.27}$$

This is equivalent to $\omega_k^2 - c^2 \vec{k} \cdot \vec{k} = 0$. The momentum 4-vector is defined by (2.26) as

$$p^\mu = (\hbar\omega/c, \vec{p}) \tag{2.28}$$

In considering Compton scattering, we start by asking the question: What is conserved in the collision between the photon and the electron?

We expect conservation of energy (1 equation) and momentum (3 equations) which can be combined into a 4-vector equation

$$p + k = p' + k' \tag{2.29}$$

The notation is that $p = (p^0, \vec{p})$, $k = (\omega/c, \vec{k})$, etc., so that there are actually four equations in (2.29). (One could write it more elaborately as $p^\mu + k^\mu = p'^\mu + k'^\mu$, with $\mu = 0, 1, 2, 3$; but it is simpler to write it as in (2.29) and keep in mind that it is a 4-vector equation.) We will take $p = (mc, 0, 0, 0)$; this choice means that we are taking the initial electron to be at rest. Rearranging the conservation equation given above and squaring both sides gives

$$(p - k')^2 = (p' - k)^2 \tag{2.30}$$

which reduces to

$$p^2 + k'^2 - 2\, p \cdot k' = p'^2 - 2\, p' \cdot k + k^2 \tag{2.31}$$

Squaring means that we take the scalar product of each side with itself using the metric. Thus $A^2 = A^\mu A^\nu g_{\mu\nu}$. We know that $p^2 = p^\mu p^\nu g_{\mu\nu} = m^2 c^2$, $p'^2 = m^2 c^2$, and $k'^2 = k^2 = 0$ since the photon has zero mass. Thus we are left with

$$p \cdot k' = p' \cdot k \tag{2.32}$$

Since $p + k = p' + k'$ by (2.29), we can rewrite the right hand side of this equation as

$$p' \cdot k = p \cdot k + k^2 - k' \cdot k \tag{2.33}$$

Of the various quantities in equations (2.32, 2.33), $p \cdot k' = m\hbar\omega'$, and $p \cdot k = m\hbar\omega$ because we have taken $p = (mc, 0)$. Further $k^2 = 0$, and from the definition of the scalar product of two four-vectors we can write

$$k \cdot k' = k^0 k'^0 - \vec{k} \cdot \vec{k}' = \frac{\hbar\omega\hbar\omega'}{c^2} - \frac{\hbar\omega}{c}\frac{\hbar\omega'}{c}\cos\theta = \frac{\hbar^2\omega\omega'}{c^2}(1 - \cos\theta) \tag{2.34}$$

Here θ is the angle between the direction of the incoming photon and the scattered photon. Using (2.34) and the results for $p' \cdot k$, $p \cdot k$ from (2.33) and substituting it into (2.32), we get

$$m\hbar\omega' = m\hbar\omega - \frac{\hbar^2\omega\omega'}{c^2}(1 - \cos\theta) \tag{2.35}$$

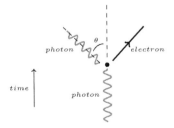

Fig. 2.1: Illustrating the Compton scattering process

which simplifies to the result

$$\omega' = \frac{\omega}{1 + \frac{\hbar\omega}{mc^2}(1 - \cos\theta)} \qquad (2.36)$$

This predicts a frequency shift for the final photon compared to the initial one, since $\omega' \neq \omega$ in general. In the case that $(\hbar\omega/mc^2) \ll 1$ we recover Thomson's original wave theory result without trouble. When is $(\hbar\omega/mc^2) \ll 1$? For a typical photon in the visible range, say, $\lambda = 500\,\text{nm}$, $\hbar\omega \approx 2.5$ eV. Thus, using the value $mc^2 \approx 0.5 \times 10^6$ eV for the electron, $\hbar\omega/mc^2 \approx 5 \times 10^{-6}$, so that the shift is completely negligible. Essentially, we have Thomson's result, $\omega' = \omega$. But, for photons of frequency in the X-ray range with $\hbar\omega \sim$ keV to MeV, $\hbar\omega/mc^2$ is not negligible compared to 1, and hence the frequency shift indicated by (2.36) is observable.

We assumed that the initial electron can be taken to be at rest. The electrons in the actual experiment are atomic electrons bound to the nuclei and hence moving in the electrostatic field of the nucleus. The typical energy for these are of the order of the ionization energies. For the Hydrogen atom, this is ≈ 13.6 eV. The speed of the electron is thus approximately given by $v^2/c^2 = 2(\frac{1}{2}mv^2)/mc^2 \approx 2 \times 13.6/(0.5 \times 10^6)$ which is very small. The assumption of the initial electron being at rest is thus accurate to this order.

Spacetime Symmetries

Recall the metric

$$ds^2 = c^2 dt^2 - \left[(dx^1)^2 + (dx^2)^2 + (dx^3)^2\right] \qquad (2.37)$$

In physics we study transformations that preserve this spacetime metric. The symmetries of this metric can be considered in two different categories.

Continuous Symmetries

- Rotations, with the angles of rotation independent of spacetime.
- Lorentz boosts, with the velocity parameters independent of spacetime.
- $t \rightarrow t + \epsilon$, ϵ independent of spacetime.
- $x_i \rightarrow x_i + a_i$, a_i independent of spacetime.

These are all symmetries of nature. In fact, the basic principle of special relativity may be restated as follows.

Physics is unchanged under the continuous symmetries of the space-time metric

$$ds^2 = c^2 dt^2 - \left[(dx^1)^2 + (dx^2)^2 + (dx^3)^2 \right]$$

which are continuously connected to the identity.

Here the qualification of being continuously connected to the identity is important. These are continuous transformations obtained by a sequence of infinitesimal transformations starting from the identity. These include rotations and Lorentz boosts. We may view a rotation by a finite angle as being made of a sequence of infinitesimal rotations composed together; similarly a Lorentz boost with a finite velocity may be obtained by composing a sequence of Lorentz boosts, each of which has an infinitesimal velocity parameter. There are continuous transformations which preserve the metric (2.37) which are not of this type and under which physics is not invariant. But such transformations can be viewed as transformations connected to identity composed with a discrete transformation like the ones discussed below.

In the presence of gravitating bodies, the spacetime metric is changed. This is the realm of the general theory of relativity. So, if we take account of this, the statement given above is only approximate; we have to qualify it as being valid as long as we are not close to gravitating bodies or if one can neglect gravitational effects, such as would apply to physics in a small region over which the curvature of spacetime is negligible.

Discrete Symmetries

- Parity (P): $x_i \to -x_i$, $t \to t$
- Time-reversal (T): $t \to -t$, $x_i \to x_i$

These are not symmetries of nature in general. The weak interactions do not conserve these symmetries.

Natural Units

Natural units refer to units in which $c = 1$, $\hbar = 1$.

We may regard c as a conversion factor from length measurements to time measurements. Such a factor arose historically because we had independently defined a unit for time and a unit for space, before we realized that they are both of the same nature. Realizing this, we can measure length in seconds, so that the basic unit of length (which is one second) would be 299792458 m if we use the meter as the unit of length. This means that energy, mass, and momentum all have the same units, namely units of energy.

In a similar way, we can think of $\hbar$ as a unit conversion factor, this time between energy units and length, via $length = \hbar c/(energy)$. In natural units, where we set $\hbar = c = 1$, all measurements in physics can be done in energy units. Some examples are:

- electron mass = 0.51 MeV
- proton mass $\simeq$ 938 MeV
- 1 fermi $(10^{-15}\text{m}) = (197\,\text{MeV})^{-1} = 5.076 \times 10^{-3}\,(\text{MeV})^{-1}$
- The charge of the electron has no dimension. Often, the relevant combination which appears in physics is

$$\frac{e^2}{4\pi} \approx \frac{1}{137} = \text{pure number with no dimensions}$$

  The combination $e^2/4\pi$ is called the fine structure constant, often denoted by α_e.
- Newton's constant of gravitation

$$G = \frac{1}{M_{\text{Pl}}^2}, \qquad M_{\text{Pl}} = 1.22 \times 10^{19}\,\text{GeV}$$

  M_{Pl} is known as the Planck mass.
- Temperature, 1 eV $\simeq 1.16 \times 10^4\,\text{K}$

These give us a good feel of various scales in physics. For example, a typical atomic transition has energy ~ 1 eV. We can ask: To what temperature must we heat up a gas so that it will glow via spectroscopic transitions? We need heat that is typically of the order of an eV to compensate for the Boltzmann factor and effect these transitions with non-negligible probability, so we need about 10^4 K.

Chapter 3

Quantum Mechanics and the Propagator

Let us now turn to the other great pillar of twentieth century physics, namely, quantum mechanics. We want to extract the essence of the subject in a few ideas which we can take to the realm of particle interactions. The key concept will be the propagator, which will denote the probability amplitude for a particle introduced at a certain point in spacetime to be detected at another spacetime point. If the particle is subject to interactions, either with other particles or with an externally applied field, all that should be reflected in how this probability amplitude is modified. So the propagator provides a simple and easy language to talk about particle interactions. Also being an idea posed directly in terms of spacetime points, it can be made consistent with relativity in a fairly straightforward way.

But let us start with quantum mechanics in the more familiar Schrödinger formulation and work towards the propagator. In quantum mechanics, to describe the state of a particle you need a wave function, $\Psi_\alpha(x)$, which is the probability amplitude to find the particle at location x if it is prepared in state α. In other words, if you consider a region of volume d^3x around a point x, then the probability of finding the particle in this region is $|\Psi_\alpha(x)|^2 d^3x$. Here α is a set of quantum numbers, needed to characterize the state of the particle completely. For example, a bound electron in the Hydrogen atom has the quantum numbers n (called the principal number), l (related to the square of the orbital angular momentum), m (azimuthal quantum number, the eigenvalue of one of the components of angular momentum) and m_s (spin); thus the label α in this case would stand for the collection n, l, m, m_s. The free particle (with spin) has the quantum numbers $\vec{k}$ (momentum) and m_s (spin).

We also have the standard result that if we prepare a system in state α, the probability amplitude to measure this as being in state β is given by the inner product

$$\langle \beta | \alpha \rangle = \int d^3x \; \Psi_\beta^*(x) \, \Psi_\alpha(x) \tag{3.1}$$

The probability is given by the absolute square of this, namely, $|\langle \beta | \alpha \rangle|^2$. Unitary transformations are operators U which can act on the states (or on the corresponding wave functions) and which obey the condition $U^\dagger U = \mathbb{1}$. A unitary operator may be written in an exponential form as $U = \exp(i\mathcal{O})$ where $\mathcal{O}$ is a hermitian operator. Unitary operators play a special role in quantum mechanics because they preserve the inner product (3.1). So they are the transformations of interest consistent with the conservation of probability.

Observables

In quantum mechanics we are concerned with observables. To carry out any observation, we have to slightly perturb the system we are observing. The response of the system to this perturbation, which may be of infinitesimal strength, is what constitutes the observation. From what we said, any change in a quantum system, consistent with the conservation of probability, is a unitary transformation. So observables can be defined by what leads to the unitary transformation. Because unitary operators may be viewed as the exponential of hermitian operators, the latter will turn out to define observables.

What are the transformations of interest which give us observables? In general, there is an infinity of them, but the most important ones are related to transformations of spacetime. This is not surprising from what we said of the importance of spacetime. The correlation of these transformations with observables is very much the same as they are in classical mechanics. So let us consider a few examples.

- **Translations in position**

    Momentum is the generator of such transformations. We consider the momentum operator

    $$\hat{p}_i = -i\frac{\partial}{\partial x_i} \tag{3.2}$$

    The wave function transforms by being acted on by this operator as follows:

    $$\Psi(x+a) = e^{ia_i \hat{p}_i} \Psi(x) \tag{3.3}$$

Notice that this is consistent with the Taylor series expansion

$$\Psi(x+a) \approx \Psi(x) + a \cdot \frac{\partial \Psi}{\partial x} = (1 + i\, a_i \hat{p}_i)\, \Psi(x) \qquad (3.4)$$

for small a. We may regard $U = e^{i a_i \hat{p}_i}$ as the unitary operator generating the translations in space, with the infinitesimal version given by (3.4).

- **Translations in time**

  Time-translations are generated by the Hamiltonian operator H.

  $$\Psi(x, t+\epsilon) = e^{-iH\epsilon}\, \Psi(x, t) \qquad (3.5)$$

  By a Taylor series expansion, we can express this in differential form as

  $$i\frac{\partial \Psi}{\partial t} = H\, \Psi \qquad (3.6)$$

  This is basically the Schrödinger equation. $U = e^{-iH(t-t')}$ is the unitary operator for translations in time by $t - t'$.

- **Rotations**

  The basic transformation is

  $$x_i \to x_i' = R_{ij} x_j \;\cong\; x_i + \epsilon_{ijk}\theta_k x_j \;+\text{terms of order } \theta^2 \qquad (3.7)$$

  Here R_{ij} is a rotation matrix which may be expressed in terms of the angles of rotation θ_k. For infinitesimal rotations, with infinitesimal angles, we can write $R_{ij} \simeq \delta_{ij} + \epsilon_{ijk}\theta_k$. The action of rotations is expressed in terms of the wave functions by the product of the angular momentum operator and the angles,

  $$\Psi(x') = e^{-i\theta_k J_k}\, \Psi(x) \qquad (3.8)$$

  J_k, $k = 1, 2, 3$, (or $\vec{J}$) is the total angular momentum operator.

- **Lorentz (boost) transformations**

  Just as for the other transformations, we have an operator K_i which will represent the effect of Lorentz transformations on the wave functions,

  $$\Psi(x') = e^{-i\omega_i K_i}\, \Psi(x) \qquad (3.9)$$

  We do not need the explicit form of K_i for most of what we do. The quantity ω_i is related to the velocities of Lorentz boost transformations. For example, if $\vec{v} = (v, 0, 0)$, then $\tanh \omega_1 = v$. For a general transformation, the identification of ω_i in terms of the v_i is more involved.

We have states (or wave functions) and observables. But how do we specify a particular physical system? For example, when we say the Hydrogen atom, those are just words. We need a mathematical characterization in terms of the states, observables, etc. to do a meaningful analysis. To specify a particular physical system, we need to specify a basic set of relevant observables, in terms of which other observables can be given. For a point particle this would mean the position and momentum operators and spin. We must further specify the Hamiltonian as a function of the basic observables, so the time-evolution is clear. (For a system which is more complicated than a point particle, there will be more observables, but the same idea holds.)

Consider an example. When we say we have a free point particle, we mean that the basic observables are $\vec{x}$, $\vec{p}$ with the Hamiltonian

$$H = \frac{\vec{p} \cdot \vec{p}}{2\,m} = \frac{p^2}{2\,m} \tag{3.10}$$

The electron in the Hydrogen atom (ignoring spin) is characterized by $\vec{x}$, $\vec{p}$ and

$$H = \frac{p^2}{2m} - \frac{e^2}{r} \tag{3.11}$$

where r is the radial coordinate, $r^2 = \vec{x} \cdot \vec{x}$. The free relativistic point particle without spin has $(\vec{x}, \vec{p})$ and

$$H = \sqrt{p^2 + m^2} \tag{3.12}$$

Transitions

Free particles do not get us very far, interactions are important and they lead to transitions. For example, an electron in an atom can make a transition from a higher energy state to a lower state emitting a photon. This is basically the process of spectroscopic transitions. The realization of this process must arise out of the usual time-evolution of the wave function $\Psi_{\text{Atom}*}$ of the atom in quantum mechanics via the Hamiltonian. We should thus be able to find the transition

$$\Psi_{\text{Atom}*} \to \Psi_{\text{Atom}} \, \Psi_\gamma$$

by solving the Schrödinger equation with the Hamiltonian which must contain a part H_{int} which realizes this transition. The probability amplitude of this transition is of the form

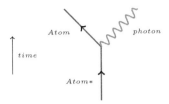

Fig. 3.1: Emission of a spectral line by an atom

$$\mathcal{A}\left(|i\rangle \to |f\rangle\right) \simeq -i \int \Psi_f^* \, H_{int} \, \Psi_i \; d^3x \, dt \tag{3.13}$$

which can also be written as

$$\mathcal{A}\left(|i\rangle \to |f\rangle\right) \simeq -i \int dt \, \langle f | \, H_{int} \, | i \rangle \tag{3.14}$$

where $|i\rangle$ represents the initial state $\Psi_i = \Psi_{\text{Atom}*}$ and $|f\rangle$ represents the final state $\Psi_f = \Psi_{\text{Atom}} \Psi_\gamma$. The result (3.13) or (3.14) is to first order in the perturbation, and can be obtained by expanding e^{-iHt} to first order in H_{int}. This is standard time-dependent perturbation theory in quantum mechanics. We may represent the transition process we are considering by a diagram as shown in Fig. 3.1. We have the atom in an excited state (denoted as Atom*) which evolves in time for some time and then emits a photon, decaying into a lower energy state (denoted as Atom).

Keeping this picture in mind, let us look again at Compton scattering. The basic process is as shown in Fig. 2.1, but in terms of visualizing this in quantum mechanics, it may be represented as in Fig. 3.2, where the electron absorbs the incoming photon to make a transition to some higher energy state. This electron then propagates for some time (and distance) and then emits a photon which is detected as the outgoing photon. We need a Hamiltonian H_{int} to obtain the transition corresponding to the absorption of the incoming photon by the electron. We also need a way to calculate the probability amplitude for the electron to propagate as a free particle for some time and distance; this is governed by the Hamiltonian for the free particle. Finally the emission of the outgoing photon by the electron also requires a Hamiltonian to effect the transition. The last step will, in fact, involve the conjugate of the matrix element (with appropriate changes of the momentum labels, etc.) of the very same Hamiltonian which described the absorption of the incoming photon by the electron, i.e.,

$$-i \int \Psi_e^* \, H_{int} \, \Psi_e \, \Psi_\gamma \to -i \int \Psi_e^* \, \Psi_\gamma^* \, H_{int} \, \Psi_e$$

This description of the process shows that the key ingredients are the vertices where the absorption or emission happens, described by some H_{int}, which, in turn, should arise from the basic interactions between the particles involved, and propagators, which are the amplitudes for the free propagation of the particles.

Another example of a simple process of interest would be the scattering of α-particles by an atomic nucleus, as in the original experiment which led to the nuclear model of the atom. We can describe it again by a similar diagram (see Fig. 3.3) where the α-particle emits a photon which is then absorbed by the nucleus thus effecting a transfer of momentum from the α-particle to the nucleus. The photon has free propagation between the emission and absorption. Again, identifying the suitable vertices and the calculation of the free particle propagation are the key elements in understanding this process.

So let us begin a theory of transitions by developing the idea of propagators, which goes back to Ernst Stueckelberg and to Richard Feynman (1948). Suppose we introduce into our system under study a particle at some point $\vec{y}$ at the time y_0 and the particle propagates to the point $\vec{x}$ at time x_0. We want to know the probability amplitude for the particle to propagate from $(y_0, \vec{y})$ to $(x_0, \vec{x})$. We know time-evolution is generated by the Hamiltonian. In our case, we must thus consider the time-evolution of the state $|\vec{y}\rangle$ by the time-interval $(x_0 - y_0)$ (which gives $e^{-iH(x_0-y_0)}|\vec{y}\rangle$) and calculate the overlap of the result with $|\vec{x}\rangle$. So the amplitude we need is given by the matrix element

$$G(x,y) = \langle \vec{x}| e^{-iH(x_0-y_0)} |\vec{y}\rangle \tag{3.15}$$

If we consider a nonrelativistic free particle, $H = \hat{p}_i\hat{p}_i/2m$, and in the case of a relativistic free particle, $H = \sqrt{\hat{p}_i\hat{p}_i + m^2}$, where $\hat{p}$ is the spatial

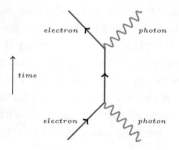

Fig. 3.2: Compton scattering

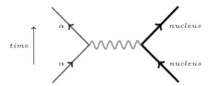

Fig. 3.3: Rutherford scattering

momentum operator. (There are three components to this momentum operator, corresponding to $i = 1, 2, 3$. In what follows, we will often write $\vec{p}^2$ for $p_i p_i$.) We will consider the latter case since we will need to do things in a relativistic way. Then we can write

$$G(x, y) = \langle \vec{x} | e^{-i\sqrt{\hat{p}^2 + m^2}(x_0 - y_0)} | \vec{y} \rangle \tag{3.16}$$

The difficulty in evaluating this expression is that $\hat{p}$ is an operator which is not diagonal in the coordinate representation of states we have indicated. In other words, while we have $\hat{x} | \vec{x} \rangle = \vec{x} | \vec{x} \rangle$ for the position operator $\hat{x}$, $| \vec{x} \rangle$ are not eigenstates of the momentum operator. In the present case, however, we are fortunate. The Hamiltonian does not depend on both $\hat{x}$ and $\hat{p}$, so we may solve the problem by going to the momentum representation $\hat{p} | \vec{p} \rangle = \vec{p} | \vec{p} \rangle$. In nonrelativistic quantum mechanics, this is achieved by inserting the completeness relation

$$\mathbb{1} = \int \frac{d^3 p}{(2\pi)^3} | \vec{p} \rangle \langle \vec{p} | \tag{3.17}$$

just after the exponential in (3.16). In the relativistic case, the normalization of the states must be compatible with Lorentz invariance and the correct completeness relation is

$$\mathbb{1} = \int \frac{d^3 p}{(2\pi)^3} \frac{1}{2\omega_p} | \vec{p} \rangle \langle \vec{p} | \tag{3.18}$$

where $\omega_p = \sqrt{\vec{p}^2 + m^2}$. (The Lorentz invariance of (3.18) will be demonstrated soon, confirming it as the correct completeness relation.) Using this relation,

$$\begin{aligned}
G(x, y) &= \int \frac{d^3 p}{(2\pi)^3} \frac{1}{2\omega_p} \langle \vec{x} | e^{-i\sqrt{\hat{p}^2 + m^2}(x_0 - y_0)} | \vec{p} \rangle \langle \vec{p} | \vec{y} \rangle \\
&= \int \frac{d^3 p}{(2\pi)^3} \frac{1}{2\omega_p} e^{-i\sqrt{\vec{p}^2 + m^2}(x_0 - y_0)} \langle \vec{x} | \vec{p} \rangle \langle \vec{p} | \vec{y} \rangle \\
&= \int \frac{d^3 p}{(2\pi)^3} \frac{1}{2\omega_p} e^{-i\omega_p(x_0 - y_0) + i\vec{p} \cdot (\vec{x} - \vec{y})}
\end{aligned} \tag{3.19}$$

where we have used the result

$$\langle \vec{x} | \vec{p} \rangle = e^{i \vec{p} \cdot \vec{x}} \tag{3.20}$$

which is well known from the transformation to the momentum-diagonal states in quantum mechanics.

We have obtained a rather neat looking expression for the probability amplitude $\langle \vec{x}, x^0 | \vec{y}, y^0 \rangle$. The relativistic invariance of this result can be seen as follows. Recall that $p \cdot (x - y) = p_0(x^0 - y^0) - \vec{p} \cdot (\vec{x} - \vec{y})$, with $p_0 = \sqrt{\vec{p}^2 + m^2} = \omega_p$ for a relativistic particle of mass m, so that the exponent in (3.19) is the Lorentz invariant scalar product of the 4-vector p and the 4-vector $x - y$. What about the measure of integration d^3p/ω_p? To see how this works out, consider now the Dirac delta function

$$\delta(p_0^2 - \vec{p} \cdot \vec{p} - m^2) = \delta[(p_0 - \omega_p)(p_0 + \omega_p)] \tag{3.21}$$

where we will consider p_0 as a free variable. When the argument of the Dirac δ-function is a function of the variables we consider in integration, we can use the rule

$$\delta[f(z)] = \sum_{\{z_0\}} \frac{\delta(z - z_0)}{\left| \frac{\partial f}{\partial z} \right|_{z_0}} \tag{3.22}$$

where the summation is over the zeros of the argument, namely, $f(z_0) = 0$. In applying this to the δ-function in (3.21), we find

$$\delta[(p_0 - \omega_p)(p_0 + \omega_p)] = \frac{1}{2\,\omega_p} \left(\delta(p_0 - \omega_p) + \delta(p_0 + \omega_p) \right) \tag{3.23}$$

Further since the sign of p_0 cannot be changed by a Lorentz transformation, integration over the positive values of p_0 will be a Lorentz invariant operation. Carrying this out, we get

$$\int_{p_0 > 0} dp_0 \, \frac{d^3p}{(2\pi)^3} \delta(p_0^2 - \vec{p} \cdot \vec{p} - m^2) \, e^{-ip_0(x_0 - y_0) + i\vec{p} \cdot (\vec{x} - \vec{y})}$$

$$= \int \frac{d^3p}{(2\pi)^3} \frac{1}{2\,\omega_p} \, e^{-i\omega_p(x_0 - y_0)} \, e^{i\vec{p} \cdot (\vec{x} - \vec{y})} \tag{3.24}$$

Since the left hand side of this equation involves only Lorentz-invariant quantities such as the Lorentz-invariant scalar product in the exponent, the Lorentz-invariant argument $p_0^2 - \vec{p} \cdot \vec{p} - m^2 = p^2 - m^2$ for the δ-function, and the Lorentz-invariant measure d^4p, we see that $G(x, y)$ must be a Lorentz-invariant function of $(x - y)$. (The use of the $(1/2\,\omega_p)$ factor for the completeness relation (3.18) is also justified by this argument.) Thus we conclude that $G(x, y)$ must be a function of $(x_0 - y_0)^2 - (\vec{x} - \vec{y})^2$, which is the

Fig. 3.4: Representing the propagator (solid line) between arbitrary vertices shown as F_1 and F_2

only invariant we can make out of the vector $(x - y)_\mu$. It is then possible to evaluate $G(x, y)$ by considering the special case $x_0 = y_0$. In this case, switching to spherical coordinates in $\vec{p}$-space, (3.19) becomes

$$
\begin{aligned}
G(R) &= \frac{1}{8\pi^3} \int_0^\infty dp\, p^2 \frac{1}{2\,\omega_p} \int_0^\pi d\theta \sin\theta \int_0^{2\pi} d\varphi\, e^{ipR\cos\theta} \\
&= \frac{2\pi}{8\pi^3} \int_0^\infty dp\, p^2 \frac{1}{2\,\omega_p} \int_{-1}^1 dz\, e^{ipRz} \\
&= \frac{1}{4\pi^2} \int_0^\infty dp\, p^2 \frac{1}{2\,\omega_p} \left(\frac{e^{ipR} - e^{-ipR}}{ipR} \right) = \frac{1}{4\pi^2 R} \int_0^\infty dp\, \frac{p}{\omega_p} \sin(pR) \\
&= \frac{1}{4\pi^2 R} \int_0^\infty dp\, \frac{p}{\sqrt{p^2 + m^2}} \sin(pR) \qquad (3.25)
\end{aligned}
$$

where $R = |\vec{x} - \vec{y}|$, and in the second line of this set of equations we used $z = \cos\theta$. (In these equations, we also write $p = |\vec{p}|$ for brevity.) The remaining integration can be done to obtain explicit formulae in terms of Bessel functions, this will be done a little later.

The explicit expressions are important as they give us a feeling for what the propagator is, but for most of what we want to do, an explicit formula is not needed. So we will now write the propagator in a way which is most useful for simplification of amplitudes for physical processes. In that case, the propagator appears connecting the vertices of the diagrammatic representation in an expression of the form

$$
I = \int d^4x\, d^4y\, F_1(x)\, G(x, y)\, F_2(y) \qquad (3.26)
$$

where $F_1(x)$ and $F_2(y)$ are functions representing the contribution from vertices, which can involve wave functions of incoming and outgoing particles and so on, but whose precise form we do not need for now. (These are shown as shaded regions in Fig. 3.4.) The integrations in (3.26) cover both regions $x_0 > y_0$ and $y_0 > x_0$, so we need the expression

$$G(x, y) = \int \frac{d^3k}{(2\pi)^3} \frac{1}{2\omega_k} e^{-i\omega_k(x_0 - y_0) + i\vec{k}\cdot(\vec{x} - \vec{y})}, \qquad x_0 > y_0$$

$$= \int \frac{d^3k}{(2\pi)^3} \frac{1}{2\omega_k} e^{-i\omega_k(y_0 - x_0) + i\vec{k}\cdot(\vec{y} - \vec{x})}, \qquad y_0 > x_0 \qquad (3.27)$$

The second line follows from similar reasoning as for $x_0 > y_0$, with the time-evolution given by $e^{-iH(y_0 - x_0)}$. In (3.26) we can also Fourier decompose the functions F_1, F_2,

$$F_1(x) = \int \frac{d^4p}{(2\pi)^4} F_1(p) e^{-ip_0 x_0 + i\vec{p}\cdot\vec{x}}$$

$$F_2(y) = \int \frac{d^4q}{(2\pi)^4} F_2(q) e^{-iq_0 y_0 + i\vec{q}\cdot\vec{y}} \qquad (3.28)$$

In using these in (3.26), we encounter several integrals. It is simplest to start with the integration over the spatial dimensions, using

$$\int d^3x \; e^{i(\vec{p} + \vec{k})\cdot\vec{x}} = (2\pi)^3 \, \delta^{(3)}(\vec{p} + \vec{k})$$

$$\int d^3y \; e^{i(\vec{q} - \vec{k})\cdot\vec{y}} = (2\pi)^3 \, \delta^{(3)}(\vec{q} - \vec{k}) \qquad (3.29)$$

Recall the following properties of delta functions:

$$\int_{-\infty}^{\infty} dx \; e^{ikx} = 2\pi \, \delta(k)$$

$$\int_{-\infty}^{\infty} dk \; e^{ikx} = 2\pi \, \delta(x)$$

$$\int dp \; \delta(p - k) f(p) = f(k) \qquad (3.30)$$

The last is the so-called sifting property of the δ-function. (The δ-function is like a sieve, letting all values of the variable get eliminated except for the one where the argument of the δ-function vanishes. That one comes through, as in a sieve.) Using (3.27) and (3.29) in (3.26), we can now carry out the k-integration to get

$$\int \frac{d^3k}{(2\pi)^3} (2\pi)^3 \delta^{(3)}(\vec{p} + \vec{k}) \, (2\pi)^3 \delta^{(3)}(\vec{q} - \vec{k}) \, f(k) = (2\pi)^3 \, \delta^{(3)}(\vec{p} + \vec{q}) \, f(k) \Big]_{\vec{k} = \vec{q}} \qquad (3.31)$$

for any function $f(k)$. The surviving δ-function gives the conservation of the 3-momentum between the vertices; the amplitude (3.26) will vanish unless

$\vec{p} + \vec{q} = 0$. The time-integration is trickier since we have to keep track of the different expressions for $G(x, y)$ for different ranges. For $x_0 > y_0$, we get

$$\int_{-\infty}^{\infty} dx_0 \, e^{-i(p_0 + \omega_k)x_0} \int_{-\infty}^{x_0} dy_0 \, e^{i(\omega_k - q_0)y_0}$$

$$= \int_{-\infty}^{\infty} dx_0 \, e^{-i(p_0 + \omega_k)x_0} \, e^{i(\omega_k - q_0)x_0} \frac{1}{\epsilon + i(\omega_k - q_0)}$$

$$= 2\pi \, \delta(p_0 + q_0) \frac{(-i)}{\omega_k - i\epsilon - q_0} \tag{3.32}$$

In this line of simplification, for the y_0-integration, for convergence at $y_0 \to -\infty$, we introduced an extra factor $e^{\epsilon y_0}$, where ϵ is a small real positive number. Eventually it will be taken to be zero. (In actual calculations, the time-integrations should not extend to $\pm\infty$, since we start at some finite time, and observe the final states at a finite time. Since the time taken for the interaction is small compared to the time over which the process is observed, we idealize (or simplify) by taking the limits to be very large. So the trick of using ϵ is justifiable and will not affect physical results in the end.) For $y_0 > x_0$, using the second expression in (3.27),

$$\int_{-\infty}^{\infty} dx_0 \, e^{-i(p_0 - \omega_k)x_0} \int_{x_0}^{\infty} dy_0 \, e^{-i(\omega_k + q_0)y_0}$$

$$= \int_{-\infty}^{\infty} dx_0 \, e^{-i(p_0 - \omega_k)x_0} \, e^{-i(\omega_k + q_0)x_0} \frac{1}{\epsilon + i(\omega_k + q_0)}$$

$$= 2\pi \, \delta(p_0 + q_0) \frac{(-i)}{\omega_k - i\epsilon + q_0} \tag{3.33}$$

Combining (3.31, 3.32, 3.33), we get

$$I = \int_{p,q} F_1(p)F_2(q) \frac{(2\pi)^4 \, \delta^{(4)}(p+q)}{2\omega_k} (-i) \left[\frac{1}{\omega_k - i\epsilon + q_0} + \frac{1}{\omega_k - i\epsilon - q_0} \right]$$

$$= \int_{p,q} F_1(p)F_2(q) \frac{(2\pi)^4 \, \delta^{(4)}(p+q)}{2\omega_k} (-i) \left[\frac{2\omega_k}{\omega_k^2 - q_0^2 - i\eta} \right]$$

$$= \int_{p,q} F_1(p)F_2(q) \, (2\pi)^4 \, \delta^{(4)}(p+k) \, (2\pi)^4 \delta^{(4)}(q-k) \left[\frac{i}{k_0^2 - \omega_k^2 + i\eta} \right] \frac{d^4k}{(2\pi)^4}$$

$$= \int d^4x \, d^4y \, F_1(x) \left[\int \frac{d^4k}{(2\pi)^4} e^{-ik\cdot(x-y)} \frac{i}{k^2 - m^2 + i\eta} \right] F_2(y) \tag{3.34}$$

In the second line of this equation, $\eta = i \, 2\omega_k \epsilon$. It can be treated as another small parameter we need to keep for a while, until the calculations are completed. It also provides a prescription for how the singularity arising from the zero of the denominator is to be avoided when the k_0-integration is to be done. In the third line, we have introduced the δ-functions such that when the k-integration is done, we recover the previous line which has $k = q$. The advantage of doing this is to rewrite the expression back in terms of $F_1(x)$, $F_2(y)$. We also realize, from the last line, that for all purposes of amplitude calculations, we can take the propagator as

$$G(x, y) = \int \frac{d^4k}{(2\pi)^4} e^{-ik\cdot(x-y)} \frac{i}{k^2 - m^2 + i\eta} \tag{3.35}$$

where k_0 is also to be considered as a free variable of integration. This is what we were after, a simple manifestly Lorentz invariant expression for the propagator.

We are now in a position to turn our attention to Feynman diagrams. These diagrams are symbolic and very intuitive representations of equations used to calculate the probability amplitude of an event. In a Feynman diagram, the incoming and outgoing lines represent wave functions (or their conjugates). The points of intersection (called vertices) are the functions like F_1, F_2 and the line connecting the vertices is the propagator. The nature of the vertex will depend on the nature of the interaction. The idea is that, once we know the interaction, the construction of a Feynman diagram for a process is a very intuitive and easy one. Then one can immediately write down the amplitude for the process, since there is a direct transcription between the lines and vertices in a diagram and the mathematical expression.

Take for example two species of spinless particles, φ with mass $= M$ and χ with mass $= m$. For this example, let us assume that the theory of these particles is such that, for the vertex, say at x, we have an expression like

$$V_1 = \frac{\lambda}{2} \int d^4x \, \varphi^2(x) \chi(x) \tag{3.36}$$

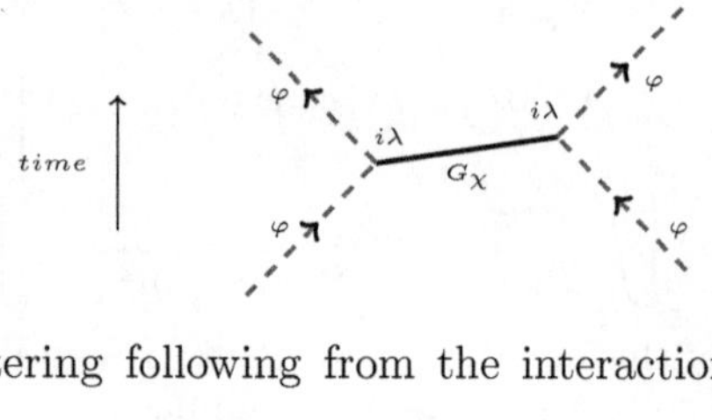

Fig. 3.5: $\varphi\varphi$ scattering following from the interaction (3.36), to lowest nontrivial order

where λ is the coupling constant. (The factor $\frac{1}{2}$ is convenient because we can assign the first φ to the first particle, the second to the second particle or vice versa, giving two possibilities in any process.) An example of a Feynman diagram for the process of scattering of two φ-particles is shown in Fig. 3.5. Taking one of the particles at x to be the incoming wave function and the other as the outgoing wave function, and following similar assignments at the other vertex at y, we can calculate $\mathcal{A}$ as

$$\mathcal{A} = (i\lambda)^2 \int d^4x \, d^4y \; \varphi_{in}(x) \, \varphi_{out}(x) \, G_\chi(x,y) \, \varphi_{in}(y) \, \varphi_{out}(y) \qquad (3.37)$$

We will discuss this in more detail in the next lecture.

Remark 3.1.

More on the propagator

The propagator is such an important quantity that it is worthwhile to spend some more time on it and obtain an explicit formula for it, by working out the remaining integral in (3.25). In that expression, we introduce the change of variable $|\vec{p}| = p = m \sinh \lambda$, $\omega_p = \sqrt{\vec{p}^2 + m^2} = m \cosh \lambda$, $dp = d\lambda \, m \cosh \lambda$, so that

$$G(R) = \frac{m}{4\pi^2 R} \int_0^\infty d\lambda \, (\sinh \lambda) \, \sin(mR \sinh \lambda)$$
$$= \frac{1}{4\pi^2 R} \left(-\frac{\partial}{\partial R} \right) \int_0^\infty d\lambda \, \cos(mR \sinh \lambda) \qquad (3.38)$$

The modified Bessel function of order zero, $K_0(z)$, is defined by

$$K_0(z) = \int_0^\infty d\lambda \, \cos(z \sinh \lambda) \qquad (3.39)$$

and $\partial_z K_0(z) = -K_1(z)$, the latter being the modified Bessel function of order 1. (The integrand in (3.39) does not decrease as λ becomes large since the cosine function can range from -1 to 1. Nevertheless, we get a convergent integral because the cosine oscillates rapidly; two values of λ which differ by $\delta\lambda = (\pi/mR \cosh \lambda)$ will have alternating signs for the cosine, which happens over a small interval $\delta\lambda$ at large λ. Hence most of the contribution to the integral from high values of λ will cancel out. This may be seen as an application of the Riemann-Lebesgue lemma.) Using the definition of the modified Bessel function

$$G(R) = \left(\frac{m}{4\pi^2 R} \right) K_1(mR) \qquad (3.40)$$

We already know that $G(x, y)$ must be a function of $(x_0 - y_0)^2 - (\vec{x} - \vec{y})^2$. Therefore to get the full result, we can proceed as follows. We write $R = |\vec{x} - \vec{y}| = \sqrt{-\Delta^2}\big|_{x_0 = y_0}$, where we define $\Delta^2 = (x_0 - y_0)^2 - (\vec{x} - \vec{y})^2$. The generalized form of $G(x, y)$ is then

$$G(x, y) = \frac{m}{4\pi^2 \sqrt{-\Delta^2}} K_1(m\sqrt{-\Delta^2}) \tag{3.41}$$

For small values of the argument, $K_1(z) \approx 1/z$; we can use this for the massless limit

$$G(x, y) = \frac{1}{4\pi^2} \left(\frac{1}{-\Delta^2} \right), \qquad \text{as } m \to 0 \tag{3.42}$$

It is also instructive to consider the direct evaluation of the propagator for $m = 0$. Starting with the expression in (3.19), setting $m = 0$, we find

$$
\begin{aligned}
G &= \frac{1}{8\pi^2} \int_0^\infty dp\, p \int_{\cos\theta = -1}^1 d(\cos\theta)\, e^{-ip\tau + ipR\cos\theta} \\
&= \frac{1}{8\pi^2} \int_0^\infty dp\, \frac{1}{iR} \left[e^{-ip(\tau - R)} - e^{-ip(\tau + R)} \right] \\
&= \frac{1}{8\pi^2 iR} \left[\frac{1}{\epsilon + i(\tau - R)} - \frac{1}{\epsilon + i(\tau + R)} \right] \\
&= -\frac{1}{4\pi^2} \frac{1}{\Delta^2 - i\eta} \tag{3.43}
\end{aligned}
$$

where $\tau = x_0 - y_0$. In doing the p-integration, we introduced a factor $e^{-\epsilon p}$ to get convergence of the integral at $p \to \infty$, where ϵ is a small, real, positive number; this is similar to what we did in (3.32). Eventually we will take $\epsilon \to 0$; this trick will not affect physical results. (Such factors would not be needed if we do more exact calculations with propagators tied into vertices for actual processes.) In the last line $\eta = 2\epsilon\tau > 0$; it may be regarded as another small real positive number. Among other things, it gives us a prescription for how we should treat the potential singularity at $\Delta^2 = 0$ in (3.42). The analytic continuation to be used is $R^2 \to -\Delta^2 + i\eta$.

For finite m, as $-\Delta^2$ becomes large (which corresponds to large spatial separation with fixed time difference), we can use

$$K_1(z) \approx \sqrt{\frac{\pi}{2z}}\, e^{-z} \tag{3.44}$$

to write

$$G(x, y) \sim \frac{1}{4\pi^2} \sqrt{\frac{m\pi}{2}} \frac{1}{(\sqrt{-\Delta^2})^{\frac{3}{2}}} e^{-m\sqrt{-\Delta^2}} \tag{3.45}$$

Notice that the propagator is not zero even though spacelike separation means that the two points cannot be connected by a signal, even one that travels at the speed of light in vacuum. Rather we get exponential fall-off of the propagator with a range $\sim 1/m$. This is related to the entanglement properties of quantum mechanics. But this does not mean any violation of relativity. For the question of how measurements at different points affect each other, what is relevant is the commutator, which, one can show, vanishes for spacelike separation.

If we consider a time-like interval, for which $\Delta^2 \gg 0$, we can set $z = im|\Delta|$ and obtain

$$G(x, y) \sim \frac{1}{4\pi^2} \sqrt{\frac{m\pi}{2}} \, i^{-3/2} \, \frac{1}{|\Delta|^{3/2}} \, e^{-im|\Delta|} \qquad (3.46)$$

Chapter 4

Scattering Processes and Feynman Diagrams

We shall now embark on a more detailed exploration of Feynman diagrams. These were invented by Richard Feynman in the late 1940s, based on certain intuitive ideas, as a method for calculating the probability amplitudes for various processes involving particle interactions. Subsequently, they have been derived more rigorously from quantum field theory. The great success of this approach is due to the fact that the diagrams themselves are fairly easy to construct based on some simple intuitive rules, yet each diagram is a mnemonic for the mathematical expression of the probability amplitude corresponding to the process that the diagram represents. So there is an easy translation from the diagrams to the amplitudes, bypassing much of the elaborate machinery of quantum field theory. We will now go over how this picture-to-mathematics dictionary is set up and how we can use it.

The processes of interest to us could be scatterings, decays or could even be processes which lead to corrections to the energy eigenvalues of a physical system. We have already seen some examples of processes represented as Feynman diagrams, Figs. 3.1, 3.2, 3.3. Each such diagram gives a visualization of the process as a time-sequence, given by incoming particles absorbing or emitting other particles, some of which may propagate to another point to be absorbed at another vertex and so on. We have also discussed one of the elements of the translation to a mathematical expression: Whenever we have a propagator in a diagram between two vertices, in the amplitude for the process represented by the diagram, it corresponds to the mathematical expression for the propagator of that type of particle, say, (3.35) for a spin zero particle. While propagators represent the possibility of particles going from one point in spacetime to another during the intermediate stages of a process, the vertices tell us how the interaction happens, what kind of particle absorption or emission can happen. So, to complete the correspondence of diagrams and amplitudes, we need to know how to represent the vertices. We will do this now; we will also need to rephrase more precisely the rules for Feynman diagrams.

The starting point is the observation that:

> For every species of particle there is a corresponding field which is a spacetime dependent quantity.

The nature of this field will depend on whether the particle has spin, charge, etc. For every particle species listed in our table in the beginning (Lecture 1), there is a field. Thus, there is a field for the electron, for the neutrino, for the photon, for the up quark, for the down quark, etc. For each field, there is a corresponding expression for the propagator.

And using the fields we can make up the mathematical expressions for different types of allowed interactions. (Ultimately, these expressions are to be determined by experiment, this is where the key physics of the interaction is.) Each such expression will turn out to be a term in the action for the theory, so we will refer to it as an interaction term. This is the product of fields (or their derivatives) representing the particles which can participate in the interaction at a single spacetime point. The spacetime argument for all the fields at a single vertex must be the same, since the interaction must be local, with no action-at-a-distance, consistent with relativity. There is also integration over all values of spacetime coordinates for the vertex, since the interaction can happen anywhere, anytime, in principle. We also have a constant coefficient for each type of vertex which gives the strength of the interaction at that vertex. These coefficients are called coupling constants.

The interaction terms give us the nature of vertices we can use in constructing Feynman diagrams. A vertex corresponding to a particular interaction term is viewed as a spacetime point with a number of lines coming out of it or going into it. Each line represents one of the fields in the interaction term.[1] Ultimately, each line represents a particle by the field-particle correspondence. A Feynman diagram is made of a number of vertices, some of them or all of them may be of the same type. Some particles propagate from one vertex to another, these are expressed as propagators in the amplitude. The remaining lines which are the fields corresponding to incoming particles, respectively outgoing particles, of the whole process will be replaced by wave functions, respectively their conjugates, each such function

---

[1]Thus, for a scalar field φ, an interaction term of the form $\lambda \int d^4x \; \varphi^4(x)$ will be represented as a point with a valency of four, i.e., four lines meeting at the point. λ is the coupling constant.

being labeled by the momentum and other observables of the particle. Labeling the vertices by spacetime points x, y, etc., we can summarize this result for Feynman diagrams as follows. The probability amplitude for the process visualized as a Feynman diagram is given by

$$\mathcal{A} = \prod_{\text{vertices}} (i \text{ Coupling constant}) \int d^4x\, d^4y \cdots$$

$$\times \prod \text{Wave functions of incoming particles}$$

$$\times \prod \text{Wave functions of outgoing particles} \times \text{Propagators}$$

$$(4.1)$$

This formulation of the rules for Feynman diagrams may seem rather involved, but they are fairly simple in actual usage; this will become clearer with some examples. As a first case, consider two species of spin zero particles. We will denote their fields by φ and χ, where φ is taken to have mass M and χ is taken to have mass m. The wave functions, and their conjugates, denoted by the same letter as the field, can be taken as

$$\varphi_{in}(x) = \frac{1}{\sqrt{2\Omega_p V}} e^{-ipx} = \frac{1}{\sqrt{2\Omega_p V}} e^{-ip_0 x_0 + i\vec{p}\cdot\vec{x}}$$

$$\chi_{in}(x) = \frac{1}{\sqrt{2\omega_k V}} e^{-ikx} = \frac{1}{\sqrt{2\omega_k V}} e^{-ik_0 x_0 + i\vec{k}\cdot\vec{x}}$$

$$\varphi_{out}(x) = \frac{1}{\sqrt{2\Omega_p V}} e^{ipx} = \frac{1}{\sqrt{2\Omega_p V}} e^{ip_0 x_0 - i\vec{p}\cdot\vec{x}} \qquad (4.2)$$

$$\chi_{out}(x) = \frac{1}{\sqrt{2\omega_k V}} e^{ikx} = \frac{1}{\sqrt{2\omega_k V}} e^{ik_0 x_0 - i\vec{k}\cdot\vec{x}}$$

where $p_0 = \Omega_p = \sqrt{\vec{p}^2 + M^2}$, $k_0 = \omega_k = \sqrt{\vec{k}^2 + m^2}$; $\vec{p}$ and $\vec{k}$ are the momenta of the φ and χ particles respectively.[2] We are considering the particle to be in a cubical box of volume V for making it easier to normalize the plane waves. (Recall that without this, the normalization integral will result in a δ-function. While it is possible to work with such δ-functions, it is a little easier to keep the particle in a box of finite volume. We will take $V \to \infty$ at the end of the calculation.)

As a simple example of a vertex, we take

$$V_1 = \frac{\lambda}{2} \int d^4x\, \varphi^2(x)\, \chi(x) \qquad (4.3)$$

---

[2]In the exponent of the wave functions, we have the invariant scalar products like $p \cdot x$ and $k \cdot x$; since we will have to deal with many such factors, to avoid clutter in notation, from now on we will simply write px, kx, etc. for the dot products. Thus $px = p \cdot x = p_0 x_0 - \vec{p} \cdot \vec{x}$, etc.

Here λ is a constant, it is the coupling constant. (We use the symbol V for the volume of the box in which the fields live, so we use V_1 for the vertex to avoid confusion.)

First of all, one might wonder how we can come up with such a vertex. Here we are just using it as an example to illustrate the method, such a vertex need not be suitable for really physical interactions. In reality, all the physics we know is in the nature of the particles involved, their propagators, and the vertices describing their interactions. So the vertices are ultimately distilled from experiments, aided by theoretical insights based on symmetries and general principles of relativity and quantum mechanics. But for now, let us see how to understand the processes for a vertex like (4.3). It can describe a variety of processes. It is best to illustrate by examples.

First order in λ

We can replace the fields by wave functions, there are various choices of incoming and outgoing ones.

(1) φ's are taken to be outgoing, χ is taken to be incoming. The diagram is as shown below. The process describes the decay of a χ-particle into two φ-particles.

Fig. 4.1: Decay of χ into two φ's

(2) Take the φ's to be incoming, χ to be outgoing; this will describe the fusion of two φ-particles to form a χ-particle.

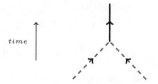

Fig. 4.2: Fusion of two φ's into χ

Fig. 4.3: Emission of χ by a φ

(3) Take one φ to be incoming and the other φ to be outgoing; take the χ to be outgoing. This will describe the emission of a χ-particle by the φ-particle.

(4) Similarly, if we take one φ and χ to be incoming with the other φ to be outgoing, we get the absorption of χ by φ.

Second order in λ

When we consider diagrams which involve two vertices of the type (4.3), there are several possible physical processes. We shall consider only a few examples at this point. We give the diagrams, see Fig. 4.4, and the process is indicated below each diagram. The time direction will help to identify which are incoming and which are outgoing.

Notice that the rule for constructing a diagram is very simple. The basic vertex tells us how many particles can come into or leave a vertex. Then we take a number of vertices, depending on the order in λ to which we wish to calculate, and draw all possible diagrams, where we can put in propagators between some of the vertices. Each diagram describes the amplitude or part of the amplitude for a process; the physical process of interest is given by the choice of the external lines as wave functions or their conjugates. We can then transcribe the diagram to a mathematical expression using (4.1). (The calculation of the amplitude involves integrations over the coordinates of the vertex, so the actual positions of the vertices are not important. For example, in the first diagram in Fig. 4.4, for the solid line representing the propagator, the end points are not necessarily at the same time. Only the overall topology of the diagram is important.)

As we go to higher orders in λ there will be many more types of processes as well as higher order corrections to the processes we have indicated.

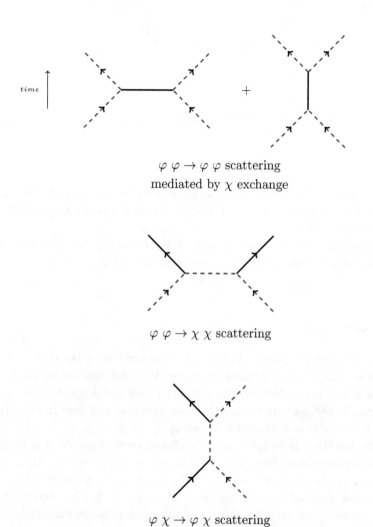

$\varphi\,\varphi \to \varphi\,\varphi$ scattering
mediated by χ exchange

$\varphi\,\varphi \to \chi\,\chi$ scattering

$\varphi\,\chi \to \varphi\,\chi$ scattering

Fig. 4.4: Examples of processes to second order in λ

A decay rate calculation

Continuing with the examples, we can now calculate the decay rate of a χ-particle into two φ-particles. This is given by Fig. 4.1, which we show again in Fig. 4.5, with the assignment of momenta indicated. Following (4.1), the

Fig. 4.5: Decay of a χ-particle into two φ-particles

amplitude is

$$
\mathcal{A} = (i\lambda) \frac{1}{\sqrt{2\Omega_{p_1} V}} \frac{1}{\sqrt{2\Omega_{p_2} V}} \frac{1}{\sqrt{2\omega_k V}} \int d^4x \, e^{-ikx + ip_1 x + ip_2 x}
$$

$$
= (i\lambda) \frac{1}{\sqrt{2\Omega_{p_1} V}} \frac{1}{\sqrt{2\Omega_{p_2} V}} \frac{1}{\sqrt{2\omega_k V}} (2\pi)^4 \, \delta^{(4)}(k - p_1 - p_2) \tag{4.4}
$$

The δ-function tells us that the amplitude for the process is zero unless we have conservation of energy (corresponding to the time-component of the momenta) and 3-momentum. Thus we need $\vec{k} = \vec{p}_1 + \vec{p}_2$. Further $\delta(k_0 - p_{01} - p_{02})$ requires $\sqrt{(\vec{p}_1 + \vec{p}_2)^2 + m^2} = \sqrt{\vec{p}_1^2 + M^2} + \sqrt{\vec{p}_2^2 + M^2}$, which can be satisfied only if $m \geq 2M$.

The probability is found by taking the absolute square (or the square of the modulus) of $\mathcal{A}$. In doing so, we will encounter the square of the δ-function, which is awkward, being infinite. The reason is that, in the naive product, because of the first δ-function, we can put $k = p_1 + p_2$ in the argument of the second, so that

$$
\delta^{(4)}(k - p_1 - p_2) \, \delta^{(4)}(k - p_1 - p_2) \to \delta^{(4)}(k - p_1 - p_2) \, \delta^{(4)}(0) = \infty
$$

To resolve this issue, we must look at where these δ-functions came from. We start by writing one of the δ-functions back as an integral,

$$
(2\pi)^4 \, \delta^{(4)}(k - p_1 - p_2) \, (2\pi)^4 \, \delta^{(4)}(k - p_1 - p_2)
$$

$$
= (2\pi)^4 \, \delta^{(4)}(k - p_1 - p_2) \times \int d^4x \, e^{-ikx + ip_1 x + ip_2 x}
$$

$$
= (2\pi)^4 \, \delta^{(4)}(k - p_1 - p_2) \int d^4x
$$

$$
= (2\pi)^4 \, \delta^{(4)}(k - p_1 - p_2) \, V \tau \tag{4.5}
$$

In the second line, because of the δ-function multiplying it, the exponent of the integrand can be set to zero. This leads to $\int d^4x$ which is the total spatial volume V multiplied by the total time τ, which we now take to be finite. (We see that the source of the infinity in the naive product is because, earlier, we considered an infinite time-interval and infinite volume.) In a real measurement, the observation time is finite. When we consider infinite times for the integrations, it is an idealization where we are saying that the observation time is large compared to the time over which the interaction is effective. This is correct for most calculations, but when we encounter an infinity we must keep τ finite, taking it to be infinite only at the end, if needed. With this understanding of the square of the δ-function, we get

$$|\mathcal{A}|^2 = \lambda^2 \frac{(2\pi)^4\,\delta^{(4)}(k - p_1 - p_2)}{8\,\Omega_{p_1}\,\Omega_{p_2}\,\omega_k\,V^3}\,V\tau \tag{4.6}$$

The decay rate, or the probability of decay per unit time, is given by $|\mathcal{A}|^2/\tau$, which is independent of τ. A further qualification is that this gives the decay rate for precisely chosen values $\vec{p}_1$, $\vec{p}_2$ of the final state momenta. In practice, we cannot resolve momenta with infinite precision, so what we observe is the decay rate to a set of final states of momenta with a little spread around the values $\vec{p}_1$ and $\vec{p}_2$. This means that we must sum over a small set of states to get the decay rate. The number of states for a range of momenta d^3p is given by $Vd^3p/(2\pi)^3$. Doing this for the two final particles, the decay rate is

$$
\begin{aligned}
\Gamma &= \frac{|\mathcal{A}|^2}{\tau}\,V\frac{d^3p_1}{(2\pi)^3}\,V\frac{d^3p_2}{(2\pi)^3}\\
&= \lambda^2\frac{(2\pi)^4\,\delta^{(4)}(k - p_1 - p_2)}{8\,\Omega_{p_1}\,\Omega_{p_2}\,\omega_k}\,\frac{d^3p_1}{(2\pi)^3}\,\frac{d^3p_2}{(2\pi)^3}
\end{aligned}
\tag{4.7}
$$

Notice that all factors of V in (4.7) have disappeared, so that taking $V \to \infty$ is not a problem at this stage. The total decay rate is given by integrating over all momenta of the final state particles,

$$\Gamma_{tot} = \frac{\lambda^2}{8\,\omega_k}\int \frac{d^3p_1}{(2\pi)^3}\frac{1}{\Omega_{p_1}}\frac{d^3p_2}{(2\pi)^3}\frac{1}{\Omega_{p_2}}\,(2\pi)^4\,\delta^{(4)}(k - p_1 - p_2) \tag{4.8}$$

The integral in this expression is completely Lorentz invariant, because the δ-function is fully 4-dimensional and the measure of integration over the momenta, with the $1/\Omega$ factors, is invariant. However, Γ_{tot} in (4.8) is not invariant because of the $1/\omega_k$. Because the integral is invariant, we can evaluate it in any Lorentz frame, the most convenient is to choose the rest frame for the initial χ-particle. If we take the initial particle χ to be at rest, $\vec{k} = 0$ and $\omega_k = m$. Writing Γ_{tot} for this frame as $\Gamma_{tot}^{(0)}$,

$$\Gamma_{tot}^{(0)} = \frac{\lambda^2}{8\,m}\int \frac{d^3p_1}{(2\pi)^3}\frac{1}{\Omega_{p_1}}\frac{d^3p_2}{(2\pi)^3}\frac{1}{\Omega_{p_2}}\,(2\pi)^4\delta^{(4)}(k - p_1 - p_2)$$

$$= \frac{\lambda^2}{8\,m} \int \frac{d^3 p_1}{(2\pi)^2} \frac{1}{\Omega_{p_1}^2} \, \delta(m - 2\,\Omega_{p_1})$$

$$= \frac{\lambda^2}{8\,m} \frac{1}{2\pi} \int_M^\infty d\Omega \, \frac{\sqrt{\Omega^2 - M^2}}{\Omega} \, \delta(\Omega - (m/2))$$

$$= \frac{\lambda^2 \sqrt{m^2 - 4M^2}}{16\pi\,m^2} \tag{4.9}$$

For the general result, we may then write

$$\Gamma_{tot} = \frac{m}{\omega_k} \, \Gamma_{tot}^{(0)} \tag{4.10}$$

Comments

(1) When we have a collection of (uncorrelated independent) χ-particles, say, N in number, each has the decay probability rate given by (4.9), so that the decay rate equation for N is

$$\frac{dN}{dt} = -\Gamma_{tot} \, N$$

which gives the standard exponential decay formula.

(2) The lifetime of the particle in its rest frame is given as $1/\Gamma_{tot}^{(0)}$. The speed v of the initial χ-particle is given by the relation $m/\omega_k = \sqrt{1 - v^2}$. The formula (4.10) shows that the lifetime of a moving χ-particle is longer:

$$\text{Lifetime at speed } v = \frac{\text{Lifetime at rest}}{\sqrt{1 - v^2}}$$

This is the expected time-dilation effect of relativity. We see that the fact that Γ_{tot} is not Lorentz-invariant is correct; in fact, it is noninvariant precisely in the manner needed to encode the time-dilation effect expected on the basis of the theory of relativity.

(3) Strictly speaking, since we have identical particles in the final state, the lifetime should be half of what we have written, because there is a Gibbs factor $1/2!$. We have not yet talked about identical particles, so we will leave this issue for now.

A scattering amplitude

We will now consider a scattering amplitude, say, two particles of the φ-type via χ exchange. These are described by the diagrams given earlier, we repeat them here with momenta indicated, see Fig. 4.6. The amplitude for the first diagram is easy to write down. We need a factor $(i\lambda)^2$ because there are two vertices. We need $G(x, y)$ for the χ-propagator. We also need the wave functions for the external lines. Thus

$$
\mathcal{A}_1 = (i\lambda)^2 \prod \frac{1}{\sqrt{2\Omega_p V}} \int d^4x d^4y \ e^{-i(p_1 - k_1)x} \ e^{-i(p_2 - k_2)y} \ G(x, y)
$$

$$
= (i\lambda)^2 \prod \frac{1}{\sqrt{2\Omega_p V}} \int (2\pi)^8 \delta^{(4)}(p_1 + q - k_1) \ \delta^{(4)}(p_2 - q - k_2)
$$

$$
\times \ \frac{i}{q^2 - m^2 + i\eta} \frac{d^4q}{(2\pi)^4}
$$

$$
= (i\lambda)^2 \prod \frac{1}{\sqrt{2\Omega_p V}} (2\pi)^4 \delta^{(4)}(p_1 + p_2 - k_1 - k_2) \frac{i}{(p_1 - k_1)^2 - m^2 + i\eta}
$$

$$(4.11)$$

In the last line, we carried out the q-integration using one of the δ-functions. Also, we use the shorthand notation

$$
\prod \frac{1}{\sqrt{2\Omega_p V}} = \frac{1}{\sqrt{2\Omega_{p_1} V}} \frac{1}{\sqrt{2\Omega_{p_2} V}} \frac{1}{\sqrt{2\Omega_{k_1} V}} \frac{1}{\sqrt{2\Omega_{k_2} V}} \tag{4.12}
$$

There is a similar expression for the other diagram

$$
\mathcal{A}_2 = (i\lambda)^2 \prod \frac{1}{\sqrt{2\Omega_p V}} (2\pi)^4 \delta^{(4)}(p_1 + p_2 - k_1 - k_2) \frac{i}{(p_1 + p_2)^2 - m^2 + i\eta}
$$

$$(4.13)$$

The total amplitude is $\mathcal{A}_1 + \mathcal{A}_2$. Notice that the momentum carried by the propagator is consistent with conservation at each vertex.

One can square this amplitude to get the probability and calculate the scattering rate. One can also see that the notion of a potential energy for the interaction is buried in the expression for the amplitude. We will not carry out the needed simplifications here, beyond making some remarks at the end, as a more complete calculation will be presented later.

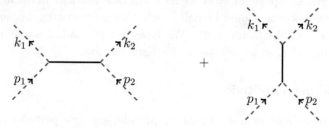

Fig. 4.6: The scattering of two φ-particles via the exchange of a χ-particle

Back to particles and their fields

The description of processes via Feynman diagrams makes it clear that the real physics is contained in two sets of quantities:

- The wave functions for the incoming and outgoing particles and the propagators for particles, which are determined by the mass, spin, etc. of the particle
- The vertices which give the possible interactions between particles.

Our use of the χ and φ particles in the discussions above is only an example to show the general structure of how we calculate with diagrams. In a realistic case, the physical theory (which is itself abstracted from experiments) must tell us what the real observed particles are and how their interaction vertices are constructed. Thus going back to the list of particles in Lecture 1, we must be able to give the wave functions and propagators for each species and then to write down all the vertices by which they interact. This will be the subject matter for most of the rest of this set of lectures.

We start by considering a simple and familiar example, the electromagnetic interaction. The particle associated with the electromagnetic field is the photon, which can be described by a 4-vector field. If we consider the Maxwell equations, we notice that a 4-vector composed of the electrostatic potential (A_0) as the time-component and the traditional vector potential ($\vec{A}$) (as the spatial components) can be used to obtain the electric and magnetic fields. In other words, we can use a 4-vector $A_\mu = (A_0, -\vec{A})$ to describe the electromagnetic field. As a reminder, the standard electric and magnetic fields are related to these by

$$\vec{E} = -\frac{\partial \vec{A}}{\partial t} - \nabla A_0, \qquad \vec{B} = \nabla \times \vec{A} \tag{4.14}$$

Now we need a propagator for the photon (γ). Photons are massless particles, so we can use a form similar to (3.35) with $m = 0$; but we have four components for A_μ, so we expect it to be of the form

$$D_{\mu\nu}(x, y) = -\int \frac{d^4 k}{(2\pi)^4} e^{-ik(x-y)} \frac{i}{k^2 + i\epsilon} \eta_{\mu\nu} \tag{4.15}$$

We need a quantity with indices μ, ν on the right hand side; but it must be Lorentz invariant, so we choose it to be the metric $\eta_{\mu\nu}$. We have seen this in the first lecture; it has the following properties:

$$\eta_{\mu\nu} = \begin{cases} \eta_{00} = 1 \\ \eta_{ij} = -\delta_{ij}, \qquad i, j = 1, 2, 3 \\ \eta_{0i} = 0 \end{cases} \tag{4.16}$$

(We used $g_{\mu\nu}$ for the spacetime metric, but from now on, we will reserve it for the metric on a general spacetime and use the symbol $\eta_{\mu\nu}$ for the metric for flat spacetime.) We will also need a wave function for the photon. Being the free particle wave function, it should be of the form

$$A_\mu(x) = \frac{1}{\sqrt{2\omega_k V}}\, \epsilon_\mu(k)\, e^{-ikx} = \frac{1}{\sqrt{2\omega_k V}}\, \epsilon_\mu(k)\, e^{-i\omega_k x_0 + i\vec{k}\cdot\vec{x}} \qquad (4.17)$$

Again, since A_μ is a 4-vector, we need a quantity which is a 4-vector on the right hand side to balance the indices (and, hence, the transformation properties). This is indicated by $\epsilon_\mu(k)$; it is the polarization vector of the photon.

Remark 4.1.

An aside on the number of states

The formula for the number of states is familiar from Statistical Mechanics. We know that to find the number of states we compute the ratio of the volume of phase space to $(2\pi\hbar)^3$. In our case this is $V d^3 p/(2\pi)^3$, since we use units with $\hbar = 1$.

One way to obtain the result directly is to consider particles in a given volume. For simplicity, consider a one-dimensional box of length L, say, from $x = 0$ to $x = L$. For free particles, wave functions are of the form $\psi \sim e^{ikx}$. Choose the periodic boundary condition $\psi(0) = \psi(L)$. (The final result will not be sensitive to the precise nature of the boundary condition.) This condition gives $e^{ikx} = e^{ikL} = 1$, which implies that $k = \frac{2\pi n}{L}$, where n is an integer, $n = 0, \pm 1, \pm 2, \cdots$. As L becomes large, the difference in the value of k between consecutive values of n, namely, $\Delta k = 2\pi/L$ becomes infinitesimal, so that k can be considered as almost a continuous variable. Summation over n can be approximated by integration. Thus we can expect

$$\sum_n f(k) = \int dn\, f(k), \qquad \text{as } L \to \infty$$

$$= \int \frac{L\, dk}{2\pi} f(k) \qquad (4.18)$$

In three dimensions, we get a similar factor for each dimension, giving

$$\sum_{n_1, n_2, n_3} f(k) = \int \frac{L^3\, dk_1\, dk_2\, dk_3}{(2\pi)^3} f(k) = \int V \frac{d^3 k}{(2\pi)^3} f(k) \qquad (4.19)$$

This gives the result for the number of states. This is only from the translational degrees of freedom of the particle and so it applies to a particle with no spin. For particles with spin, a similar result holds for each independent spin direction.

Remark 4.2.
Simplification of the amplitude

The amplitude for the scattering of two φ particles via χ exchange was obtained to the lowest nontrivial order as $\mathcal{A}_1 + \mathcal{A}_2$, with the expressions for $\mathcal{A}_1$ and $\mathcal{A}_2$ given in (4.11) and (4.13). To calculate the cross section, we must take the square $|\mathcal{A}_1 + \mathcal{A}_2|^2$, which gives the probability, then find the rate and divide by the flux of incoming particles. We will carry out such a calculation in detail later. But for now, we will consider the simplification of one of the terms, say, $\mathcal{A}_1$ for special cases to illustrate the nature of the interaction. Even though this is not absolutely essential for our later discussions, it is a good instructive calculation. We take φ's to be heavy particles, compared to the momenta involved. Then $p_{10} = \Omega_{p_1} \approx M + (\vec{p}_1^2/2M)$, $p_{20} \approx M + (\vec{p}_2^2/2M)$, etc. This means that we can write

$$(p_{10} - k_{10})^2 \approx \left(\frac{\vec{p}_1^2 - \vec{k}_1^2}{2M} \right)^2 \ll (\vec{p}_1 - \vec{k}_1)^2 \qquad (4.20)$$

Thus

$$\mathcal{A}_1 \approx (i\lambda)^2 \prod \frac{1}{\sqrt{2\Omega_p V}} (2\pi)^4 \delta^{(4)}(p_1 + p_2 - k_1 - k_2) \frac{(-i)}{(\vec{p}_1 - \vec{k}_1)^2 + m^2} \qquad (4.21)$$

We can notice several things about this amplitude. First of all, we have the simplification,

$$(\vec{p}_1 - \vec{k}_1)^2 = \vec{p}_1^2 + \vec{k}_1^2 - 2\vec{p}_1 \cdot \vec{k}_1 = \vec{p}_1^2 + \vec{k}_1^2 - 2|\vec{p}_1|\,|\vec{k}_1| \cos\theta$$

where θ is the angle between the incoming momentum $\vec{p}_1$ and the outgoing momentum $\vec{k}_1$. If we neglect the change in the energy (elastic scattering, which is reasonable for nonrelativistic scattering), $|\vec{p}_1| \approx |\vec{k}_1|$, and

$$(\vec{p}_1 - \vec{k}_1)^2 \approx 4\,|\vec{p}_1|^2 \sin^2(\theta/2) \qquad (4.22)$$

If the exchanged particle has zero mass, $m = 0$, then we get a factor like (4.22) in the denominator of $\mathcal{A}_1$. In $|\mathcal{A}_1|^2$ we get a factor

$$\frac{1}{16\,|\vec{p}_1|^4 \sin^4(\theta/2)}$$

which is characteristic of Rutherford scattering. (We have used a scalar particle; for the Rutherford scattering, we need a photon exchange, but the mathematics is similar.)

A second observation is about how a potential description is possible in the nonrelativistic case. We start with the relation

$$\int d^3x \, e^{i\vec{q}\cdot\vec{x}} \frac{e^{-mr}}{r} = 2\pi \int_0^\infty dr\, r^2 \left(\frac{e^{iqr} - e^{-iqr}}{iqr} \right) \frac{e^{-mr}}{r}$$

$$= \frac{2\pi}{iq} \int_0^\infty dr \left[e^{-(m-iq)r} - e^{-(m+iq)r} \right]$$

$$= \frac{2\pi}{iq} \left[\frac{1}{m-iq} - \frac{1}{m+iq} \right]$$

$$= \frac{4\pi}{\vec{q}^2 + m^2} \tag{4.23}$$

In these formulae, q denotes $|\vec{q}|$. Using (4.23), we may write

$$\frac{1}{(\vec{p}_1 - \vec{k}_1)^2 + m^2} = \frac{1}{4\pi} \int d^3x \, e^{i(\vec{p}_1 - \vec{k}_1)\cdot\vec{x}} \, \frac{e^{-mr}}{r} \tag{4.24}$$

This shows that the factor $\lambda^2/[(\vec{p}_1 - \vec{k}_1)^2 + m^2]$, which appears in the amplitude $\mathcal{A}_1$ in (4.21) may be viewed as arising from an interaction potential between the φ-particles, the potential being

$$V(r) = \frac{\lambda^2}{4\pi} \frac{e^{-mr}}{r} \tag{4.25}$$

So this simplification we have done shows how the potential description can be recovered in the nonrelativistic limit. The specific potential (4.25) obtained in this problem is of the Yukawa type. This is because it is due to the exchange of a massive particle, namely, χ in our case. Notice that if $m \neq 0$, the potential has a finite range, of the order of $1/m$.

Chapter 5

Photons and the Electromagnetic Field

We are now ready to start discussing a more realistic theory, namely, of photons and the electromagnetic interaction, and on quantum electrodynamics (QED), which is truly a marvelous sub-theory embedded in the Standard Model. Photons are the quanta of the electromagnetic field. The Maxwell equations show that the electric and magnetic fields are dynamical, evolving in time as given by the equations or, equivalently, in a way controlled by a Hamiltonian. Thus they can, and must, be quantized just as any dynamical system should be. The eigenstates of the Hamiltonian, the energy eigenstates, for the free Maxwell theory (without currents or charge densities) are the photons. These particles are therefore central to electromagnetic interactions. While all this can be obtained by applying the principles of quantization to the fields themselves, here we will continue with our strategy of focusing on propagators and vertices and constructing Feynman diagrams.

We have already talked about two key results for the electromagnetic field or, in particle language, for the photon. We wrote down the propagator for the photon as

$$D_{\mu\nu}(x,y) = -\int \frac{d^4k}{(2\pi)^4} \, e^{-ik(x-y)} \, \frac{i}{k^2 + i\epsilon} \, \eta_{\mu\nu} \tag{5.1}$$

We also wrote down the wave function for a photon as

$$A_\mu(x) = \frac{1}{\sqrt{2\omega_k V}} \, \epsilon_\mu(k) \, e^{-ikx} = \frac{1}{\sqrt{2\omega_k V}} \, \epsilon_\mu(k) \, e^{-i\omega_k x_0 + i\vec{k}\cdot\vec{x}} \tag{5.2}$$

In this equation for the wave function, ϵ_μ is the polarization vector. (Also, as a reminder, our notation is such that $kx = k \cdot x = k_0 x_0 - \vec{k} \cdot \vec{x}$.) There are two independent components for the polarization of a photon. This can be seen easily from the Maxwell equations, which are, in the standard form using $\vec{E}$ and $\vec{B}$ fields,

$$\nabla \cdot \vec{B} = 0$$

$$\nabla \times \vec{E} + \frac{\partial \vec{B}}{\partial t} = 0 \tag{5.3}$$

$$\nabla \cdot \vec{E} = 0$$

$$\nabla \times \vec{B} - \frac{\partial \vec{E}}{\partial t} = 0 \tag{5.4}$$

The first two of these equations hold even in the presence of a charge density or current, and are called the sourceless Maxwell equations. They lead to the existence of the electrostatic and vector potentials,

$$\vec{E} = -\frac{\partial \vec{A}}{\partial t} - \nabla A_0, \qquad \vec{B} = \nabla \times \vec{A} \tag{5.5}$$

with $A^\mu = (A_0, \vec{A})$, $A_\mu = \eta_{\mu\nu} A^\nu = (A_0, -\vec{A})$. Equations in (5.4) are modified if we have charge and current densities. Here we have written them out for the case of vacuum.

If we take a plane wave ansatz

$$\vec{E} = E_0 \, \vec{\epsilon} \, e^{-i\omega t + i\vec{k}\cdot\vec{x}}, \qquad \vec{B} = B_0 \, \vec{\epsilon}' \, e^{-i\omega t + i\vec{k}\cdot\vec{x}} \tag{5.6}$$

we find that $\vec{B}$ is determined in terms of $\vec{E}$ by the second equation in (5.3), namely, Faraday's law. This gives $\vec{k} \times \vec{\epsilon} = \omega\vec{\epsilon}'$. Further, the condition $\nabla \cdot \vec{E} = 0$ becomes $\vec{k} \cdot \vec{\epsilon} = 0$, which shows that $\vec{\epsilon}$ must be orthogonal to the direction of propagation given by $\vec{k}$. This leaves two independent directions for $\vec{\epsilon}$ which are the two possible polarization states for the electromagnetic wave, or for the photon, once we shift to the quantum point of view. In the 4-dimensional language, we may represent the polarization vector as

$$\epsilon_\mu = (0, \vec{\epsilon}), \qquad \vec{k} \cdot \vec{\epsilon} = 0 \tag{5.7}$$

The two independent polarizations may be chosen in many ways, since a vector orthogonal to $\vec{k}$ can be rotated around $\vec{k}$ and will still remain orthogonal to it. A simple choice for the two independent polarizations is

$$\vec{\epsilon}^{(1)} = \frac{(-k_2, k_1, 0)}{\sqrt{k_1^2 + k_2^2}}, \qquad \vec{\epsilon}^{(2)} = \frac{\vec{k} \times \vec{\epsilon}^{(1)}}{|k|} \tag{5.8}$$

where $\vec{k} = (k_1, k_2, k_3)$. Any rotation of (5.8) around $\vec{k}$ will do as well. One could also consider combinations like $\frac{1}{\sqrt{2}}\left[\vec{\epsilon}^{(1)} \pm i\,\vec{\epsilon}^{(2)}\right]$ which correspond to (left and right) circular polarizations.

Once we have the propagator and the wave function, we can consider processes involving the photon. But for this, we also need the vertices. One way to think about them is to consider all possible vertices, work out experimental consequences and then eliminate many as being incompatible with experiment. This would be the experimental way to determine the vertices and, in fact, this is more or less what was done historically, going back to the nineteenth century (although it was not phrased in our language of vertices and propagators). But now we have a better understanding, and while experiments ultimately tell us what the vertices should be, we can eliminate many choices from the outset based on symmetry and other considerations. So here we will discuss the vertices from a more theoretical point of view.

There is a quantity which serves as the focal point of most of the discussion in physics; this is the Lagrangian or action for a theory. We shall see that the action contains information about propagators and vertices. Further, the action should have the symmetries displayed by the physics. Ultimately, various terms in the action are distilled from experiments, but the process is guided by symmetries and general principles of quantum mechanics. We would thus want to identify the key concepts which go into the construction of the action for all particle interactions; that would be the essence of particle physics. We can now see how this strategy unfolds by taking electrodynamics as an example.

For the free electromagnetic field, the action is given by

$$S = \int d^4x \, \frac{1}{2}(\vec{E} \cdot \vec{E} - \vec{B} \cdot \vec{B}) = \int d^4x \, \frac{1}{2}(E^2 - B^2) \qquad (5.9)$$

Notice that d^4x is invariant under Lorentz transformations; so is the combination $E^2 - B^2$, although it is less obvious. (This invariance will become apparent as we go on.) We will start by checking that the action (5.9) does lead to the Maxwell equations. Since the sourceless equations are identities if we use the potentials in (5.5), we do not need to derive them; we only need to show how (5.4) arise as the variational equations for (5.9). For this, it is useful to first rewrite the electric field as

$$E_i = \frac{\partial A_i}{\partial t} - \partial_i A_0 = \partial_0 A_i - \partial_i A_0 \qquad (5.10)$$

Traditionally the spatial vector components are identified via $A^\mu = (A^0, \vec{A})$, so that A_i carry an additional minus sign. The components of the magnetic field are

$$B^i = -\frac{1}{2}\epsilon^{ijk}(\partial_j A_k - \partial_k A_j) \qquad (5.11)$$

Here ϵ^{ijk} is the completely antisymmetric symbol in three dimensions, with $\epsilon^{123} = 1$. In terms of these, we see that

$$E^2 - B^2 = (\partial_0 A_i - \partial_i A_0)^2 - \frac{1}{2}(\partial_j A_i - \partial_i A_j)(\partial_j A_i - \partial_i A_j) \qquad (5.12)$$

The action for the electromagnetic field can thus be written as

$$S = \int d^4x \left[\frac{1}{2}(\partial_0 A_i - \partial_i A_0)^2 - \frac{1}{4}(\partial_j A_i - \partial_i A_j)(\partial_j A_i - \partial_i A_j)\right] \qquad (5.13)$$

Upon varying the fields, we get

$$\delta S = \int d^4x \left[E_i\left(\partial_0\delta A_i - \partial_i\delta A_0\right) - \partial_j\delta A_i(\partial_j A_i - \partial_i A_j)\right]$$

$$= \int d^4x \left[\left[-\frac{\partial E_i}{\partial t} + \partial_j(\partial_j A_i - \partial_i A_j)\right]\delta A_i + (\partial_i E_i)\,\delta A_0\right] \qquad (5.14)$$

We carried out a partial integration to go from the first line of this equation to the second.[1] Since the variations δA_0 and δA_i can be arbitrary functions, the only way δS can be zero (for any δA_0, δA_i) is if the coefficients of these variations in (5.14) vanish. The equations of motion (or the variational equations) are thus

$$-\frac{\partial E_i}{\partial t} + \partial_j(\partial_j A_i - \partial_i A_j) = 0$$

$$\partial_i E_i = 0 \qquad (5.15)$$

It is easy to verify that $\partial_j(\partial_j A_i - \partial_i A_j)$ agrees with the components of $\nabla \times \nabla \times \vec{A}$, so that these equations are identical to (5.4), thus identifying the action (5.9) or (5.13) as the correct action for the Maxwell equations.

We can combine the terms in the action (5.13) as follows.

$$S = \int d^4x \left[\frac{1}{2}(\partial_0 A_i - \partial_i A_0)(\partial_0 A_j - \partial_j A_0)\,\eta^{00}(-\eta^{ij})\right.$$

$$\left.-\frac{1}{4}(\partial_j A_i - \partial_i A_j)(\partial_k A_l - \partial_l A_k)\,(-\eta^{jk})(-\eta^{il})\right]$$

$$= \int d^4x \left[-\frac{1}{4}\,F_{\mu\nu}\,F_{\alpha\beta}\,\eta^{\mu\alpha}\,\eta^{\nu\beta}\right] \qquad (5.16)$$

where

$$F_{\mu\nu} = \partial_\mu A_\nu - \partial_\nu A_\mu \qquad (5.17)$$

The $F_{\mu\nu}$, which is usually referred to as the field strength tensor, is in terms of the 4-vector ∂_μ and the 4-vector A_μ; the contractions over the indices

---

[1]Recall that in deriving the equations of motion via the variational principle we must consider variations which vanish on the boundaries, so these partial integrations are justified.

are done using the spacetime metric in the action. Thus we see that the action is indeed Lorentz invariant.

It is also useful to write the action in a slightly different way, by carrying out some partial integrations.[2]

$$
\begin{aligned}
S &= \int d^4x \left[-\frac{1}{4} F_{\mu\nu} F_{\alpha\beta} \, \eta^{\mu\alpha} \, \eta^{\nu\beta} \right] \\
&= -\frac{1}{2} \int d^4x \left[\partial_\mu A_\nu \left(\partial^\mu A^\nu - \partial^\nu A^\mu \right) \right] \\
&= -\frac{1}{2} \int d^4x \, A_\nu (-\Box) A^\nu + \frac{1}{2} \int d^4x \, (\partial_\mu A^\mu)(\partial^\nu A_\nu) \\
&= -\frac{1}{2} \int d^4x \, A_\mu (-\Box) A_\nu \, \eta^{\mu\nu} + \frac{1}{2} \int d^4x \, (\partial_\mu A^\mu)^2
\end{aligned}
\tag{5.18}
$$

where $\Box$ is the differential operator

$$
\Box = \partial_\mu \partial^\mu = \eta^{\mu\nu} \frac{\partial}{\partial x^\mu} \frac{\partial}{\partial x^\nu} = \frac{\partial^2}{\partial t^2} - \nabla^2
\tag{5.19}
$$

Notice that $\Box$, known as the d'Alembertian or the wave operator, is Lorentz invariant by construction. Since there are only two independent polarizations, there is redundancy in using the four components of A_μ; so one can choose them to obey a condition

$$
\partial_\mu A_\nu \, \eta^{\mu\nu} = \partial_\mu A^\mu = \nabla \cdot \vec{A} + \frac{\partial A_0}{\partial t} = 0
\tag{5.20}
$$

This is known as the Lorentz gauge condition. (The redundancy is related to what is known as the gauge symmetry of the Maxwell theory. We will discuss this in more detail later and we will see that it is always possible to choose certain conditions on the A_μ, such as this.) With this choice, the action (5.18) reduces to

$$
S = -\frac{1}{2} \int d^4x \, \eta^{\mu\nu} \left[A_\mu (-\Box) A_\nu \right]
\tag{5.21}
$$

We have already seen that the action (5.9) which is identical to (5.16) is Lorentz invariant. The Lorentz gauge condition (5.20) is invariant as well, so is the action (5.21).We have thus demonstrated the Lorentz invariance of the Maxwell theory, at least in vacuum.

However, more to our point is that the differential operator in (5.21) is related to the propagator. For this, we consider the inverse of the differential

---

[2]These partial integrations produce boundary terms as well; we take the boundary terms to be zero, taking the fields or their derivatives to vanish on the boundary or to obey some suitable periodic boundary conditions.

operator involved. For a matrix M, with matrix elements M_{ij}, the inverse is defined by $(M^{-1})_{ik} M_{kj} = \mathbb{1} = \delta_{ij}$, where $\mathbb{1}$ is the identity matrix. For functions, the analogue of the identity matrix is the Dirac δ-function. The definition of the inverse of $\Box$, which we will denote by $D(x,y)$, is thus $\Box_x D(x,y) = \delta^{(4)}(x-y)$. We will actually use $i\Box$; thus its inverse $D(x,y)$ is given by

$$i \Box_x D(x,y) = \delta^{(4)}(x-y) \tag{5.22}$$

We can write $D(x,y)$ by Fourier transform as

$$D(x,y) = \int \frac{d^4k}{(2\pi)^4} D(k) e^{-ik(x-y)} \tag{5.23}$$

(Recall that in our very abbreviated notation $k(x-y) = k_0(x_0 - y_0) - \vec{k} \cdot (\vec{x} - \vec{y})$.) Applying $i\Box$ to this,

$$i \Box_x D(x,y) = \int \frac{d^4k}{(2\pi)^4} D(k) i \left(-k_0^2 + \vec{k} \cdot \vec{k} \right) e^{-ik(x-y)} \tag{5.24}$$

We want the right hand side to be

$$\delta^{(4)}(x-y) = \int \frac{d^4k}{(2\pi)^4} e^{-ik(x-y)} \tag{5.25}$$

This can be achieved if we choose $D(k) = (i/(k_0^2 - \vec{k}^2))$, so that

$$D(x,y) = \int \frac{d^4k}{(2\pi)^4} \frac{i}{k_0^2 - \vec{k} \cdot \vec{k} + i\epsilon} e^{-ik(x-y)} \tag{5.26}$$

In this expression, we have also put in the $i\epsilon$ to handle the potential singularity at $k_0^2 = \vec{k}^2$. Notice that this is the propagator, for the photon for one component (one choice of μ, ν, specifically one spatial component for this case).

This calculation shows that there is a simple relation between the term in the action which is quadratic in the fields and the propagator. We may restate this as follows.

Prop 5.1 (Rule 1). In the action for any field, the term which is quadratic in the fields is of the form $\frac{1}{2} \int$ (field) K (field), where K is a differential operator. The propagator for the corresponding particle is given by the inverse of $-i K$.

(The $i\epsilon$ has to be put in separately. Also if we have complex fields, we write the quadratic term as $\int$(field*) K(field); the propagator is given by the inverse of $-i K$ again.) We have not justified this rule; we have only shown that our calculation of the inverse to $i\square$ is very suggestive of this rule. The full justification for this comes from quantum field theory, which will also pick the correct $i\epsilon$ prescription. We shall take Prop. 5.1 as a working rule and proceed. In applying this rule to the action (5.21), we will get the propagator (5.1); this can be done for each of the components separately. Note that the A_0-term has a different sign compared to the A_i-terms in (5.21); this is nicely reflected in the different signs for the corresponding propagators due to the sign difference between the spatial and time-components of $\eta_{\mu\nu}$ and is consistent with (5.1).

We must now consider vertices which capture the interaction of photons with charged particles. For this, it is useful to recall the standard way of coupling charged particles to electric and magnetic fields. This is familiar from the nonrelativistic quantum mechanics of single particles, like the electron. The rule used there is the minimal coupling, which involves replacing the momentum operator $\hat{p}$ by $\hat{p} - qA$, where q is the charge of the particle. Since $\hat{p} = -i\nabla$, this amounts to $\nabla \to \nabla - iq\vec{A}$, or, in the fully relativistic sense, $(\partial/\partial x^\mu) \to (\partial/\partial x^\mu) + iqA_\mu$, with $A_\mu = (A_0, -\vec{A})$. There is a deeper reason for this rule, based on gauge symmetry, which we shall explore later. But for now, we will take this as another working rule and proceed.

Prop 5.2 (Rule 2). The coupling of a charged particle (of charge q) to the electromagnetic field or the photon is given by replacing the derivative ∂_μ of the field by $\partial_\mu + iqA_\mu$ for all terms in the action.

Now that we have this rule, we are ready to construct Lagrangians and vertices. The electron is a particle of spin $\frac{1}{2}$, so is the proton. We have not yet discussed particles with spin. So the simplest case to consider at this stage would be a particle of zero spin. If a particular example is desired to make this more concrete, think of the π^+ (or π^-) meson. Let us denote the field for this by ϕ. (Recall what we said earlier: Every particle species has a corresponding field.) What can we write for the action for the free particle? The π-meson has a mass, so mass is important. Further, we know that the propagator for a massive spin-zero particle (and hence the pion propagator) must have the form (3.35), namely,

$$G(x, y) = \int \frac{d^4 p}{(2\pi)^4} e^{-ip(x-y)} \frac{i}{p^2 - m^2 + i\epsilon} \tag{5.27}$$

The action must also be Lorentz-invariant. So we can write it down as

$$S = \frac{1}{2} \int d^4 x \, \phi \left[-\frac{\partial^2}{\partial t^2} + \nabla^2 - m^2 \right] \phi \tag{5.28}$$

In accordance with Rule 1, this will give the propagator (5.27). Further, S is Lorentz-invariant, since it only involves the combination $\Box$ and the field ϕ, which is a Lorentz-invariant quantity, being a scalar. We can rewrite S, by partial integrations, as

$$S = \frac{1}{2} \int d^4x \left[\left(\frac{\partial \phi}{\partial t} \right)^2 - (\nabla \phi)^2 - m^2 \phi^2 \right] \tag{5.29}$$

Now we can use Rule 2 to include the coupling to the photon by upgrading S to the form

$$S = \frac{1}{2} \int d^4x \left[\left(\frac{\partial \phi}{\partial t} + ieA_0\, \phi \right)^2 - \left(\partial_i \phi + ieA_i \phi \right)^2 - m^2 \phi^2 \right] \tag{5.30}$$

where we take $q = e$. We are almost done, but there is a catch. In this action, the term linear in A_i, for example, is (up to the overall factor of $\frac{1}{2}$)

$$-ie \int A_i (\phi\, \partial_i \phi + \partial_i \phi\, \phi)$$

Since the field ϕ is real, this term is not real and the action is not real. We can compensate by adding the complex conjugate, but then this coupling term will vanish. (Similar argument applies to the A_0 term as well. Another way to notice this is to write the term given above, by partial integration as $-ie \int A_i \partial_i (\phi^2) = ie \int \partial_i A_i\, \phi^2$. Combining this with the similar term from the A_0 part, we get $ie \int (\partial_i A_i - \partial_0 A_0) \phi^2 = -ie \int (\partial_\mu A^\mu) \phi^2$ which vanishes by the Lorentz gauge condition (5.20). Thus by choosing a subsidiary condition, we can make the interaction vanish. Clearly that is not good.) The only way to avoid this is to make ϕ complex. In that case, we will need to use ϕ^* for some of the terms in S. In fact, we can see that

$$S = \int d^4x \left[\left(\frac{\partial \phi^*}{\partial t} - ieA_0\, \phi^* \right) \left(\frac{\partial \phi}{\partial t} + ieA_0\, \phi \right) \right.$$

$$\left. - (\partial_i \phi^* - ieA_i \phi^*)(\partial_i \phi + ieA_i \phi) - m^2 \phi^* \phi \right]$$

$$= \int d^4x \left[|\partial_0 \phi + ieA_0\, \phi|^2 - |\partial_i \phi + ieA_i \phi|^2 - m^2 \phi^* \phi \right]$$

$$= \int d^4x \left[\eta^{\mu\nu}(\partial_\mu \phi^* - ieA_\mu \phi^*)(\partial_\nu \phi + ieA_\nu \phi) - m^2 \phi^* \phi \right] \tag{5.31}$$

is a Lorentz invariant (and real-valued) action. Further, by construction, it has the correct propagator, it is in accord with Rule 2 and it does not have vanishing coupling between A_μ and the field ϕ. (The pre-factor of $\frac{1}{2}$ was used in (5.28) and (5.29) because the variation with respect to ϕ gave a factor of 2. Here, we have ϕ and ϕ^*, which can be varied independently, and do not produce a factor of 2. So we do not use the pre-factor of $\frac{1}{2}$.) We may state the arguments which led to (5.31) as another rule we must take account of.

Prop 5.3 (Rule 3). The fields corresponding to charged particles are in general complex and the action must involve the derivatives and their complex conjugates in such a way that it is real and respects Rules 1 and 2.

(Note: It is possible to separate out the real and imaginary parts of the field and write things in a way that all fields look real. For example, this may be done for ϕ by writing it as $\phi = \frac{1}{\sqrt{2}}(\phi_1 + i\phi_2)$. This will recover the factors of $\frac{1}{2}$ for the real components ϕ_1, ϕ_2. However, if one does this, there are two real fields for every charged field. This way of writing out the fields is not in contradiction to our Rule 3; it is a restatement of it. Also we may note that since we have a complex field, we identify K from the quadratic term of the action written as (field*)K(field) and the propagator is given by the inverse of $-iK$.)

If we expand out the terms in (5.31), the terms involving products of A's and ϕ's are

$$S_{int} = \int d^4x \, \left[-ieA_\mu \left(\phi^* \partial_\nu \phi - \partial_\nu \phi^* \, \phi \right) + e^2 \phi^* \phi \, A_\mu \, A_\nu \right] \eta^{\mu\nu} \qquad (5.32)$$

Remark 5.1.
About charged particles and minimal coupling

We know that the dynamics of a charged particle in an electromagnetic field is governed by the Lorentz force. The Lagrangian for this is given by

$$L = \frac{1}{2} m \, \dot{x}^i \dot{x}^i - qA_0 - qA_i \dot{x}^i$$
$$= -\frac{1}{2} m \, \eta_{ij} \, \dot{x}^i \dot{x}^j - qA_0 - qA_i \dot{x}^i \qquad (5.33)$$

Since we use a metric tensor with the spatial components being $-\delta_{ij}$, there are a few minus signs we must keep track of. So in the second line of this equation we explicitly introduce the spatial metric. From the Lagrangian, we find

$$\frac{\partial L}{\partial \dot{x}^i} = -m \, \eta_{ij} \, \dot{x}^j - q \, A_i, \qquad \frac{\partial L}{\partial x^i} = -q \, \frac{\partial A_k}{\partial x^i} \, \dot{x}^k - q \, \frac{\partial A_0}{\partial x^i} \qquad (5.34)$$

The action is given by the integral of L from some initial time t_i to a final time t_f; thus the variation of the action is obtained as

$$\delta S = \int_{t_i}^{t_f} dt \left[\frac{\partial L}{\partial x^i} - \frac{d}{dt}\left(\frac{\partial L}{\partial \dot{x}^i}\right) \right] \delta x^i + \Theta(t_f) - \Theta(t_i)$$

$$\Theta(t) = \left[-m\,\eta_{ij}\dot{x}^j - q\,A_i \right] \delta x^i \tag{5.35}$$

Since the boundary term can be ignored for the variational principle, the Euler-Lagrange equation (or the equation of motion) is given by

$$\frac{d}{dt}\left(\frac{\partial L}{\partial \dot{x}^i}\right) = \frac{\partial L}{\partial x^i} \tag{5.36}$$

In the present case this becomes

$$-m\,\eta_{ij}\ddot{x}^j - q\frac{\partial A_i}{\partial x^k}\dot{x}^k - q\frac{\partial A_i}{\partial t} = -q\frac{\partial A_k}{\partial x^i}\dot{x}^k - q\frac{\partial A_0}{\partial x^i} \tag{5.37}$$

(In taking derivatives, we must keep in mind that A_i can depend on time through its argument x and also it can have a separate explicit dependence. This gives the additional $\partial A/\partial t$ term.) Rearranging terms, this becomes

$$m\,\ddot{x}^i = -q\,E^i - q\,\eta^{ij}\left(\partial_k A_j - \partial_j A_k\right)\dot{x}^k \tag{5.38}$$

Working out the components of the last term, this can be seen to be identical to the Lorentz force equation

$$m\frac{d^2\vec{x}}{dt^2} = q\,\vec{E} + q\,(\dot{\vec{x}} \times \vec{B}) \tag{5.39}$$

This confirms (5.33) as the action for the charged particle in an electromagnetic field. (In making this identification, we must keep in mind that the components of $\vec{A}$ are usually identified as A^i.)

The Hamiltonian for the charged particle is obtained as

$$H \equiv \frac{\partial L}{\partial \dot{x}^i}\,\dot{x}^i - L == -\frac{1}{2}m\,\eta_{ij}\dot{x}^i\dot{x}^j + qA_0 \tag{5.40}$$

This can be written in terms of the canonical momenta, but we will leave it as it is for now.

In transcribing this to quantum mechanics, the basic observation is that the wave function $\psi \sim e^{iS}$ and so it changes under a small change of x^i as $\delta\psi = i\,\Theta\,\psi$. This tells us that

$$-i\frac{\partial\psi}{\partial x^i} = \left[-m\,\eta_{ij}\dot{x}^j - q\,A_i\right]\psi \tag{5.41}$$

The Hamiltonian operator in the quantum theory is thus given by

$$H = \frac{1}{2\,m}\,\eta^{ij}(\partial_i + i\,q\,A_i)(\partial_j + i\,q\,A_j) + q\,A_0 \tag{5.42}$$

This shows how the prescription $\partial_i \to \partial_i + i\,q\,A_i$ emerges.

It is also useful to see how this works out for a relativistic particle. The action is then given by

$$S = -m \int \sqrt{\eta_{\mu\nu}dx^\mu dx^\nu} - q \int A_\mu\, dx^\mu \qquad (5.43)$$

The free part of the action is the spacetime length of the path of the particle. Minimization of this length gives the classical trajectory; thus the true trajectory of the particle is the path of minimal spacetime distance between the initial and final points. Relativistic particle mechanics amounts to a spacetime generalization of the familiar result that the minimization of the Euclidean distance in three dimensions gives a straight line.

We can parametrize the path in terms of a single variable τ, taking x^μ as functions of τ. Writing $dx^\mu = \dot{x}^\mu\, d\tau$, this action can be written as

$$S = \int d\tau \left[-m\, \sqrt{\eta_{\mu\nu}\dot{x}^\mu \dot{x}^\nu} - q\, A_\mu \dot{x}^\mu \right] \qquad (5.44)$$

From the variation of the action, we find

$$\Theta = -m\, \eta_{\mu\nu} \frac{\dot{x}^\nu}{\sqrt{\dot{x}^2}} - q\, A_\mu \qquad (5.45)$$

This leads to

$$\left[-i \frac{\partial}{\partial x^\mu} + q\, A_\mu \right] \psi = -m\, \eta_{\mu\nu} \frac{\dot{x}^\nu}{\sqrt{\dot{x}^2}}\, \psi \qquad (5.46)$$

In other words, $-m\dot{x}_\mu/\sqrt{\dot{x}^2}$ should be interpreted as the operator $-i\partial_\mu + q\,A_\mu$. By taking the square of the operator, we get the condition

$$\left[\eta^{\mu\nu}\, (\partial_\mu + i\,q\,A_\mu)(\partial_\nu + i\,q\,A_\nu) + m^2 \right]\psi = 0 \qquad (5.47)$$

This is the Klein-Gordon equation for a relativistic spin zero particle. There are inconsistencies in treating this as a wave equation within the realm of one-particle quantum mechanics. But it can be consistently interpreted as a field equation for a spin zero particle.

Chapter 6

Processes with Photons

In the last lecture we talked about the photon propagator and how we can couple charged particles to the electromagnetic field (and the photon). The principle we have enunciated seems very general and one can ask if it is truly universal. Is the coupling of the photon to any charged particle given by this principle? The answer is that it works for a charged point particle. If we consider a composite particle, then we can apply the same principle to the charged point particles which make up the composite particle of interest. The coupling of the photon to a field which represents the whole composite particle has to be obtained from the coupling of the fundamental constituents. This may show different or additional vertices at the level of the composite particles. We will comment again on this matter later. But for now, we continue with the construction of diagrams and processes with photons.

We wrote down the action for a spin zero particle (like the charged π-meson) as

$$S = \int d^4x \; [\partial_t \phi^* \, \partial_t \phi - \nabla \phi^* \, \nabla \phi - m^2 \phi^* \phi]$$

$$= \int d^4x \; \phi^* (-\Box - m^2) \phi \tag{6.1}$$

where $\Box = \frac{\partial^2}{\partial t^2} - \nabla^2$. The coupling of this field/particle (taken to be of charge e) to the photon was introduced by the prescription $\partial_\mu \to \partial_\mu + ieA_\mu$, which led to the following action for a charged spin zero particle coupled to the photon,

$$S = \int d^4x \; [|\partial_t \phi + ieA_0 \, \phi|^2 - |\partial_i \phi + ieA_i \, \phi|^2 - m^2 \phi^* \phi] \tag{6.2}$$

The term in S which is quadratic in the field ϕ (with no A's), namely,

$$S^{(2)} = \int d^4x \; \phi^* (-\Box - m^2) \phi, \tag{6.3}$$

determines the propagator, while the terms with higher numbers of fields of any kind will tell us what the vertices (relevant for interactions) are. The higher-than-quadratic terms in (6.2) are given by

$$S_{int} = \int d^4x \; \left[-ieA_\mu \left(\phi^* \partial_\nu \phi - \partial_\nu \phi^* \, \phi \right) + e^2 \phi^* \phi \, A_\mu \, A_\nu \right] \eta^{\mu\nu} \qquad (6.4)$$

Notice that there is a term with ϕ, ϕ^* and A_μ, and there is a term with two A's and a ϕ and a ϕ^*. Thus there are two types of vertices given by this. They can be represented diagrammatically as shown in Fig. 6.1.

If we make up various possible Feynman diagrams using these and substitute wave functions appropriately, we can calculate the probability amplitudes for various processes. The wave functions for a real scalar field have been given before. Here we are dealing with a complex scalar field, so we need a rule to identify the incoming and outgoing wave functions appropriately. The correct assignment is given as follows.

- $\phi \rightarrow \dfrac{1}{\sqrt{2\Omega_p V}} e^{-ipx}$ for incoming charged particle (of momentum p_μ),

  $\phi^* \rightarrow \dfrac{1}{\sqrt{2\Omega_p V}} e^{-ipx}$ for incoming antiparticle (which will have the opposite charge)

- $\phi^* \rightarrow \dfrac{1}{\sqrt{2\Omega_p V}} e^{ipx}$ for outgoing charged particle,

  $\phi \rightarrow \dfrac{1}{\sqrt{2\Omega_p V}} e^{ipx}$ for outgoing antiparticle.

The rationale for this is easy to see. The charge should have opposite signs for the particle and the antiparticle. If we look at the term $-ieA_\mu(\phi^* \partial_\nu \phi - \partial_\nu \phi^* \, \phi) \, \eta^{\mu\nu}$, we see that interchanging the role of ϕ and ϕ^* gives a minus sign, equivalent to changing the charge e to $-e$. Further wave functions for the incoming particles must correspond to the factor e^{-ipx}. Therefore, for the amplitude for any process, ϕ must be replaced by the wave function with the factor e^{-ipx} for incoming particles and ϕ^* with the wave function with the same e^{-ipx} factor for incoming antiparticles. The assignment for the outgoing particles then follows from a similar argument.

Fig. 6.1: Basic vertices corresponding to the terms in (6.4)

As an example, let us take the first vertex and write down the amplitude for the emission of a photon by the charged particle. It is evidently given by

$$
\mathcal{A} = i(-ie)\frac{\eta^{\mu\nu}}{\sqrt{8\,\omega_k\Omega_p\Omega_{p'}V^3}} \int d^4x \; \epsilon_\mu(k)e^{ikx} \left[e^{ip'x}\partial_\nu e^{-ipx} - (\partial_\nu e^{ip'x})e^{-ipx}\right]
$$

$$
= -ie\frac{1}{\sqrt{8\,\omega_k\Omega_p\Omega_{p'}V^3}} \int d^4x \; \epsilon_\mu(p_\nu + p'_\nu)\eta^{\mu\nu}\, e^{i(k+p'-p)x}
$$

$$
= -ie\,\epsilon \cdot (p+p')\,\frac{(2\pi)^4(\delta^{(4)}(p-k-p'))}{\sqrt{8\,\omega_k\Omega_p\Omega_{p'}V^3}} \tag{6.5}
$$

where $\omega_k = |\vec{k}|$, $\Omega_p = \sqrt{p^2 + m^2}$, $\Omega_{p'} = \sqrt{p'^2 + m^2}$. This gives the amplitude for the emission of a photon of momentum k and polarization ϵ_μ by the charged particle of momentum p. (Strictly speaking, when you work out the δ-function, you will see that this amplitude is zero, because there is no solution to $p - k - p' = 0$. After all a charged particle moving at constant velocity cannot radiate. Nevertheless the formula illustrates how we can calculate the amplitudes.)

One can consider many other processes arising from the basic vertices (6.4). For any process, we draw all possible Feynman diagrams obtained by combining the basic vertices, and assign the external lines to the incoming and outgoing particles in all possible ways, keeping in mind the rules of assignment given above. The total amplitude is the sum of the amplitudes corresponding to all possible diagrams. The calculations can be ordered in powers of the interaction strength (as given by e) and will be consistent with the conservation laws.

As an example, consider again the scattering of a photon by the charged particle. This is the analogue of Compton scattering but with a spin zero particle rather than the electron. Since we have two cubic vertices and one quartic vertex to consider, the relevant diagrams, to the lowest non-trivial order (of order e^2), are given in Fig. 6.2. For this process, the total amplitude is given by

$$
\mathcal{A} = \mathcal{A}_1 + \mathcal{A}_2 + \mathcal{A}_3 \tag{6.6}
$$

There are many other processes of interest as well. For example, we can consider the scattering of two charged particles, say, the particle and antiparticle, against each other. The diagrams for this are given in Fig. 6.3. They are similar to the diagrams we considered in equations (4.11, 4.13). There are also diagrams which involve more vertices, but with the same

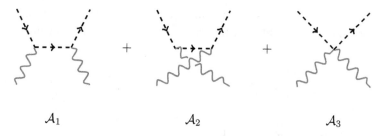

$$\mathcal{A}_1 \qquad\qquad \mathcal{A}_2 \qquad\qquad \mathcal{A}_3$$

Fig. 6.2: Compton process with spin zero particles

choice of external lines, so that the physical process is the same. For example, consider the diagrams shown in Fig. 6.4. The 3-particle vertices carry a factor of e while the 4-particle one has a factor of e^2, as seen from (6.4). As a result these diagrams have a factor of e^4. They can be interpreted as higher order corrections to the basic scattering process of Fig. 6.3, if we view e^2 (or $(e^2/4\pi) \approx 1/137$) as an expansion parameter.

We can also consider diagrams where not all incoming and outgoing particles are actually particles; some of them may represent external fields. Take for instance the bremsstrahlung effect. (The word is German for "braking radiation".) This describes the emission of radiation by a charged particle when it is accelerated or slowed down. We can describe this by Feynman diagrams with two external photon lines, where one of them is the outgoing wave function for the photon while the other is replaced by the external field A_μ, which is the agency causing the acceleration or deceleration. The diagrams would thus look like the ones for Compton scattering, but with one of the photons replaced by the external field. (We show this by an X at the end of the photon line; see Fig. 6.5 for one such diagram.) The external field could be the Coulomb field of a nucleus (as is often the case for charged particles going through a material medium) or something

Fig. 6.3: The scattering of two charged particles

Fig. 6.4: Higher order corrections to scattering of charged particles

else which keeps the charged particles in their trajectory; examples of the latter include radiation from a confined plasma, with A_μ being the field which keeps it confined or the fields of the magnets in a synchrotron which guide the particles around the ring.

The cross section

Most of the scattering processes of interest are two-particle scatterings. This is particularly true in high energy physics where most of the experiments are of this nature. Typically in accelerators, we have either two beams moving in opposite directions which are brought to collision at certain points, or we have one beam which is accelerated and brought to collision with a fixed target. The density or flux of particles is such that (i.e., dilute enough that) essentially all collisions are two-particle collisions. In these cases, a very important quantity is the scattering cross section.

Consider the geometry of the scattering process shown in Fig. 6.6, where, for simplicity, we consider incoming particles scattering against a fixed target. The detectors measure the number of particles scattered into a small solid angle $d\Omega$ at orientation (θ, φ). It is from this data that we work back to identify the nature of the interaction between the particles involved. Clearly, the number of particles is not the quantity which can be compared across different measurements or with theory. For example, if we increase the rate at which the incident particles approach the target, the number of particles scattered off in the direction (θ, φ) will also increase. A good

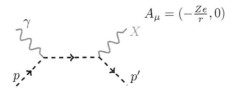

Fig. 6.5: One of the Feynman diagrams which describe bremsstrahlung to the lowest order

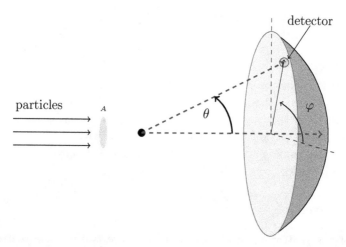

Fig. 6.6: Geometry of a typical scattering on a fixed target

way to measure the rate at which the incident particles are coming in is to look at the number of particles crossing a unit area transverse to their direction (area A in Fig. 6.6) per unit time. This is called the incident flux (or intensity or luminosity). What we are saying is that different labs or even different experiments may have different luminosities, so the number of particles scattered in a given direction is not what is intrinsic to the process. Likewise, if we continue running the scattering process over a long time with identical incoming flux, then the total number observed will increase in proportion to the running time as well. Thus a quantity which is relevant is

$$d\sigma = \text{Number of scattered particles per unit time observed in solid angle}$$
$$d\Omega \text{ in the direction } (\theta, \varphi) \text{ per unit of flux}$$
$$= \frac{\text{Rate of scattering into } d\Omega(\theta, \varphi)}{\text{Flux}} \tag{6.7}$$

Once $d\sigma$ is given for any scattering process, we can multiply it by the flux (which may depend on which accelerator or which lab is used) to get the number observed at $d\Omega(\theta, \varphi)$ per unit time. A further multiplication by the total running time T will give the total number of events observed at $d\Omega(\theta, \varphi)$. Notice that the total number is thus given by $d\sigma \times (N_{inc}/A\,t) \times T$. From this we see that $d\sigma$ has the dimensions of an area; it is called the differential cross section for the scattering. We can also define the total cross section (also with units of area) by integrating over all angles,

$$\int_{\text{all angles}} d\sigma = \sigma$$

σ multiplied by the flux and the running time will give all events counting the final state particles scattered into all directions.

The cross section is a measure of the effectiveness of scattering where the effects of the local experimental set-up have been divided out. In other words, it abstracts the essence of the physics from the particular circumstances of experiments. Thus it is the quantity which can be compared to the theoretical calculations. The theoretical calculation is also simplified from this point of view. We can use any convenient set-up, such as particles uniformly distributed in a cubical volume V, and calculate $d\sigma$. The flux appropriate for the theoretical set-up also gets divided out and the $d\sigma$ so obtained, which is no longer sensitive to the arbitrariness of the theoretical set-up, can be compared to experiment.

Chapter 7

Cross Section and Dimensional Analysis

We have discussed the notion of the cross section. It is a central notion in particle physics, in many ways the bread and butter of particle physicists. As emphasized, it is a measure of the strength of the interaction which leads to the scattering, and by simple multiplications with the flux and running time, it gives the number of events. The expression for the cross section will, of course, depend on the momenta of the particles involved and on the nature of the interaction. But, amazingly, the fact that the cross section has the dimensions of an area is actually powerful enough to make some general statements. For this, we first note that the action is a quantity with no dimensions at all. It has the dimension of *Energy* × *Time*, which is dimensionless in natural units. Another way to think about this is to note that in the usual units, S had the dimensions of $\hbar$, but since we use units in which $\hbar = 1$, S has no dimension. Thus $\dim[S] = 0$. Equivalently, we may say that we are really using $S/\hbar$ when we speak of the action.

Let us now return to the electromagnetic interaction of a charged particle. Recall that the dimension of any quantity can be expressed in terms of the energy unit. Thus if we look at the leading term in the action for ϕ,

$$S^{(2)} = \int d^4x \, \left[\partial_\mu \phi^* \, \partial_\nu \phi \, \eta^{\mu\nu} - m^2 \phi^* \phi \right], \tag{7.1}$$

we can count dimensions (in units of energy) as follows. From the first term

$$2 \dim[\phi] + 2 \, (\text{for the 2 } \partial\text{'s}) - 4 \, (\text{for the 4 } x\text{'s in } d^4x) = \dim[S] = 0$$
$$\implies \quad \dim[\phi] = 1 \tag{7.2}$$

Notice that this is consistent with the second term, since $\dim[m] = 1$. In a similar way, from the leading term in the action for the photon,

$$S^{(2)} = -\frac{1}{2} \int d^4x \, \eta^{\mu\nu} A_\mu (-\Box) A_\nu, \tag{7.3}$$

we find $\dim[A] = 1$. Now let us look at an interaction term,

$$S^{(3)} = -ie \int d^4x \; \eta^{\mu\nu} \, A_\mu \left[\phi^* \partial_\nu \phi - (\partial_\nu \phi^*) \, \phi \right] \tag{7.4}$$

In the integrand, A_μ, ϕ, ϕ^* and ∂_ν each carry dimension 1, giving a total of 4; the measure of integration d^4x has dimension -4. So the total is zero. Since $S^{(3)}$ has to be dimensionless, being a term in the action, we find $\dim[e] = 0$.

Now let us look at the probability amplitude for a scattering of charged particles, as in Fig. 6.3. The amplitude has e^2, so the probability, and hence the cross section, has e^4. Further imagine we consider very highly energetic particles with energy $E \gg m$, so that mass is negligible for the calculation compared to energy. So the only quantity of dimension characterizing the particles is the energy E, or if we consider scattering in the center of mass frame, the CM energy $\sqrt{(p_{10} + p_{20})^2}$. For the total cross section, since we integrate over all final allowed values of momenta and energies, it can only depend on the energy of the incoming particles. Since e^4 has no dimension, we conclude that for very high energy scattering

$$\sigma \sim \frac{\alpha_e^2}{s} \tag{7.5}$$

where $s = (p_1 + p_2)^2$, $\alpha_e = (e^2/4\pi)$. For the electromagnetic interaction, just on dimensional grounds we can conclude that the interaction cross section goes down as the incident energy increases. This has a direct impact on accelerator building, particularly for $e^+ e^-$ machines where we consider head-on collisions of e^+ and e^- of equal energy. As we increase the energy, the cross section goes down, we get less and less of collisions to study. As a result, any increase in energy must be accompanied by an increase in flux (or luminosity) to get similar number of events. (Strictly speaking, since e^+ and e^- are spin-$\frac{1}{2}$ particles, we are jumping ahead a bit here. We have shown the result (7.5) for spin zero particles; later we will see that the same form is obtained for spin-$\frac{1}{2}$ particles as well.)

As another simple exercise, consider the interaction vertex

$$S_{int} = \lambda \int d^4x \; \varphi^3 \chi^2 \tag{7.6}$$

where φ and χ correspond to spin zero particles. We have considered such fields before. The terms in the action which are quadratic in the fields are of the form

$$S^{(2)} = \frac{1}{2} \int d^4x \; \left[\eta^{\mu\nu} (\partial_\mu vf \, \partial_\nu vf) - M^2 vf^2 \; + \; \eta^{\mu\nu} (\partial_\mu \chi \, \partial_\nu \chi) - m^2 \chi^2 \right] \tag{7.7}$$

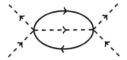

Fig. 7.1: One of the diagrams for the scattering of two φ particles

We find again that $\dim[\varphi] = \dim[\chi] = 1$. Looking at the vertex (7.6), we find $\dim[\lambda] = -1$. Now we can consider the scattering of, say, two φ-particles, one of the contributing diagrams being the one shown in Fig. 7.1. The amplitude will have a factor of λ^2, because there are two vertices of the type (7.6). Thus, at high energies, the cross section will behave as

$$\sigma \sim \lambda^4 s \tag{7.8}$$

The cross section grows with the CM energy of the collision.

This example (of a vertex like (7.6)) is just to show how dimensional analysis works; there is no such interaction allowed at the fundamental level. Cross sections are bounded at high energies for reasons of unitarity or conservation of probability, so the result of cross sections growing with energy cannot hold, for arbitrarily high energy, in a fundamental theory. We will discuss this matter in more detail when we take up weak interactions.

Resonances

Consider the scattering process shown in Fig. 7.2. We can calculate this process as usual. Because of the propagator, the amplitude will contain a factor

$$\frac{1}{(p_1 - p_1')^2 - M^2 + i\epsilon}. \tag{7.9}$$

This shows the possibility of a resonance. The quantity $q = p_1 - p_1'$ is the transfer momentum (momentum transferred from particle 1 to particle 2) and when $q^2 = M^2$, the amplitude, and hence the cross section, will have a very large value; the cross section will show a peak as a function of q^2 (or

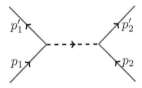

Fig. 7.2: A simple scattering diagram to illustrate resonance

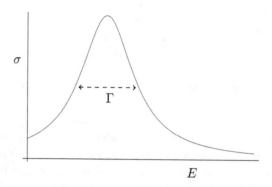

Fig. 7.3: A typical plot of cross section versus energy when there is a resonance

energy). As we have written, the peak value is infinite as $\epsilon \to 0$, but this is not so when higher order corrections are included. The term $i\epsilon$ will get replaced by a (noninfinitesimal) factor $\approx i\Sigma_I$, and the cross section has a factor

$$\frac{1}{(q^2 - M^2)^2 + \Sigma_I^2} \tag{7.10}$$

Σ_I is related to the finite width of the peak. If we do a scan of the cross section as a function of the invariant transfer momentum q^2, because its profile will have a factor like (7.10), we will find a peak at the (mass)^2 of the propagating particle with a width related to Σ_I. The quantity Σ_I is also related to the decay rate Γ for the particle which propagates between the two vertices by $\Sigma_I = \Omega_q\Gamma \approx M\Gamma$. Thus a scan of cross section can give the mass and decay rate (and thus the lifetime) of the particle which is mediating the scattering. This is very useful for the detection of unstable particles; they are observed as resonances from which the mass and decay rate can be read off.

If the cross section is written as a function of energy, rather than q^2, the decay rate Γ is identical to the width. In this case, we have directly,

$$\text{Mean lifetime} = \frac{1}{\Gamma} = \frac{1}{\text{Resonance width}} \tag{7.11}$$

How do we calculate the cross section?

The calculation of the cross section for a process is not difficult, we just have to use the Feynman rules and implement the definition of the cross section correctly. We will show how this can be done with a simple example, following the complete logical sequence from the vertices to the final answer, even though this is not very essential for the rest of the material we discuss.

We will consider the example of the scattering of two charged particles due to their electromagnetic fields. The electromagnetic interaction of a single scalar field is given by

$$S_{int} = \int d^4x \, \left[-ieA_\mu \left(\phi^* \partial_\nu \phi - \partial_\nu \phi^* \, \phi\right) + e^2 \phi^* \phi \, A_\mu \, A_\nu\right] \eta^{\mu\nu} \qquad (7.12)$$

We will consider two different fields, denoted as ϕ and χ, with masses m and M respectively, but with equal charges. The particles are not identical, so this case will be simpler, avoiding some Gibbs factors. For this system, we may write the interaction term as

$$S_{int} = \int d^4x \, \left[-A_\mu J_\nu + e^2 \phi^* \phi A_\mu A_\nu + e^2 \chi^* \chi A_\mu A_\nu\right] \eta^{\mu\nu}$$
$$J_\nu = ie \left(\phi^* \partial_\nu \phi - \partial_\nu \phi^* \, \phi\right) + ie \left(\chi^* \partial_\nu \chi - \partial_\nu \chi^* \, \chi\right) \qquad (7.13)$$

Consider the scattering to the lowest order in e. This is given by the Feynman diagram shown in Fig. 7.4, where we use k_1, k_2 for the ϕ-particles and p_1, p_2 for the χ-particles. The amplitude is of order e^2. It is given by substituting wave functions for the incoming and outgoing particles, and using the photon propagator for the internal photon line. The assignment of wave functions is as discussed in the last lecture and the amplitude is thus given by

$$\mathcal{A} = e^2 \int d^4x d^4y \, \left(u_{k_2}^* \partial_\mu u_{k_1} - \partial_\mu u_{k_2}^* \, u_{k_1}\right)\right]_x \int \frac{d^4k}{(2\pi)^4} e^{-ik(x-y)} \frac{(-i\,\eta^{\mu\nu})}{k^2 + i\epsilon}$$
$$\times \left(u_{p_2}^* \partial_\nu u_{p_1} - \partial_\nu u_{p_2}^* \, u_{p_1}\right)\right]_y$$
$$= \frac{(2\pi)^4 \delta^{(4)}(k_1 + p_1 - k_2 - p_2)}{\sqrt{16\, \omega_{k_1} \, \omega_{k_2} \, \omega_{p_1} \, \omega_{p_2}}\, V^2} \, \mathcal{M} \qquad (7.14)$$

where

$$\mathcal{M} = ie^2 \frac{(k_1 + k_2) \cdot (p_1 + p_2)}{(k_1 - k_2)^2} \qquad (7.15)$$

Squaring this amplitude using the standard trick

$$(2\pi)^4 \delta^{(4)}(k_1 + p_1 - k_2 - p_2) \, (2\pi)^4 \delta^{(4)}(k_1 + p_1 - k_2 - p_2)$$
$$= (2\pi)^4 \delta^{(4)}(k_1 + p_1 - k_2 - p_2) \, V\tau, \qquad (7.16)$$

we get, for the rate,

$$\frac{|\mathcal{A}|^2}{\tau} = \frac{(2\pi)^4 \delta^{(4)}(k_1 + p_1 - k_2 - p_2)}{16\, \omega_{k_1} \, \omega_{k_2} \, \omega_{p_1} \, \omega_{p_2}\, V^3} \, |\mathcal{M}|^2 \qquad (7.17)$$

Fig. 7.4: The electromagnetic scattering of two charged particles. The thicker line represents the χ-particle of mass M.

We must again sum this over a small range of the final states which means that we should have a factor of $V(d^3k_2/(2\pi)^3)\,V(d^3p_2/(2\pi)^3)$ for the two particles in the final state. We then get

$$\sum_{\text{small range}} \frac{|\mathcal{A}|^2}{\tau} = \frac{(2\pi)^4\delta^{(4)}(p_1 + k_1 - p_2 - k_2)}{16\,\omega_{k_1}\omega_{k_2}\omega_{p_1}\omega_{p_2}\,V}\,|\mathcal{M}|^2 \frac{d^3k_2}{(2\pi)^3}\frac{d^3p_2}{(2\pi)^3} \qquad (7.18)$$

We must now divide this by the flux of incoming particles. The flux we use must be in the calculational framework we have set up; this will give the cross section which will be independent of the particular set-up and then we can use the result for any situation by multiplying by the flux available in that situation to get the rate of events. So we must know the flux in our set-up. This is slightly tricky. We have normalized our single particle wave functions to 1, so we have one initial particle of each kind in the volume V. Thus the density is essentially $1/V$. If we take one of the incoming particles, say, ϕ to be at rest (so that $k_1 = (m, 0, 0, 0)$), then this particle will see a stream of the χ-particle approaching with a velocity $|\vec{p}_1|/\omega_{p_1}$. Thus the flux will be

$$F = \frac{|\vec{p}_1|}{\omega_{p_1} V} \qquad (7.19)$$

A similar result should hold with $|p_1|/\omega_{p_1}$ replaced by $|k_1|/\omega_{k_1}$ if we consider the rest frame of the χ-particle. The general relativistic formula for the flux, consistent with these two limits, is

$$F = \frac{\sqrt{(k_1 \cdot p_1)^2 - m^2\,M^2}}{\omega_{k_1}\omega_{p_1} V} \qquad (7.20)$$

Dividing the result (7.18) by the flux, the differential cross section is found to be

$$d\sigma = \frac{(2\pi)^4\delta^{(4)}(k_1 + p_1 - k_2 - p_2)}{16\,\omega_{k_2}\,\omega_{p_2}\,\sqrt{(k_1 \cdot p_1)^2 - m^2\,M^2}}\,|\mathcal{M}|^2 \frac{d^3k_2}{(2\pi)^3}\frac{d^3p_2}{(2\pi)^3} \qquad (7.21)$$

Since d^3k/ω_k is a Lorentz-invariant measure of integration, the cross section is seen to be invariant. But it is useful to simplify it in special frames which are of interest in practical situations.

Rest frame of the incoming χ-particle

We can carry out the integration over one set of spatial momenta easily because of the δ-function. Since we choose the rest frame for the incoming χ-particle (i.e., $\vec{p}_1 = 0$), the scattering angle θ can be defined by the momenta of the ϕ-particle by

$$\vec{k}_1 \cdot \vec{k}_2 = |\vec{k}_1|\,|\vec{k}_2|\cos\theta \tag{7.22}$$

It is thus useful to carry out the p_2-integration. This will set $\vec{p}_2 = \vec{k}_1 + \vec{p}_1 - \vec{k}_2 = \vec{k}_1 - \vec{k}_2$ in all the remaining expressions. Further, we can write

$$\frac{d^3k_2}{(2\pi)^3} = \frac{k_2^2\,dk_2}{8\pi^3}\,d\Omega = \frac{k_2\,\omega_{k_2}\,d\omega_{k_2}}{8\pi^3}\,d\Omega \tag{7.23}$$

where Ω is the solid angle subtended by the outgoing $\vec{k}_2$-direction relative to the incoming $\vec{k}_1$ direction. Explicitly, $d\Omega = \sin\theta\,d\theta\,d\varphi$. We have also used $\omega_{k_2}\,d\omega_{k_2} = k_2 dk_2$ which follows from the variation of $\omega_{k_2}^2 = k_2^2 + m^2$. Using (7.23) we can also do the integration over the ω's which removes the δ-function and sets

$$\omega_{k_2} = \omega_{k_1} + \omega_{p_1} - \omega_{p_2} = \omega_{k_1} + M - \sqrt{M^2 + (\vec{k}_1 - \vec{k}_2)^2} \tag{7.24}$$

We thus get

$$d\sigma = \frac{1}{64\,\pi^2}\,\frac{k_2}{\omega_{p_2}}\,\frac{|\mathcal{M}|^2}{\sqrt{(k_1\cdot p_1)^2 - m^2 M^2}}\,d\Omega \tag{7.25}$$

To simplify this further, notice that we can write

$$
\begin{aligned}
(k_1 + k_2)\cdot(p_1 + p_2) &= (\omega_{k_1} + \omega_{k_2})(M + \omega_{p_2}) - (\vec{k}_1 + \vec{k}_2)\cdot\vec{p}_2 \\
&= (\omega_{k_1} + \omega_{k_2})(M + \omega_{p_2}) + k_1^2 - k_2^2 \\
&= (\omega_{k_1} + \omega_{k_2})(M + \omega_{p_2}) + \omega_{k_1}^2 - \omega_{k_2}^2 \\
&= (\omega_{k_1} + \omega_{k_2})\left[M + \omega_{p_2} - \omega_{k_1} + \omega_{k_2}\right] \\
&= 2M\,(\omega_{k_1} + \omega_{k_2})
\end{aligned}
\tag{7.26}
$$

$$(k_1 - k_2)^2 = -2\,(\omega_{k_1}\omega_{k_2} - m^2 - k_1 k_2 \cos\theta) \tag{7.27}$$

$$\sqrt{(k_1\cdot p_1)^2 - m^2 M^2} = M\,\sqrt{\omega_{k_1}^2 - m^2} \tag{7.28}$$

With these formulae, we can simplify the cross section as

$$d\sigma = \frac{\alpha_e^2}{4}\,\frac{k_2}{k_1}\,\frac{1}{\sqrt{1 + (\vec{k}_1 - \vec{k}_2)^2/M^2}}\,\frac{(\omega_{k_1} + \omega_{k_2})^2}{(\omega_{k_1}\omega_{k_2} - m^2 - k_1 k_2 \cos\theta)^2}\,d\Omega \tag{7.29}$$

where $\alpha_e = e^2/4\pi$ is the fine structure constant. In the limit of M being very large compared to the momentum transfer $|\vec{k}_1 - \vec{k}_2|$, (7.24) shows that $\omega_{k_1} \approx \omega_{k_2}$; so the scattering is elastic and the recoil effect on the large mass M is negligible. In this case, the cross section simplifies as

$$d\sigma = \frac{\alpha_e^2}{4\,\omega_{k_1}^2\,v^4}\frac{1}{\sin^4(\theta/2)}\,d\Omega \tag{7.30}$$

where $v = k_1/\omega_{k_1}$ is the speed of the incoming ϕ-particle. This is the classic (and classical) Rutherford scattering formula.

Ultrarelativistic scattering in CM frame

Another interesting limit to consider is the ultrarelativistic regime, where the masses are negligible compared to the energies of the particles. It is then useful to consider the scattering in the center of momentum (CM) frame since this applies to the geometry often realized in particle colliders. In this case,

$$\vec{k}_1 + \vec{p}_1 = 0 \tag{7.31}$$

Thus, $\omega_{k_1} \approx \omega_{p_1}$. Define the square of the CM energy as

$$s = (k_1 + p_1)^2 \approx 4\,\omega_{k_1}^2 \tag{7.32}$$

Carrying out the integration over p_2 and the magnitude of k_2 in (7.21), we get

$$d\sigma \approx \frac{|\mathcal{M}|^2}{128\pi^2\sqrt{(k_1 \cdot p_1)^2}}\,d\Omega \tag{7.33}$$

where we have also used $\delta(2\omega_{k_1} - 2\omega_{k_2}) = \frac{1}{2}\delta(\omega_{k_1} - \omega_{k_2})$. Further, we have the simplifications

$$\sqrt{(k_1 \cdot p_1)^2} \approx \frac{s}{2}$$
$$(k_1 - k_2)^2 \approx -2\omega_{k_1}^2\,(1 - \cos\theta)$$
$$(k_1 + k_2) \cdot (p_1 + p_2) \approx 2\omega_{k_1}^2\,(3 + \cos\theta) \tag{7.34}$$

Simplifying $\mathcal{M}$ using these formulae, we get

$$d\sigma \approx \frac{\alpha_e^2}{4\,s}\left(\frac{3 + \cos\theta}{1 - \cos\theta}\right)^2\,d\Omega \tag{7.35}$$

Notice the fall-off of the cross section with increasing CM energy as we expected from the dimensional analysis.

Other particles

So far we have developed the general framework to think about particle interactions and have basically concentrated on spin zero particles and the photon. (The photon is a spin 1 particle, but is rather special, being a massless particle.) But the world has many other species of particles; in fact, at the fundamental level, at least at our present level of understanding, there are no charged spin zero particles. There is an uncharged one, the Higgs boson. Matter, as we know it, is made of spin-$\frac{1}{2}$ particles. So let us recall the list of particles, the leptons, quarks and force exchange particles, from the first lecture; it is shown again in Table 7.1. We have not separately indicated the antiparticles. All leptons and quarks are spin-$\frac{1}{2}$ particles, while γ, $W^{\pm}$, Z^0 and gluons are all spin-1 particles. The Higgs boson has spin zero.

From the general description of processes via Feynman diagrams, we know that to study the interaction of these particles we will need wave functions for the spin-$\frac{1}{2}$ and spin-1 particles (other than the photon, since

Table 7.1: List of fundamental particles

Type	Species			Spin	Electric charge
Leptons	e	μ	τ	$\frac{1}{2}$	-1
	ν_e	ν_μ	ν_τ	$\frac{1}{2}$	0
Quarks	u	c	t	$\frac{1}{2}$	$\frac{2}{3}$
	d	s	b	$\frac{1}{2}$	$-\frac{1}{3}$
Force Carriers	γ (Photon)			1	0
	$W^{\pm}$			1	± 1
	Z^0			1	0
	g (Gluons, 8 types)			1	0
	Graviton			2	0
Condensate	H (Higgs)			0	0

we have already discussed the photon wave functions). Effectively, we will need to construct a Lagrangian for all the particles, since we know that the term in the Lagrangian which is quadratic in the fields will give us the wave functions and the propagator and the higher terms will give the vertices from which the Feynman diagrams can be constructed. Before we do that, it is good to mention the spin-statistics connection, which is a very useful theorem to keep in mind.

Spin and statistics

We will not give the precise statement of the spin-statistics theorem, it involves some more ideas from quantum field theory, and can be found in standard books on field theory. We give the connection between spin and statistics as it is operational in physics.

Prop 7.1 (Spin-statistics relation). Identical particles with spin$= (n + \frac{1}{2})$, where n is an integer, obey the Pauli exclusion principle and hence they are fermions and obey Fermi-Dirac statistics.

Identical particles with integer values for spin are bosons, they obey Bose-Einstein statistics.

This theorem tells us that quarks and leptons are fermions, while the force carriers and the Higgs particle are bosons.

The nature of the statistics will be reflected in multiparticle wave functions. For example, consider the two-particle wave function of noninteracting identical fermions. It is given by

$$\Phi_{\alpha_1 \alpha_2}(x_1, x_2) = \frac{1}{\sqrt{2!}} [\phi_{\alpha_1}(x_1) \phi_{\alpha_2}(x_2) - \phi_{\alpha_1}(x_2) \phi_{\alpha_2}(x_1)] \qquad (7.36)$$

where the indices α_1, α_2 label the states of single-particles, x_1, x_2 indicate the position vectors, $\phi_\alpha(x)$ being the single particle wave function in state α. Notice that this wave function encodes the exclusion principle; it vanishes when $x_1 = x_2$ or when $\alpha_1 = \alpha_2$.

For a two-particle system of noninteracting identical bosons, the wave function is

$$\Phi_{\alpha_1 \alpha_2}(x_1, x_2) = \frac{1}{\sqrt{2!}} [\phi_{\alpha_1}(x_1) \phi_{\alpha_2}(x_2) + \phi_{\alpha_1}(x_2) \phi_{\alpha_2}(x_1)] \qquad (7.37)$$

The connecting sign here being plus, the probability amplitude for two bosons to have the same quantum numbers is not zero. In fact, there is an enhancement of the probability of the bosons to have the same quantum numbers.

Dirac Equation

We now turn to the more detailed discussion of spin-$\frac{1}{2}$ particles. It is important to consider the particle and antiparticle together, since interactions can involve pair production and other processes which involve both types. Specifically, we will talk about the electron, although the discussion for other leptons and for quarks is similar. The basic equation for their dynamics is the Dirac equation. It is one of the most important equations which emerged in twentieth century physics.

A spin-$\frac{1}{2}$ particle of nonzero mass has $2s + 1 = 2$ independent spin states, say, the spin-up and spin-down states with respect to some particular direction. The antiparticle has two as well, so we need four components for the wave function or four components for the field representing such a particle species. We may take this as the matrix, or column vector,

$$\Psi(x) = \begin{bmatrix} \psi_1(x) \\ \psi_2(x) \\ \psi_3(x) \\ \psi_4(x) \end{bmatrix} \tag{7.38}$$

Here ψ's are complex, thus, so is Ψ. The conjugate can be represented as a row vector. Hence, for the part of the Lagrangian which is quadratic in the fields, we should expect a term of the form $\Psi^\dagger K \Psi$, where K is a 4×4 matrix. Indeed this is so; the action for the Dirac equation is

$$S = \int d^4x \, \bar{\Psi}(i\gamma^\mu \partial_\mu - m)\Psi \tag{7.39}$$

where $\gamma^\mu = (\gamma^0, \gamma^1, \gamma^2, \gamma^3)$ are four 4×4-matrices which obey the commutation algebra

$$\gamma^\mu \gamma^\nu + \gamma^\nu \gamma^\mu = 2\, \eta^{\mu\nu}\, \mathbb{1} \tag{7.40}$$

where $\eta^{\mu\nu}$ is the spacetime metric and $\mathbb{1}$ is the unit 4×4-matrix. The matrices γ^μ are called the Dirac γ-matrices. The algebra (7.40) is a version of Clifford algebras. Notice that if we have one set of matrices γ^μ obeying (7.40), then $S^{-1}\gamma^\mu S$ also obey the same relation, for any invertible matrix S. Thus, there is some freedom in the choice of the γ-matrices. We will choose an explicit set of formulae for the γ^μ, which are in a form useful for later discussions. Our choice is given by

$$\gamma^0 = \begin{pmatrix} 0 & 1_{2\times 2} \\ 1_{2\times 2} & 0 \end{pmatrix} \qquad\qquad \gamma^1 = \begin{pmatrix} 0 & -\sigma_1 \\ \sigma_1 & 0 \end{pmatrix} \tag{7.41}$$

$$\gamma^2 = \begin{pmatrix} 0 & -\sigma_2 \\ \sigma_2 & 0 \end{pmatrix} \qquad\qquad \gamma^3 = \begin{pmatrix} 0 & -\sigma_3 \\ \sigma_3 & 0 \end{pmatrix} \qquad (7.42)$$

where $1_{2\times2}$ stands for the 2×2 unit matrix and σ_i are the Pauli matrices; i.e.,

$$1_{2\times2} = \begin{pmatrix} 1 & 0 \\ 0 & 1 \end{pmatrix}, \quad \sigma_1 = \begin{pmatrix} 0 & 1 \\ 1 & 0 \end{pmatrix}, \quad \sigma_2 = \begin{pmatrix} 0 & -i \\ i & 0 \end{pmatrix}, \quad \sigma_3 = \begin{pmatrix} 1 & 0 \\ 0 & -1 \end{pmatrix}$$

$$(7.43)$$

The action (7.39) also involves $\bar{\Psi}$ which is given by $\bar{\Psi} = \Psi^\dagger \gamma^0$. Notice that we take the hermitian conjugate of (7.38) as expected, but we need an additional factor of γ^0 for reasons of Lorentz invariance. This is because γ^0 is hermitian, but the γ^i are antihermitian (which is traceable to the different signs for the space and time components of $\eta^{\mu\nu}$ in (7.40)) and hence we have to use the additional γ^0. The 4×4 square matrix $(i\gamma^\mu \partial_\mu - m)$ can be written out in terms of the 2×2 submatrices as

$$i\gamma^\mu \partial_\mu - m = \begin{bmatrix} -m & i(\partial_0 - \sigma_i\partial_i) \\ i(\partial_0 + \sigma_i\partial_i) & -m \end{bmatrix} \qquad (7.44)$$

If we also split Ψ into the two-component form as

$$\Psi(x) = \begin{bmatrix} U(x) \\ V(x) \end{bmatrix}, \qquad (7.45)$$

then the action becomes

$$S = \int d^4x \, \left[U^\dagger i(\partial_0 + \vec{\sigma} \cdot \nabla) U + V^\dagger i(\partial_0 - \vec{\sigma} \cdot \nabla) V - m(V^\dagger U + U^\dagger V) \right]$$

$$(7.46)$$

Chapter 8

More on the Dirac Equation

In the last lecture, we started our discussion of the Dirac theory of spin-$\frac{1}{2}$ fermions. It provides a relativistically invariant description of such particles. Dirac himself arrived at this by trying to factorize the wave operator $\Box$ into a product of first order differential operators. He realized he could do it if he allowed for a matrix equation. He introduced the γ^μ matrices with their algebra to ensure that the square of the first order operator, namely, $(\gamma^\mu \partial_\mu)^2$, would indeed give the wave operator, little knowing if it had anything deeper to do with Lorentz symmetry. It was only later it was realized that the γ-matrices led to a representation of the Lorentz transformations. Almost magically, in attempting something very unusual, yet very down-to-earth and mundane as trying to factorize $\Box$, Dirac obtained one of the deepest results in physics.

Let us start by recalling the action for the Dirac particle,

$$S = \int d^4x \ \bar{\Psi}(i\gamma^\mu \partial_\mu - m)\Psi \tag{8.1}$$

Since the γ-matrices were given in terms of 2×2 submatrices, it is convenient to separate our four-component wave function into two 1×2 wave functions U, V,

$$\Psi(x) = \begin{bmatrix} \psi_1(x) \\ \psi_2(x) \\ \psi_3(x) \\ \psi_4(x) \end{bmatrix} = \begin{bmatrix} U \\ V \end{bmatrix}, \qquad U = \begin{bmatrix} \psi_1(x) \\ \psi_2(x) \end{bmatrix}, \qquad V = \begin{bmatrix} \psi_3(x) \\ \psi_4(x) \end{bmatrix} \tag{8.2}$$

The γ-matrices were given in the last lecture as

$$\gamma^0 = \begin{pmatrix} 0 & 1_{2\times2} \\ 1_{2\times2} & 0 \end{pmatrix} \qquad\qquad \gamma^1 = \begin{pmatrix} 0 & -\sigma_1 \\ \sigma_1 & 0 \end{pmatrix}$$

$$\gamma^2 = \begin{pmatrix} 0 & -\sigma_2 \\ \sigma_2 & 0 \end{pmatrix} \qquad\qquad \gamma^3 = \begin{pmatrix} 0 & -\sigma_3 \\ \sigma_3 & 0 \end{pmatrix} \tag{8.3}$$

$$1_{2\times2} = \begin{pmatrix} 1 & 0 \\ 0 & 1 \end{pmatrix}, \quad \sigma_1 = \begin{pmatrix} 0 & 1 \\ 1 & 0 \end{pmatrix}, \quad \sigma_2 = \begin{pmatrix} 0 & -i \\ i & 0 \end{pmatrix}, \quad \sigma_3 = \begin{pmatrix} 1 & 0 \\ 0 & -1 \end{pmatrix} \quad (8.4)$$

The equation of motion for the Dirac action, the Dirac equation as it is called, is obtained by varying with respect to $\bar{\Psi}$ and reads

$$(i\gamma^\mu \partial_\mu - m)\Psi = 0 \tag{8.5}$$

First of all, let us look at free particle solutions. These are plane waves, so we can find them by taking the ansatz $\psi = A\,e^{-ipx} = A\,e^{-ip_0 x^0 + i\vec{p}\cdot\vec{x}}$. For the solutions, it is convenient to use a slightly different choice of γ-matrices, which we denote by $\tilde{\gamma}$'s, given by

$$\tilde{\gamma}^0 = \begin{pmatrix} 1_{2\times2} & 0 \\ 0 & -1_{2\times2} \end{pmatrix} \qquad \tilde{\gamma}^1 = \begin{pmatrix} 0 & \sigma_1 \\ -\sigma_1 & 0 \end{pmatrix}$$

$$\tilde{\gamma}^2 = \begin{pmatrix} 0 & \sigma_2 \\ -\sigma_2 & 0 \end{pmatrix} \qquad \tilde{\gamma}^3 = \begin{pmatrix} 0 & \sigma_3 \\ -\sigma_3 & 0 \end{pmatrix} \tag{8.6}$$

This is related to the previous choice by

$$\gamma^\mu = S\tilde{\gamma}^\mu S^{-1}, \quad S = \frac{1}{\sqrt{2}} \begin{pmatrix} 1 & 1 \\ 1 & -1 \end{pmatrix} \tag{8.7}$$

In terms of the choice $\tilde{\gamma}$, using the plane wave ansatz in the Dirac equation, we get

$$(\tilde{\gamma} \cdot p - m)A = 0 \tag{8.8}$$

Here A is a 4-component column vector which is independent of x. This equation is a matrix equation which can be written in terms of the 2×2 submatrix form as

$$\begin{bmatrix} p_0 - m & -\vec{\sigma} \cdot \vec{p} \\ \vec{\sigma} \cdot \vec{p} & -p_0 - m \end{bmatrix} (A) = 0 \tag{8.9}$$

As with any matrix equation of this form, if the determinant of the square matrix $\tilde{\gamma} \cdot p - m$ is not zero, the only solution to this equation is the trivial one, $A = 0$. Thus, for nontrivial solutions, we need

$$\det(\tilde{\gamma} \cdot p - m) = \begin{vmatrix} p_0 - m & -\vec{\sigma} \cdot \vec{p} \\ \vec{\sigma} \cdot \vec{p} & -p_0 - m \end{vmatrix} = 0 \tag{8.10}$$

This condition simplifies to

$$(p_0^2 - \vec{p}^2 - m^2)^2 = 0 \tag{8.11}$$

which gives four possible types of solutions, two with $p_0 = \sqrt{\vec{p}^2 + m^2}$ and two with $p_0 = -\sqrt{\vec{p}^2 + m^2}$. Explicitly, we can write them as[1]

$$\left.\begin{aligned} \Psi &= u^{(\alpha)}(p)\, e^{-ipx} = u^{(\alpha)}(p)\, e^{-i\sqrt{\vec{p}^2+m^2}\,t + i\vec{p}\cdot\vec{x}} \\ \Psi &= v^{(\alpha)}(p)\, e^{ipx} = v^{(\alpha)}(p)\, e^{i\sqrt{\vec{p}^2+m^2}\,t - i\vec{p}\cdot\vec{x}} \end{aligned}\right\} \text{ where } \alpha = 1,2 \quad (8.12)$$

Once the condition (8.11) is satisfied, we can solve (8.9) to find how the various components of A are related. (We can normalize it as well; this will be given later.) We will not go through this in detail here, but the final result can be summarized neatly in a matrix form,

$$A = \frac{1}{\sqrt{2\,m(E+m)}} \begin{bmatrix} E+m & \vec{\sigma}\cdot\vec{p} \\ \vec{\sigma}\cdot\vec{p} & E+m \end{bmatrix} W \qquad (8.13)$$

There are 4 independent choices for W which give the 4 solutions,

$$W = \begin{pmatrix} 1 \\ 0 \\ 0 \\ 0 \end{pmatrix} \to u^{(1)}, \qquad W = \begin{pmatrix} 0 \\ 1 \\ 0 \\ 0 \end{pmatrix} \to u^{(2)}$$

$$W = \begin{pmatrix} 0 \\ 0 \\ 1 \\ 0 \end{pmatrix} \to v^{(1)}, \qquad W = \begin{pmatrix} 0 \\ 0 \\ 0 \\ 1 \end{pmatrix} \to v^{(2)} \qquad (8.14)$$

The first two choices for W correspond to $u^{(\alpha)}(p)$ in (8.12), with $\alpha = 1,2$, as indicated in (8.14); the last two choices for W give $v^{(\alpha)}(p)$. Notice that when $\vec{p} = 0$, the matrix in (8.13) becomes the identity and the four solutions are just the 4 W's. These are then the spin-up, spin-down states of the particle for the first two choices for W and the spin-up and spin-down states for the antiparticle for the other two choices for W. When we consider the particle with nonzero momentum, the components get mixed by the matrix multiplying the W's, and the identification of the matrix components with the spin states is more involved. Nevertheless, we can think of, say, $u^{(1)}(p)$ as the solution for the particle which would be in the spin-up state in its own rest frame, and similarly for the others.

---

[1] A word of caution: Even though we use the same letters u, v, albeit in lower case, these have 4 components; they are not solutions for the U, V we introduced earlier. Each of the solutions given above can be, if desired, split into a U, V form as

$$u^{(1)}(p) = \begin{pmatrix} U^{(1)} \\ V^{(1)} \end{pmatrix}$$

It is the interpretation in the rest frame which makes the use of $\tilde{\gamma}$'s convenient. The solutions for our choice of γ-matrices given in (8.3) can be obtained from the similarity transformation in (8.7) by using SA in place of A in (8.13).

Calculation of Feynman diagrams with spin-$\frac{1}{2}$ particles

The Dirac theory describes spin-$\frac{1}{2}$ particles. Starting from the action (8.1), it is thus very easy to write down the rules for calculating Feynman diagrams with spin-$\frac{1}{2}$ particles. Recall that there are three ingredients needed: wave functions for the external lines, propagators for the internal lines, and the vertices to represent the interactions. We consider each in turn.

Wave functions

We have already obtained the free particle solutions, so what is needed is just to identify which one describes what particle. To motivate this, recall that a negative exponent for the time component such as in e^{-ipx} corresponds to incoming particles. Thus we identify the $u^{(\alpha)}(p)\,e^{-ipx}$ as the wave function for an incoming particle. Since $v^{(\alpha)}(p)\,e^{ipx}$ has a positive exponent, it must be interpreted as outgoing. But it must have the same charge properties as $u^{(\alpha)}(p)\,e^{-ipx}$ since they are all solutions for Ψ. The only compatible way is then to consider $v^{(\alpha)}(p)\,e^{ipx}$ as representing outgoing antiparticles. In this way, they will both correspond to the same change of charge at a vertex. The complete assignment, following these lines, is

$$\sqrt{\frac{m}{E_pV}}\;u^{(\alpha)}(p)\,e^{-ipx} \qquad \text{corresponds to an incoming particle}$$

$$\sqrt{\frac{m}{E_pV}}\;v^{(\alpha)}(p)\,e^{ipx} \qquad \text{corresponds to an outgoing anti-particle}$$

$$\sqrt{\frac{m}{E_pV}}\;\bar{u}^{(\alpha)}(p)\,e^{ipx} \qquad \text{corresponds to an outgoing particle}$$

$$\sqrt{\frac{m}{E_pV}}\;\bar{v}^{(\alpha)}(p)\,e^{-ipx} \qquad \text{corresponds to an incoming anti-particle}$$

where we have put in the correct normalization as well.

Propagator

The propagator is also easily found from the action

$$S = \int \bar{\Psi}(i\gamma^{\mu}\partial_{\mu} - m)\Psi$$

For this, recall the rule we found earlier, Rule 1 of Lecture 7. We look at the term in the action which is quadratic in the fields and identify the differential operator sandwiched between the fields. If this operator is K, the propagator is the inverse of $-iK$, or $K_x G(x,y) = i\delta^{(4)}(x-y)$. The operator K, for the Dirac theory is identified from the action given above, as $K = i\gamma^\mu \partial_\mu - m$. Thus we need

$$(i\gamma^\mu \partial_\mu - m)\, \mathbf{S}(x,y) = i\,\delta^{(4)}(x-y) \tag{8.15}$$

where we use the symbol $\mathbf{S}(x,y)$ for the spin-$\frac{1}{2}$ propagator, to easily distinguish it from the spin zero and photon propagators. Expressing $\mathbf{S}(x,y)$ in terms of its Fourier transform as

$$\mathbf{S}(x,y) = \int \frac{d^4p}{(2\pi)^4} e^{-ip(x-y)}\, \mathbf{S}(p) \tag{8.16}$$

we act on it with the differential operator K to get

$$(i\gamma^\mu \partial_\mu - m)\, \mathbf{S}(x,y) = \int \frac{d^4p}{(2\pi)^4} e^{-ip(x-y)} (\gamma \cdot p - m)\, \mathbf{S}(p) \tag{8.17}$$

Thus, if we want $\mathbf{S}$ to be our propagator, $(\gamma \cdot p - m)\, \mathbf{S}(p)$ must equal i, so that the integral on the right hand side becomes $i\,\delta^{(4)}(x-y)$. This shows that $\mathbf{S}(p)$ must be identified as

$$\mathbf{S}(p) = \frac{i(\gamma \cdot p + m)}{p^2 - m^2 + i\epsilon} \tag{8.18}$$

Using this back in (8.16) we get the propagator as

$$\mathbf{S}(x,y) = \int \frac{d^4p}{(2\pi)^4} e^{-ip(x-y)} \frac{i(\gamma \cdot p + m)}{p^2 - m^2 + i\epsilon} \tag{8.19}$$

It is easy enough to see that the matrix product in (8.17) gives the right answer:

$$\begin{aligned}
(\gamma \cdot p - m)(\gamma \cdot p + m) &= -m^2 + (\gamma \cdot p\, \gamma \cdot p) \\
&= -m^2 + \frac{1}{2}(\gamma^\mu p_\mu \gamma^\nu p_\nu + \gamma^\nu p_\nu \gamma^\mu p_\mu) \\
&= -m^2 + \frac{1}{2}(\gamma^\mu \gamma^\nu + \gamma^\nu \gamma^\mu)\, p_\mu p_\nu \\
&= -m^2 + \eta^{\mu\nu} p_\mu p_\nu \\
&= -m^2 + p^2 \tag{8.20}
\end{aligned}$$

We have used the algebraic relation defining the γ-matrices, namely, $\gamma^\mu \gamma^\nu + \gamma^\nu \gamma^\mu = \eta^{\mu\nu}$, in this simplification. The result (8.20) leads to

$$(\gamma \cdot p - m) \frac{(\gamma \cdot p + m)}{p^2 - m^2 + i\epsilon} = 1 \qquad \text{as } \epsilon \to 0 \tag{8.21}$$

Equation (8.19) gives the Dirac propagator in the form we can use in interactions.

Vertices

The vertices would come from terms in the action which are higher than quadratic in the fields. Of course, we do not see such terms in the action (8.1) because we have only looked at the action for free spin-$\frac{1}{2}$ particles. We can find the action for charged spin-$\frac{1}{2}$ particles coupled to the photon (or the electromagnetic field) very easily from Rule 2 of Lecture 7. Recall that coupling any charged particle to the photon is achieved by replacing the derivatives ∂_μ of the fields in the free action by $\partial_\mu + iqA_\mu$, where q is the charge of the particle. Since we shall shortly consider the electrodynamics of the electron-positron system, and the electron (of charge $-e$) is conventionally viewed as the particle, we use the prescription $\partial_\mu \to \partial_\mu - ieA_\mu$. The Dirac action becomes

$$
\begin{aligned}
S &= \int d^4x \ \bar{\Psi}(i\gamma^\mu(\partial_\mu - ieA_\mu) - m)\Psi \\
&= \int d^4x \ \bar{\Psi}(i\gamma^\mu\partial_\mu - m)\Psi + e \int d^4x \ (\bar{\Psi}\gamma^\mu\Psi)A_\mu
\end{aligned}
\tag{8.22}
$$

The basic vertex is thus given by the last term $e \int \bar{\Psi}\gamma^\mu\Psi\, A_\mu$. There is only one kind of vertex to consider; it is trilinear with two charged particle lines and the photon.

In general, particles have many types of interactions–strong, weak, electromagnetic, etc. However, for electrons (and positrons) there is a range of low energies (up to a few hundred MeV, depending on the process) for which it is reasonable to ignore interactions other than their coupling to photons. This is because we consider a regime where there is not enough energy to create other species of particles which are mostly of higher mass or, as in the case of neutrinos, couple to the electron-positron system very weakly via high mass intermediate states. Thus one can consider the theory of electrons and positrons coupled to the photon, as a closed theory in its own right which can be used as a good approximation for electrons, positrons and photons for energies up to a few hundred MeV. This theory is called quantum electrodynamics (QED). The action for this is easily identified. It is given by (8.22) with the Ψ being interpreted as the electron/positron field. (We must add to it the action for free photons, just to be complete.) Thus QED has only one vertex to worry about and we can consider a number of interesting processes. (At this point we are finally considering a really physical situation, a realistic theory, no more just mathematical examples to illustrate the formalism.)

Some examples in QED

As the simplest example, consider the scattering of an electron by a Coulomb potential given by the diagram Fig. 8.1. The amplitude is easily written down from the rules given before. Taking the incoming electron to have momentum p and spin state specified by α, the outgoing one to have momentum p' and spin state specified by β,

$$\mathcal{A} = ie\sqrt{\frac{m^2}{E_p E_{p'} V^2}} \int d^4x \, \bar{u}^{(\beta)}(p') \gamma^\mu u^{(\alpha)}(p) A_\mu^{ext}(x) \, e^{i(p'-p)x} \quad (8.23)$$

If we use $A_0 = -Ze/4\pi r$ and carry out the integral, we can use this to calculate the scattering cross section. We do not go through the details here, but for unpolarized incoming electrons (i.e., 50% in $\alpha = 1$ state and 50% in $\alpha = 2$) of speed v, the differential cross section is

$$d\sigma = \frac{(Ze^2/4\pi)^2}{4E^2 v^4 \sin^4(\theta/2)} \left(1 - v^2 \sin^2(\theta/2)\right) \, d\Omega \quad (8.24)$$

where θ is the scattering angle, the angle between the incoming and outgoing directions for the electron and $d\Omega$ is the infinitesimal solid angle. (Notice that the answer is close to the Rutherford scattering formula, but not quite, differing from it by the factor $\left(1 - v^2 \sin^2(\theta/2)\right)$. This is because of the spin. Think of the process in the rest frame of the electron. In this frame, the (charged) source of the potential is moving and hence constitutes a current. This generates a magnetic field to which the spin magnetic moment of the electron will respond. The magnetic field being inhomogeneous, this interaction can cause a correction to the trajectory. So the result will be somewhat different from Rutherford's formula. Since the magnetic field generated has a v/c factor, the correction is negligible at low velocities. The magnetic moment interaction leads to an electric dipole interaction upon transformation to a moving frame; so in the frame where the electron is moving and the source is at rest, this can be viewed as due to this induced electric dipole moment interaction. Also, in the nonrelativistic

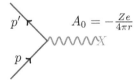

Fig. 8.1: Scattering of an electron by a Coulomb potential

case, the energy E in the denominator will be replaced by m, the mass of the electron.)

As another example, consider again Compton scattering. There are two diagrams as shown in Fig. 8.2. The amplitudes are again easily written down, following the general rules for translating diagrams into mathematical expressions. For example, the first diagram gives

$$\mathcal{A}_1 = (ie)^2 \sqrt{\frac{m^2}{E_p E_{p'} 2\omega_k 2\omega_{k'} V^4}} \; (2\pi)^4 \delta^{(4)}(p + k - p' - k')$$

$$\times \epsilon'_\nu(k') \, \bar{u}^{(\beta)}(p') \, \gamma^\nu \left[\frac{i(\gamma \cdot (p + k) + m)}{(p + k)^2 - m^2 + i\epsilon} \right] \gamma^\mu u^{(\alpha)}(p) \epsilon_\mu(k) \quad (8.25)$$

Here $\epsilon(k)$, $\epsilon'(k')$ give the polarizations of the two photons, $(\vec{k}, \epsilon(k))$ referring to the incoming photon and $(\vec{k}', \epsilon'(k'))$ referring to the outgoing one. In a similar way, the amplitude for the second diagram is given by

$$\mathcal{A}_2 = (ie)^2 \sqrt{\frac{m^2}{E_p E_{p'} 2\omega_k 2\omega_{k'} V^4}} \; (2\pi)^4 \delta^{(4)}(p + k - p' - k')$$

$$\times \epsilon_\nu(k) \, \bar{u}^{(\beta)}(p') \, \gamma^\nu \left[\frac{i(\gamma \cdot (p - k') + m)}{(p - k')^2 - m^2 + i\epsilon} \right] \gamma^\mu u^{(\alpha)}(p) \epsilon'_\mu(k') \quad (8.26)$$

Thus if we take $|\mathcal{A}_1 + \mathcal{A}_2|^2$, divide by the total time τ (which will come out of squaring the delta function) and sum over a range of final states and divide by the initial flux, we can get the cross section. We will not do this here, it is worked out in many books on quantum field theory; the result, known as the Klein-Nishina formula, reads

$$\frac{d\sigma}{d\Omega} = \frac{\alpha_e^2}{4\,m^2} \left(\frac{\omega'}{\omega}\right)^2 \left[\frac{\omega'}{\omega} + \frac{\omega}{\omega'} + 4\,(\epsilon \cdot \epsilon')^2 - 2 \right] \quad (8.27)$$

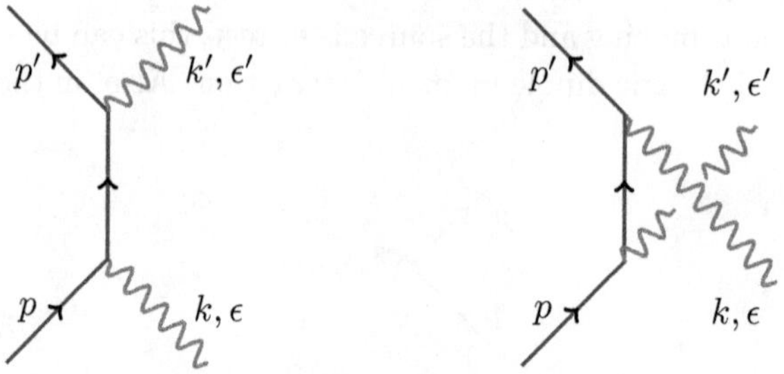

Fig. 8.2: Compton scattering

Fig. 8.3: The self-energy of an electron in vacuum and when it is bound to a nucleus

This applies in the rest frame of the initial electron. Further we have taken incoming electrons to be unpolarized and summed over the final electron polarizations.

There are many other processes we can consider in a similar way, processes which are physically important. These include bremsstrahlung, pair creation, pair annihilation, corrections to scatterings, etc.

Another interesting diagram to consider is the one shown in Fig. 8.3, which corresponds to the emission and reabsorption of a photon by an electron. The incoming and outgoing states are just single electrons, so this is a process that modifies the propagation of a single electron. But the propagator for a free electron must have the form given in (8.19), so the only possible modification is to the parameters defining an electron, like its mass; in fact, the process in Fig. 8.3 is a correction to the mass of the electron. It is referred to as the self-energy of the electron. However, the process happens in vacuum and whatever mass it might add to the electron, that is already accounted for in its measured mass. So this diagram actually does not constitute anything physical. (It is subtracted out by a process called renormalization.) But, if we consider the same diagram for an electron moving in a background field (as shown on the right in Fig. 8.3), such as the field of a nucleus in an atom, the difference between the self-energy calculated with a bound electron and self-energy of the free electron in vacuum is measurable. This is the main contribution to a particular kind of shift in the spectral lines of an atom, say, the Hydrogen atom, known as Lamb shift. The effect is tiny and to isolate it experimentally, we need to look at some energy levels which are exactly degenerate in the Dirac theory without the self-energy. (Otherwise the shift would be masked by other, more dominant, effects.) An example would be the $2S\frac{1}{2}$ and $2P\frac{1}{2}$

states of the Hydrogen atom. The experimentally observed difference and the theoretical prediction are

$$E_{2S\frac{1}{2}} - E_{2P\frac{1}{2}} = 1057.8576(21) \text{ MHz} \qquad \text{(Experiment)}$$
$$= 1057.833(2)(4) \text{ MHz} \qquad \text{(Theory)}$$
$$= 1057.843(2)(6) \text{ MHz} \qquad \text{(Theory)}$$

The self-energy diagram we have shown is not the only contribution; it is the major one, but there are other corrections (all of which involve absorption and emission of a photon by an electron) which contribute to the theoretical result. These have been included in the theoretical estimate.[2] Notice the impressive level of agreement between theory and experiment. All these Feynman diagrams, with all these squiggly lines, do lead to something physical and measurable.

There are many other higher order corrections of importance as well. For example, we considered the scattering of an electron by an external field in diagram Fig. 8.1. Some examples of higher order corrections to this process are shown in Fig. 8.4. A part of the effect of these corrections may be summarized as an addition to the magnetic moment of the electron which is related to its spin vector $\vec{S} = \frac{1}{2}\vec{\sigma}$ as

$$\vec{\mu} = g\,\frac{e}{2m}\,\vec{S} \qquad (8.28)$$

The factor g, which is known as the gyromagnetic ratio, should be exactly 2 to the lowest order in Dirac's electron theory. The inclusion of the higher order corrections gives

$$\frac{g-2}{2} = 1\,159\,652\,180.73(0.28) \times 10^{-12} \qquad \text{(Experiment)}$$
$$= 1\,159\,652\,181.13(0.11)(0.37)(0.77) \times 10^{-12} \qquad \text{(Theory)}$$

The theoretical prediction quoted includes not only the contributions from the diagrams in Fig. 8.4, but also from even higher orders, up to terms of the fourth power in α_e. (The bracketed numbers in the quoted values are the errors in the last two decimal places, from different sources.) The number of diagrams increases rapidly, with 891 diagrams, for example, at the order α_e^4. In addition, many of the diagrams are complicated, some

---

[2]The numbers in brackets indicate the possible error in the last set of digits due to uncertainties in the input parameters, such as masses, Rydberg constant, charge radius of proton. For the theoretical values the first set of errors is the estimate of uncertainty due to yet-to-be-calculated corrections and the second set is due to uncertainty in the charge radius of the proton. The input parameters taken from two different measurements lead to the two theoretical values listed.

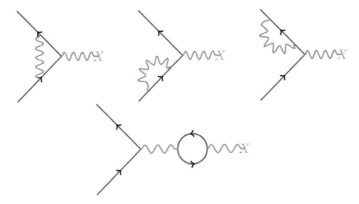

Fig. 8.4: Some of the higher order corrections to Coulomb scattering

have over 20,000 integrals. The next order, of order α_e^5, is being calculated; there are 12,672 Feynman diagrams to be calculated.

Notice once again, the impressive agreement between theory and experiment. These results, the Lamb shift and the correction to the magnetic moment of the electron, are some of the most accurate predictions and experimental verifications in the whole history of physics.

Dimensional Analysis

Turning again to the Dirac action for a charged spin-$\frac{1}{2}$ particle coupled to the electromagnetic field we can perform dimensional analysis to find the dimension of the wave functions. We wrote down the fermionic part of the action in (8.22) as

$$S = \int d^4x \ \bar{\Psi}(i\gamma^\mu\partial_\mu - m)\Psi + e\int d^4x \ \bar{\Psi}\gamma^\mu\Psi A_\mu \tag{8.29}$$

For the first term, we get -4 from d^4x, 1 from ∂_μ so that we find $\dim[\Psi] = \frac{3}{2}$. This is consistent with the second term, with e being dimensionless. Thus our dimensional estimates for the cross section will go through, essentially as in the case of spin zero particles, giving the result

$$\sigma \sim \frac{\alpha_e^2}{s} \tag{8.30}$$

for CM energies much higher than the masses of the particles involved. We see that the result (7.5) holds for spin-$\frac{1}{2}$ particles as well.

Remark 8.1.
Feynman rules: Of loops and a minus sign

The basic set of Feynman rules was given in Lecture 4. Here we make a couple of remarks which elaborate on them.

First of all, among the diagrams we have discussed, some have complete loops and some do not. We can see that the number of loops is tied in a nice way with quantum corrections. For this, it is useful to keep the factor of $\hbar$ explicitly. Since the action has the dimension of $\hbar$, it is useful to think of $S/\hbar$ as the starting point. This means that, since the propagator is the inverse of the differential operator in the term quadratic in the fields, it can be taken to have one power of $\hbar$. The vertices on the other hand have a power of $\hbar^{-1}$. Based on this, it is possible to count the powers of $\hbar$ for any diagram. For example, consider the diagrams for Compton scattering in Fig. 8.2. Each has one propagator and two vertices, so it carries a power of $\hbar^{-1}$, just as the starting classical action $S/\hbar$. Similarly, the scattering process in Fig. 8.1 has a power of $\hbar^{-1}$. However, if we look at the diagrams for the higher order corrections in Fig. 8.4, we see that they all have 3 vertices and 3 propagators, so they behave as $\hbar^0$. Clearly this is one power higher than the starting point and may be viewed as a first set of quantum corrections to the basic scattering process of Fig. 8.1. One can also see that, graphically speaking, each diagram in Fig. 8.4 has a complete loop, either made of an electron propagator and a photon propagator or just two electron propagators. This can be generalized. By working out the powers of $\hbar$, one can see that a diagram with L loops will carry a power of $\hbar^{L-1}$. So if we group diagrams by the number of loops they have, we can say that the diagrams with no loops (called the tree diagrams) with $\hbar^{-1}$ behavior are like the classical processes, while those with one loop are the first set of quantum corrections, those with two loops are the next set of quantum corrections, etc. This is a very useful re-organization of the infinite set of diagrams which constitute all the processes and all the corrections for a given theory.

Does this mean that the tree diagrams are purely classical and only calculate classical effects with no quantum concepts? Not quite. For example, how do we understand that the formula for Compton scattering does carry a factor of $\hbar$ (in one of the terms in the denominator) even at the level of kinematics, as in (2.36), which we even argued constituted a signature of the concept of the photon? The reason is that, in general, there are two sources of quantum effects. For purely classical physics, we need to consider only tree diagrams and we need to have a large number of particles, in some coherent distribution, so that the notion of a classical beam makes sense. When the number of quanta participating in the process is small, then quantum effects are visible even if we only use tree diagrams for the process. (This is the case for the Compton kinematics in (2.36).) And loop diagrams, of course, are intrinsically quantum in nature.

There is another addition to the rules for Feynman diagrams which is important. In a diagram with fermion loops, each fermion loop gives a factor of -1 multiplying the mathematical expression for the amplitude. This is due to the fermionic statistics, which is expressed in the field theory by a minus sign when we exchange the field operators. Such a rearrangement of fields is needed to bring the vertices in a proper time-sequence to write the diagram in terms of propagators. For example, at the second order in QED, we encounter the term $\bar{\Psi}(x)\gamma^\mu A_\mu(x)\Psi(x)\,\bar{\Psi}(y)\gamma^\nu A_\nu(y)\Psi(y)$. A fermion loop is obtained by replacing $\Psi\bar{\Psi}$ pairs by propagators. So let us start with replacing $\Psi(x)\bar{\Psi}(y)$ by a propagator from y to x. To get the remaining $\Psi(y)$ and $\bar{\Psi}(x)$ in the same order $(\Psi(y)\bar{\Psi}(x))$ to be replaced by a propagator, and complete the fermion loop, we need to move $\bar{\Psi}(x)$ to the right end, passing through three fermion fields. This is the origin of the minus sign.

Remark 8.2.
The story of Quantum Electrodynamics

In the modern way of looking at it, in terms of rigorously establishing it as an interacting theory, Quantum Electrodynamics (QED) may not exist as a theory solely in its own right. Despite this disheartening potential fate, QED is, by far, the field theory *par excellence* that we have. Its action can be written down based entirely on general principles of quantum field theory, including relativistic invariance and the gauge principle, and calculations can be carried out to a high enough order within perturbation theory, and the results/predictions can be checked against experiments to a very high degree of accuracy, producing some of the best tested results in all of physics. The development of QED is an interesting story as it was the motivation and the test case for many of the ideas of field theory.

The story begins shortly after the discovery of quantum mechanics in 1925. In many ways, the beginning is the work of Dirac who quantized the free electromagnetic field in 1926–27, showing that the eigenstates are the photons. His work also explained how the spontaneous and stimulated emission of light by atoms could occur, giving the fully quantum mechanical justification of the earlier work of Einstein. The Dirac equation which describes the electron appeared in 1928. The need for the positron within this theory was fully appreciated by 1930 or so. The general principles of field quantization had been formulated in the years prior to 1930 in a series of papers by Heisenberg and Pauli, Jordan and Pauli, with additional work by Jordan and Wigner on how fermions were to be quantized. In 1929, Fermi gave a quantization procedure for the Maxwell theory which improved on Dirac's pioneering work by being manifestly covariant, although there were still some issues related to the gauge condition which were not clear. By this time, one could argue that QED was already formulated, although there were still serious calculational issues. While some processes could be calculated in a painstaking way in standard perturbation theory, it was not clear how one could take this further and get a general framework. Further, it became clear that there was a serious problem with infinities. For example, the electron self-energy was calculated by Weisskopf, who found that it diverged logarithmically. While this was somewhat better than the situation in the classical theory (where the divergence is linear), a divergence is still a divergence, with its value running off to infinity, so extracting a reliable prediction was impossible. Even nondivergent results could be vitiated by divergent higher order corrections.

This gloomy state of affairs continued through much of the 1930s, although there were a few bright spots. Euler and Heisenberg calculated the first set of quantum corrections to the classical action for electrodynamics, obtaining a very nice and beautiful result. This was one of the nondivergent contributions so it could be unambiguously calculated, but again, it was unclear if it could be trusted given the divergences elsewhere in the theory. Pauli gave the first, albeit fairly restricted, proof of the connection between spin and statistics. Symmetries started getting better appreciation, following Wigner's seminal work on the representations of the Poincaré group and the work of London on gauge invariance. But these were the years leading up to the Second World War, large numbers of physicists were leaving continental Europe and their attention was being increasingly turned to the war effort. There was little time or possibility for anything but small scale incremental progress on QED.

The end of the war led to an outburst of activity, including measurements of Lamb shift and $g - 2$ for the electron. What crystallized the various efforts was the Shelter Island conference of 1947, where Kramers suggested the basic idea of renormalization. (It seems that Stueckelberg also had similar ideas earlier, but this was not widely known or appreciated.) Calculations would show corrections to the mass and charge of the electron, which could be divergent. But Kramers argued that whatever such corrections might be, these were already included in the measured values, so one should rewrite the theory in terms of the measured values. Perhaps what is left over after this would be a finite theory. A cynic could argue that this was only a way of hiding the infinities, a rather contrived one at that, but at least a procedure worth trying out emerged. Inspired by this, Hans Bethe immediately (mostly just on the train ride going back to Schenectady from the conference) calculated the Lamb shift, interpreting it as being primarily due to the difference of electron self-energies between the bound electron and a free electron. This gave a value of 1040 MHz, as opposed to the experimental value of ~1058 MHz. This was impressively close, considering that Bethe had made a nonrelativistic approximation, that it stimulated several attempts at a better calculation. Julian Schwinger developed a method of covariant perturbation theory in the interaction picture (using what we now call the Tomonaga-Schwinger equation) and was able to calculate the first set of contributions to the anomalous magnetic moment of the electron. (Often old ideas come back to life in physics: The interaction picture is essentially due to Dirac in his work on time-dependent perturbation theory; and that too has a classical ancestor in the "osculating ellipse" of Lagrange.) Schwinger's work is elegant and powerful, but it was not easy for anyone to use. In a totally independent line of development, Richard Feynman came up with the eponymous diagrams which provided a much easier method of calculation. Feynman's approach was based on intuitive ideas and to some extent on the path integral which he invented developing an earlier notion due to Dirac (again!). It was not clear how, if at all, it could be related to Schwinger's work; it was Freeman Dyson who showed the equivalence. Dyson also developed many of the ideas of diagrammatics we use today, such as proper vertices, degree of divergence, etc. and also indicated how one could show that QED is renormalizable. This meant that all potential infinities in QED are of the type that they could be absorbed into the definitions of mass, charge and normalizations of wave functions, so that all predictions would be unambiguous and finite. In other words, one could successfully implement Kramers' idea. (The full proof of renormalizability of QED took a few more years. Also, today, after the work of Ken Wilson, we understand the concept of renormalizability much better, and we regard QED as a theory which must be embedded in a larger theory, but all that is another story.)

During the war years, Sin-itiro Tomonaga in Japan had been working on QED. In fact, shortly before Schwinger's work, he had discovered the method of generating covariant perturbation theory and had published the results in Japanese journals, although he had not managed to take it to the point where predictions, such as for $g-2$, could be extracted. Although the war had just ended, communication between Japan and the United States was still not easy and the western world learnt of this work only later, when Schwinger's and Feynman's and all the related work began to be published in the U.S. and Tomonaga wrote to Robert Oppenheimer, enclosing copies of his papers.

There is an old saying about QED: Tomonaga showed it could be done, Schwinger did it, and Feynman showed how anybody could do it. This leaves out the important work of Dyson and many others, but, as with many such witticisms, it captures a germ of truth.

We will not talk more of the history of the subject, or of the many significant developments which came later. Many concepts in field theory can be traced to QED. These include the more rigorous approaches to renormalization, the β-function and the renormalization flow, the development of the notion of anomalies, dynamical mass generation (originally studied in the Schwinger model or QED in two spacetime dimensions), etc. QED has long been the place where ideas on field theory get tested out. As for the early history of the subject, Silvan Schweber's *QED and the men who made it* (Princeton University Press, 1994) is a beautiful and masterful book which is well worth reading.

Chapter 9

Other Forces: Weak Interactions

We have considered the electromagnetic interactions of charged particles or Quantum Electrodynamics (QED), and in particular, the theory of electrons (and positrons) and photons. This theory is one of the most successful theories in the whole history of physics, making precise predictions which have also been experimentally verified to very high accuracy. After centuries of wondering about it, we could finally claim we have some understanding of the nature of light. But somewhat ironically, QED as a theory in its own right may not exist. There is a way to formulate field theories from a rigorous mathematical point of view, known as constructive field theory. What is done is to set up the theory on a lattice with a finite lattice spacing and a finite number of lattice points, making everything mathematically well-defined and then taking the limit of the number of lattice points becoming infinite and the lattice spacing becoming zero, thus recovering a continuum formulation. There are indications that QED formulated in this way does not exist as an interacting field theory, meaning that the theory becomes a free theory in the continuum limit. Nevertheless, it is sensible to work with QED viewing it as part of a larger theory such as the Standard Model (with other particles and other interactions) and, as we mentioned, it has been amazingly successful.

But let us return to the point that the world is made of many more things than just electrons and photons, and there are many other particle species and interactions that we need to consider. Of immediate interest to us are the weak interactions, responsible for β-decay and a number of other processes, and the strong nuclear forces responsible for binding protons and neutrons (or quarks at a more fundamental level) into nuclei. We will consider these in turn, starting with β-decay and other weak interactions.

The story of weak interactions begins, in some sense, with the discovery of the neutron in 1932. It was quickly realized that β-decay could be viewed as the decay of a neutron into a proton and an electron, the latter being ejected from the nucleus as the β-particle. Once the electron is produced, keeping it confined would be very costly in terms of binding energy and so it is ejected. Experiments however indicated a mismatch of energy between the initial nucleus and the daughter nucleus plus the electron. This led Pauli to suggest that there is yet another particle involved which escaped detection with the techniques available at that time. This particle was named the neutrino. It was clear that it had to be neutral for reasons of charge conservation and that its mass had to be zero or very small from the energy range available to the electron. (If the neutrino has a high mass, then at least that much of the energy of the reaction goes into producing it, so that electrons with energies close to the energy difference between the parent and daughter nuclei would not be seen.) Thus the β-decay reaction was identified as

$$n \rightarrow p + e^- + \bar{\nu}_e$$

We have written the antineutrino here and also labeled it as the electron-type neutrino; these two qualifications came much later than 1932, but we may as well include these here.

We can also see that the neutrino should be a spin-$\frac{1}{2}$ particle. The neutron is a spin-$\frac{1}{2}$ particle. On the right hand side of the reaction, we have the proton and the electron which are also spin-$\frac{1}{2}$ particles; their spins can be combined into states of integer spin. Thus to balance the fractional spin of the left hand side of this reaction, the neutrino has to be a spin-$\frac{1}{2}$ particle. (We see that there would be a mismatch of angular momentum without the neutrino, which was another reason to postulate its existence.) Just from these considerations, we can write down the basic interaction vertex needed for the β-decay, as done by Fermi in 1932.

We know that spin-$\frac{1}{2}$ particles are described by spinors of the type Ψ. For the 4 species involved in the reaction, we thus need 4 types, say, Ψ_n, Ψ_p, Ψ_e and Ψ_{ν_e}. The action at the free level would be the Dirac action for each of these (except possibly for the neutrino, for reasons stated later). We need the interaction vertex. For this, we need a Ψ_n for the incoming neutron, a $\bar{\Psi}_p$ for the outgoing proton, a $\bar{\Psi}_e$ for the outgoing electron and a Ψ_{ν_e} for the outgoing antineutrino. This is in accord with the rules given in the Lecture 8. The vertex is then of the type

$$S_{int} \sim \int d^4x \, (\bar{\Psi}_e M \Psi_{\nu_e}) (\bar{\Psi}_p N \Psi_n) \tag{9.1}$$

Here M, N are 4×4 matrices with matrix indices since Ψ's are column vectors and $\bar{\Psi}$'s are row vectors, of 4 entries each. Other than that, we just need to ensure Lorentz symmetry, so we cannot have uncontracted spacetime indices left over. A basis for 4×4 matrices of the spinorial type is given by

$$\Gamma = \{\mathbb{1}, \gamma^5, \gamma^\mu, \gamma^\mu\gamma^5, \gamma^{\mu\nu} \equiv (\gamma^\mu\gamma^\nu - \gamma^\mu\gamma^\nu)\} \tag{9.2}$$

where the γ-matrices are:

$$\mathbb{1} = \begin{pmatrix} 1 & 0 \\ 0 & 1 \end{pmatrix}, \quad \gamma^5 = \begin{pmatrix} -1 & 0 \\ 0 & 1 \end{pmatrix}, \quad \gamma^0 = \begin{pmatrix} 0 & 1 \\ 1 & 0 \end{pmatrix}, \quad \gamma^i = \begin{pmatrix} 0 & -\sigma_i \\ \sigma_i & 0 \end{pmatrix} \tag{9.3}$$

(Notice that the symmetrization of indices in $\gamma^\mu\gamma^\nu$ would just give the identity, since $\gamma^\mu\gamma^\nu + \gamma^\nu\gamma^\mu = 2\,\eta^{\mu\nu}\mathbb{1}$, so only the antisymmetrized combination is linearly independent and is entered in (9.2). There are 6 independent $\gamma^{\mu\nu}$, giving 16 independent matrices in the set (9.2), adequate to span the set of 4×4 matrices.) The general interaction vertex consistent with Lorentz symmetry is thus

$$
\begin{aligned}
S_{int} = \int d^4x \Big[&\bar{\Psi}_e[a\mathbb{1} + b\,\gamma^5]\,\Psi_{\nu_e}\,\bar{\Psi}_p\,[c\mathbb{1} + d\,\gamma^5]\,\Psi_n \\
&+ \bar{\Psi}_e[f\gamma_\mu + g\,\gamma_\mu\gamma^5]\,\Psi_{\nu_e}\,\bar{\Psi}_p\,[h\gamma^\mu + k\,\gamma^\mu\gamma^5]\,\Psi_n \\
&+ l\,\bar{\Psi}_e\,\gamma_{\mu\nu}\,\Psi_{\nu_e}\,\bar{\Psi}_p\,\gamma^{\mu\nu}\,\Psi_n \Big]
\end{aligned} \tag{9.4}
$$

where a, b, $\cdots$, l are possible coupling constants. They have to be determined from experiment.[1]

From the time of Fermi's work, through the 1940s and '50s, there was a lot of analysis of the β-decay in nuclei; a number of other processes were examined as well. The idea was to carefully determine the various possible coupling constants in (9.4). The culmination of this long and arduous and careful work with experimental data was two breakthroughs in 1956 and 1957. The first was the realization that parity is not conserved in weak interactions. It was pointed out by C.N. Yang and T.D. Lee that the so-called τ-θ puzzle in weak decays could be resolved if both particles were identified as the same particle, now called the K^+ meson, but this would mean giving up on parity conservation. Parity nonconservation in weak interactions was confirmed immediately thereafter in the experiment by C.S. Wu. The second step was the elimination, with the benefit of

---

[1]In principle, in (9.1) we could also consider terms like $\bar{\Psi}_p\,M\,\Psi_{\nu_e}\,\bar{\Psi}_e\,N\,\Psi_n$. But these are related to the ones we have written by rearrangement of terms, usually referred to as a Fierz rearrangement. There is also some more simplification/reduction of terms possible in (9.4); but this is immaterial at this point.

parity nonconservation, of most of the terms in (9.4), by comparison with experiment, done by E.C.G. Sudarshan and Robert Marshak. They showed that with many of the coupling constants in (9.4) being zero, one could write the interaction as

$$S_{int} = \frac{G_F}{\sqrt{2}} \int d^4x \ \bar{\Psi}_e [\gamma_\mu - \gamma_\mu \gamma^5] \Psi_{\nu_e} \ \bar{\Psi}_p [\gamma^\mu - \gamma^\mu \gamma^5] \Psi_n \qquad (9.5)$$

with a single coupling constant G_F (called the Fermi coupling constant) whose numerical value was estimated from experiments as

$$G_F = 1.166 \times 10^5 \ (\text{GeV})^{-2} \qquad (9.6)$$

A term like $\bar{\Psi}\gamma^\mu\Psi$ is a vectorial quantity under Lorentz transformations, but $\bar{\Psi}\gamma^\mu\gamma^5\Psi$ is an axial vector, namely, it transforms as a vector, but has an additional minus sign under parity compared to a vector. For this reason, (9.5) is often referred to as the $V - A$ (V minus A) interaction.

There are many other weak processes of interest, other than β-decay. Another classic example is the decay of the muon,

$$\mu \rightarrow e + \bar{\nu}_e + \nu_\mu \qquad (9.7)$$

involving both the electron-neutrino and the mu-neutrino in the final state. The interaction describing this was identified as

$$S_{int} = \frac{G_F}{\sqrt{2}} \int d^4x \ \bar{e}\gamma_\mu(1 - \gamma^5)\nu_e \ \bar{\nu}_\mu \gamma^\mu(1 - \gamma^5)\mu \qquad (9.8)$$

where we use the symbol for the particle as the symbol for the field itself. Thus μ stands for Ψ corresponding to μ, $\bar{e}$ stands for $\bar{\Psi}_e$, etc. In the same notation, (9.5) reads

$$S_{int} = \frac{G_F}{\sqrt{2}} \int d^4x \ \bar{e}\gamma_\mu(1 - \gamma^5)\nu_e \ \bar{p}\gamma^\mu(1 - \gamma^5)n \qquad (9.9)$$

Most importantly, we have the same structure and the same strength of interaction in both cases, (9.8) and (9.5) or (9.9).

There are also a large number of weak decay processes involving mesons. We will not list them here, but a few samples are:

$$\pi^+ \rightarrow \mu^+ + \nu_\mu$$
$$K^+ \rightarrow \mu^+ + \nu_\mu$$
$$K^+ \rightarrow e^+ + \nu_e$$

There are also many processes involving baryons, a couple of examples being

$$\Lambda \ \rightarrow p + e^- + \bar{\nu}_e$$

$$\Sigma^+ \to \Lambda + e^+ + \nu_e$$

There are two features of the $V - A$ theory embodied in (9.8) and (9.9) which are important and which show the way to a more complete theory of weak interactions. First of all, we consider the action of $1 - \gamma^5$ on a spinor. Given a 4-component spinor Ψ, we find

$$\frac{1}{2}(1 - \gamma^5)\,\Psi = \begin{pmatrix} 1 & 0 \\ 0 & 0 \end{pmatrix} \begin{pmatrix} U \\ V \end{pmatrix} = \begin{pmatrix} U \\ 0 \end{pmatrix} \tag{9.10}$$

The combination $\frac{1}{2}(1-\gamma^5)$ is thus a projection operator, projecting out the upper two components of the spinor. The two-component column vector U is known as the left chiral component of Ψ. It corresponds to the upper two components in our choice of γ-matrices. In a similar way, $\frac{1}{2}(1+\gamma^5)$ projects out the lower two components which constitute the right chiral component in our choice of γ-matrices. Denoting the left chiral component by the subscript L, we can write the $V - A$ interaction in (9.8) as

$$S_{int} = \frac{4G_F}{\sqrt{2}} \int d^4x\; \bar{e}_L \gamma_\mu \nu_{eL}\; \bar{\nu}_{\mu L}\, \gamma^\mu\, \mu_L \tag{9.11}$$

Similarly we can write (9.9) in terms of chiral components as

$$S_{int} = \frac{4G_F}{\sqrt{2}} \int d^4x\; \bar{e}_L \gamma_\mu \nu_{eL}\; \bar{p}_L\, \gamma^\mu\, n_L \tag{9.12}$$

The key property is that these weak interactions only involve the left chiral components. This is also directly related to parity violation.

The parity operation on spinors corresponds to

$$\Psi(t, \vec{x}) \to \Psi^P = \gamma^0\,\Psi(t, -\vec{x}) \tag{9.13}$$

With this definition, we can check the parity invariance of the free Dirac theory easily. Consider the action with Ψ^P in place of Ψ,

$$\begin{aligned}
S[\Psi^P] &= \int d^4x\; \bar{\Psi}^P \left[i\gamma^0 \frac{\partial}{\partial t} + i\gamma^i \frac{\partial}{\partial x^i} - m \right] \Psi^P \\
&= \int d^4x\; \bar{\Psi}(-\vec{x})\gamma^0 \left[i\gamma^0 \frac{\partial}{\partial t} + i\gamma^i \frac{\partial}{\partial x^i} - m \right] \gamma^0 \Psi(-\vec{x}) \\
&= \int d^4x\; \bar{\Psi}(-\vec{x}) \left[i\gamma^0 \frac{\partial}{\partial t} + i\gamma^i \frac{\partial}{\partial (-x)^i} - m \right] \Psi(-\vec{x}) \\
&= \int d^4x\; \bar{\Psi}(\vec{x}) \left[i\gamma^0 \frac{\partial}{\partial t} + i\gamma^i \frac{\partial}{\partial x^i} - m \right] \Psi(\vec{x}) \\
&= S[\Psi]
\end{aligned} \tag{9.14}$$

In the third line we used, $\gamma^0 \gamma^0 \gamma^0 = \gamma^0$ and $\gamma^0 \gamma^i \gamma^0 = -\gamma^i$ and put the minus sign onto x^i; in the fourth line, we changed variables of integration from x^i to $-x^i$. This equation shows the parity invariance of the free Dirac theory. Notice that the extra factor of γ^0 is necessary in (9.13) to get the change of sign for the $\partial/\partial x$ term. So the parity transformation for the Dirac field must have this factor in addition to $\vec{x} \rightarrow -\vec{x}$.

Now when we apply the parity transformation to the left chiral components, we find

$$(\Psi^P)_L = \frac{1 - \gamma^5}{2} (\gamma^0 \Psi(t, -\vec{x})) = \gamma^0 \frac{1 + \gamma^5}{2} \Psi(t, -\vec{x}) = \gamma^0 \, \Psi_R(t, -\vec{x}) \quad (9.15)$$

where we used $\gamma^0 \gamma^5 = -\gamma^5 \gamma^0$ which may be verified from the explicit formulae we have given for these matrices. Equation (9.15) shows that the left and right components get exchanged under parity, apart from $\vec{x} \rightarrow -\vec{x}$. In the vertex term of the action, we can do a change of integration variables from x^i to $-x^i$ as we did for the free part. But the change from the left chiral components to the right chiral components under parity will remain. Since the interaction vertices (9.11) and (9.12) only involve the left chiral components, they cannot be invariant under parity. This is the parity violation of weak interactions, now built into the structure of the vertex.

Let us now consider the Feynman diagram giving, say, β-decay. We may represent this as shown in Fig. 9.1. We can calculate the rate for this process following the usual rules for Feynman diagrams. We do not need to do that in detail here. However, once we have the basic vertex (9.9), we know that the theory will lead to many other processes as well, including scatterings rather than just decays, and even new ones which arise from higher orders in perturbation theory.

We will now use an example of a scattering process to estimate and point out an issue with the behavior of the cross section. For this, we choose electron-neutrino scattering, which is obtainable even at the lowest

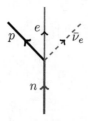

Fig. 9.1: Feynman diagram for β-decay

order in perturbation theory with the basic vertex we have discussed. The diagram for this process is shown in Fig. 9.2. (We could consider other scatterings as well, e.g., the proton-neutron scattering which results from (9.9). This process would have corrections from nuclear interactions as well. Electron-neutrino scattering has no nuclear force corrections (at this order at least) and no electromagnetic part since the neutrino is neutral. So this is a bit cleaner to consider for consequences of just the $V - A$ interaction.) The interaction terms given in (9.8, 9.9) or (9.11, 9.12) are not hermitian as written. The hermitian conjugate has to be added to them. Thus (9.8) should read

$$S_{int} = \frac{G_F}{\sqrt{2}} \int d^4x \; \Big[\bar{e}\,\gamma_\mu(1 - \gamma^5)\,\nu_e \; \bar{\nu}_\mu\,\gamma^\mu(1 - \gamma^5)\,\mu$$

$$+ \bar{\mu}\,\gamma_\mu(1 - \gamma^5)\,\nu_\mu \; \bar{\nu}_e\,\gamma^\mu(1 - \gamma^5)\,e \Big] \qquad (9.16)$$

The second term leads to the process $e + \bar{\nu}_e \to \mu + \bar{\nu}_\mu$ which is shown. Again, without getting into detailed calculations, we can estimate the high energy behavior of the scattering cross section just on dimensional grounds, as we did for the electromagnetic case. Each spin-$\frac{1}{2}$ field is of dimension $\frac{3}{2}$, as we have seen before. Thus in S_{int} in (9.16), the fields for the electron, electron-neutrino, the muon and the muon-neutrino together have a dimension of 6. The measure factor d^4x has dimension $= -4$. So we get a net value for the dimension of the integral of the product of fields to be 2, which means that G_F has dimension $= -2$, in agreement with what we found earlier. In the cross section for the process, we have two such factors (from squaring the amplitude) giving a dimension of -4. Since σ must have the dimensions of area (or its dimension $= -2$), we expect it to have the behavior

$$\sigma \sim G_F^2\, s \qquad (9.17)$$

where s is the square of the CM energy. The cross section rises with energy.

We can also consider higher order processes, say, $e + \nu_e \to e + \nu_e$, with some of the contributing diagrams shown in Fig. 9.3. In these cases, we

Fig. 9.2: Electron-(anti)neutrino scattering into muon and the mu-(anti)neurino given by the $V - A$ interaction

have two powers of G_F already in the amplitude, so the cross section must go like s^3. (There are other issues with these diagrams having to do with

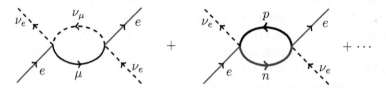

Fig. 9.3: Electron-neutrino scattering in $V - A$ theory

renormalization as well.) In any case, the conclusion from these simple dimensional analyses is that the $V - A$ theory leads to cross sections rising with energy.

But we know from quantum mechanics that this cannot go on for all energies. Cross sections have to be bounded. This is familiar from the partial wave analysis for scattering from a potential, even in the nonrelativistic case. The cross section for potential scattering is of the form

$$\sigma = \frac{4\pi}{k^2} \sum_{l=0}^{\infty} (2l + 1) \sin^2 \delta_l \tag{9.18}$$

where k is the wave vector of the incident particle, and δ_l is the phase shift for the partial wave of angular momentum l. This equation shows immediately that the cross section for each partial wave is bounded,

$$\sigma_l \leq \frac{4\pi}{k^2} (2l + 1) \tag{9.19}$$

(It is easy to see that the total cross section as in (9.18) will be bounded even if a finite set of partial waves contribute; this can be verified to be the case for $e \bar{\nu}_e$ scattering.) The result (9.19) shows that we cannot have something like (9.17) since it would violate this bound at some energy.

The bound on the cross sections is a consequence of a very general property known as unitarity of the scattering matrix which any consistent theory should have. It is also an expression of the conservation of probability. The point is that any transition is obtained by time-evolution with a Hamiltonian, so that the generic transition amplitude for $|\beta\rangle \to |\alpha\rangle$ is of the form

$$S_{\alpha\beta} = \langle \alpha | e^{-iH(t-t_0)} | \beta \rangle \tag{9.20}$$

The hermiticity of the Hamiltonian implies that this is a unitary matrix, with α, β as matrix labels. Thus $(S^\dagger S)_{\beta\beta} = 1$ and this can be expanded out as

$$\sum_\alpha S^*_{\alpha\beta} S_{\alpha\beta} = \sum_{\text{all final states } \alpha} \text{Probability of transition } (|\beta\rangle \to |\alpha\rangle) = 1$$

(9.21)

The point is that a system in state $|\beta\rangle$ either continues to be in the same state or makes a transition to some other state; so the total probability for transitions from the state $|\beta\rangle$ to all possible states $|\alpha\rangle$ (including $|\beta\rangle$) should be one. This is the expression of the conservation of probability. Clearly this does not allow the probability of transitions into some subset of possible final states such as the μ and ν_μ (of various momenta) in the first example to keep on increasing with energy. Cross section is defined by the transition rate (probability per unit time) divided by the incoming flux, so the constraint on the probability being bounded leads to a bound on the cross section as well. The rising cross section in (9.17) shows that the theory with just the $V - A$ vertex is incompatible with unitarity.

So, our conclusion is the following. The $V - A$ interaction is a major step forward in our understanding of weak interactions, nicely summing up a variety of experimental results, but it cannot be a fundamental theory. While it is valid at low energies, it must be a low-energy approximation to a more fundamental theory.

How can we modify the theory? The undesirable feature of the growth of cross sections with energy is due to the fact that the coupling parameter G_F has dimensions of $(Energy)^{-2}$. We also know from the electromagnetic theory that a vertex with two fermions and one boson (like the photon) leads to a coupling constant which is dimensionless. Thus if we can mimic the electron-photon coupling and obtain the $V - A$ interaction as some approximation to it, we have the possibility of avoiding the rise of cross sections with energy. We will take this up in the next lecture.

Remark 9.1.
The saga of V − A

Every step of progress in particle physics demands a great investment of effort (and time and money) and a lot of back and forth between theory and experiment. The story of the $V - A$ theory is as good an illustration of this point as any other. The four-fermion interaction terms in (9.4) come with many possible interaction vertices and coupling constants. A number of experimental results were needed to show that the scalar, pseudoscalar and tensor type couplings were actually not obtained in nature, leaving the vector and axial vector terms. The problem was that, as far as β-decay was concerned, most of the experiments involved nuclei and hence the neutron and proton wave functions which enter into a calculation of rates using (9.4) would be the bound state wave functions of these particles in the nucleus. But the binding of nucleons in a nucleus was not well understood at that time; one had to make potential models as effective *ad hoc* descriptions and test them out in experiments. Further, there could be issues specific to the type of nucleus, so extracting any kind of a universal result, independent of the milieu in which the nucleons are, was a very difficult task. In fact, Sudarshan and Marshak had to analyze and sift through a number of experimental results, rejecting some of the observations (which seemed to show evidence for non-$V - A$ vertices) as unreliable, to finally come up with the $V - A$ result. Even then, what emerged was not $V - A$ but rather

$$S_{int} = \frac{G_F}{\sqrt{2}} \int d^4x \; \bar{e}\gamma_\mu(1 - \gamma^5)\,\nu_e \; \bar{p}\gamma^\mu(1 - g_A\,\gamma^5)\,n \qquad (9.22)$$

where g_A was approximately 1.2. In other words, for the nucleon part we have the current $\bar{p}\gamma^\mu n - g_A\bar{p}\gamma^\mu\gamma^5 n$, which is $V - g_A\,A$. (Thus we cheated a bit in writing (9.9). As we will see, it should truly be interpreted as being valid for quarks with u, d taking the places of p, n, respectively.) This is rather strange, particularly since a purely leptonic process like $\mu \rightarrow e + \bar{\nu}_e + \nu_\mu$ seemed to be a pure $V - A$ interaction, as in (9.8). How could we hope for universality with results like these?

Since the proton and the neutron also have strong interactions, one possible way out was to argue that the strong forces could change the current $\bar{p}\gamma^\mu(1-\gamma^5)n$ to $\bar{p}\gamma^\mu n - g_A\bar{p}\gamma^\mu\gamma^5 n$. The leptons which have no strong interactions would retain the $V - A$ form, $\bar{e}\gamma_\mu(1-\gamma^5)\,\nu_e$ and $\bar{\nu}_\mu\,\gamma^\mu(1-\gamma^5)\,\mu$. (In modern language, p and n are bound states of quarks and the use of the bound state wave functions of the quarks (inside the nucleon) will correct the value of g_A (which is taken to be 1 at the level of quarks) to $g_A \simeq 1.2$ at the level of nucleons. The leptons which are fundamental would not have such a correction. But none of this was clear in the late 1950s.) We can restate the idea by saying that the interaction (9.22) should be replaced at the quark level by

$$S_{int} = \frac{G_F}{\sqrt{2}} \int d^4x \; \bar{e}\gamma_\mu(1 - \gamma^5)\,\nu_e \; \bar{u}\gamma^\mu(1 - \gamma^5)\,d \qquad (9.23)$$

When we put in the bound state wave functions for the quarks (as they are bound to form the proton and the neutron) and try to write this effectively at the level of the baryons, we should find (9.22), with $g_A \simeq 1.2$. But this possibility immediately brought up another issue: Why would strong interactions affect only the axial current? Could we not have

$$\bar{p}\gamma^\mu(1-\gamma^5)n \to g_V\bar{p}\gamma^\mu n - g_A\bar{p}\gamma^\mu\gamma^5 n,$$

with both g_V, $g_A \neq 1$? Although we could rewrite this as $g_V(\bar{p}\gamma^\mu(1 - (g_A/g_V)\gamma^5)n)$ to obtain a form similar to $\bar{p}\gamma^\mu n - g_A\bar{p}\gamma^\mu\gamma^5 n$, the factor g_V would change the overall strength of the interaction and spoil the universality between leptonic and baryonic processes.

The conserved vector current (CVC) hypothesis of Feynman and Gell-Mann showed how we could understand why g_V remains 1 even with strong interactions. The basic idea is that if we have a conserved current, then we can couple it consistently to a vector field, just as the usual electric charge is coupled to the electromagnetic field A_μ. The charge contained in a volume V is then given by the electric flux over the boundary of V; this is just Gauss' law familiar from Maxwell's theory. The flux is measured at the surface, which could be very far from the locations of the charges, and hence it is not affected by local interactions which the charges may be subject to. We can therefore envisage a simple *gedanken* experiment. Imagine we put the electron and the quarks u, u, d (which make up the proton) at some point in space, practically at zero separation. Then the flux lines for the electric field emanating from the (positively charged) u's will terminate at the d and the electron. Now consider pulling the electron far away from the quarks. We should still have as much flux emanating from the quarks as needed to terminate at the electron, appropriate to its charge of -1. The quarks may have all kinds of other (like strong) interactions, but the total electric charge of the three quarks will be what it was, namely, $+1$ in units of e. There cannot be a renormalization or any change in the value of the charge as it has to match the flux terminating on the electron. This explains why the proton has exactly the same charge (but opposite in sign) as the electron, even though the proton is subject to strong interactions. The conservation of electric current is the key to this. So Feynman and Gell-Mann suggested that the vector current $\bar{p}\gamma^\mu n$ is conserved and hence the coupling constant or the corresponding charge (which is not the electric charge) does not change even with strong interactions, i.e., g_V remains 1. But axial currents are not conserved because mass terms in the action break this conservation law, so the axial part is not protected and we can have $g_A \neq 1$. (The arguments and rationale for the $V - A$ interaction first appeared in three papers in 1958, one by Feynman and Gell-Mann, another by Sudarshan and Marshak, and the third by J. Sakurai. The analysis and sifting of various experiments to arrive at $V - A$ had been done by Sudarshan and Marshak, and their result was presented at meetings, including the Padua-Venice conference in September 1957, but the first paper published in a journal was the one by Feynman and Gell-Mann in January 1958. This unfortunate inversion of events seems to have led to some misunderstandings about the history of the subject (and between scientists as well).)

The CVC hypothesis is a beautiful idea and indeed shows a path to universality. But following this path, could one check that the change in g_A is indeed approximately 1.2? Strong interactions were not well understood, so this was a tricky proposition. But the idea was that although many things were not known, the currents corresponding to symmetry transformations would have an algebra determined by symmetry considerations, so perhaps one could use it to get some statements. This was the so-called current algebra method initiated by Gell-Mann. It was used by Adler and Weisberger to obtain a sum rule relating g_A to known (and measurable) cross sections for pion-nucleon scattering. Using experimental input for the cross sections, one could indeed check that g_A would come out around 1.2 for the nucleons. So universality for the weak interactions seemed within reach.

But what about the weak processes involving the mesons? For example, we can have the decay $\pi^+ \to \mu^+ + \nu_\mu$. While we may envisage using a current $\bar{\nu}_\mu \gamma^\mu (1 - \gamma^5)\mu$ for the leptons, we would need to add in a pion at the vertex to form a Feynman diagram which can explain the decay. For (pseudo)scalar particles, we would expect currents to be of the form $J_\mu \sim i(\phi^* \partial_\mu \phi - \partial_\mu \phi^* \, \phi)$ as we may see from the example of the electromagnetic field in (5.32). But a vertex like $J^\mu \, \bar{\nu}_\mu \gamma_\mu (1 - \gamma^5)\mu$ would entail two pions at the vertex, so how can we explain pion decay with a single incoming pion? The answer to this came from another deep theoretical insight. Yoichiro Nambu argued that one could take the current for the pion as $i f_\pi \partial_\mu \pi^+$ so that the interaction would be

$$S_{int} = \frac{G_F}{\sqrt{2}} \left[i \, f_\pi \, \partial_\mu \pi^+ \right] \bar{\nu}_\mu \gamma^\mu (1 - \gamma^5)\mu \; + \; \text{hermitian conjugate} \qquad (9.24)$$

which would correctly describe pion decay. (Another way to phrase this, if we think of the pion as a composite particle made of quarks, is that the weak interaction current which is $\bar{d}_L \gamma^\mu u_L$ has a matrix element, between the incoming pion state and the vacuum, which is of the form $\langle 0 | \bar{d}_L \gamma^\mu u_L | \pi^+ \rangle \sim f_\pi \, k^\mu$ where k^μ is the momentum of the pion.) In (9.24), f_π is a constant called the pion decay constant and is experimentally found to be around 130 MeV. The statement of the relevant meson current being $if_\pi \partial_\mu \pi^+$ is known as the PCAC (partial conservation of axial vector current) hypothesis (because it was the divergence of the current which was first discussed). Nambu's main point was that this form could be understood as arising from the spontaneous breaking of chiral symmetry, yet another theoretical input from ideas which emerged in the 1950s. So now, universality of weak interactions even including mesons seemed within reach. But there was yet another wrinkle, the course of true research never did run smooth. In extending the idea of PCAC to the K-mesons, it became clear that the currents participating in the weak processes were actually linear combinations of currents one would expect based on the states as defined by strong interaction processes (used to produce the Ks in the first place). More specifically, in modern terms, this means that in writing the interaction in terms of the quark current as in (9.23), we should actually replace $\bar{u}\,\gamma^\mu(1 - \gamma^5)\,d$ by

$$\bar{u}\,\gamma^\mu(1 - \gamma^5)\,d \,\cos\theta_C + \bar{u}\,\gamma^\mu(1 - \gamma^5)\,s\,\sin\theta_C \qquad (9.25)$$

where θ_C is the Cabibbo angle, after Nicola Cabibbo who introduced this mixing in 1963; experimentally $\theta_C \simeq 0.25$. (Later this Cabibbo mixing of the d and s quarks got generalized to the Cabibbo-Kobayashi-Maskawa mixing. In the Standard Model it can be understood as being due to the freedom of a matrix of coupling constants, rather than a single constant, for the quark-Higgs coupling. We will discuss this briefly later.)

There were many more minor wrinkles which had to be straightened out as well, but, by and large, by the early 1960s, universality had been obtained and a more fundamental theory of weak interactions could be contemplated.

Chapter 10

The Gauge Principle

We will now begin our discussion of the gauge principle, which is the foundational principle, one might even say the soul, of the Standard Model. To define what we are trying to formulate, let us start by recalling that at the end of the last lecture, we were talking about how to improve the $V - A$ theory of weak interactions. We mentioned how we can mimic the electromagnetic interaction to get a dimensionless coupling constant so that the problematic rise of cross sections with energy can be avoided. Thus, for example, we can try postulating a vertex of the form

$$S_{int} = \frac{g}{\sqrt{2}} \int d^4x \ [(\bar{e}_L\gamma^\mu\nu_{eL}) + (\bar{n}_L\gamma^\mu p_L)] \ W_\mu^-$$

$$+ \frac{g}{\sqrt{2}} \int d^4x \ [(\bar{\nu}_{eL}\gamma^\mu e_L) + (\bar{p}_L\gamma^\mu n_L)] \ W_\mu^+ \qquad (10.1)$$

where $W_\mu^\pm$ are a new type of vector particles. The term in the second line of this equation is the hermitian conjugate of the term in the first line. (We ignore the muon, its neutrino and other particles for the moment. Also the division by $\sqrt{2}$ is for later convenience.) Simple dimension counting shows that the coupling constant g has no dimension. Since each spin-$\frac{1}{2}$ field has dimension $\frac{3}{2}$, the fact that the action has zero dimension tells us that $\dim[g] + \frac{3}{2} + \frac{3}{2} + \dim[W] - 4$ (for d^4x) $= 0$. W has dimension 1, similar to the photon, so $\dim[g] = 0$. Since the coupling constant is dimensionless, there is some hope that the cross sections will be bounded, as was the case for the electromagnetic interactions.

The basic vertex corresponding to (10.1) would be of the form shown in Fig. 10.1. We can see immediately that the W's are not like photons as regards some of their properties. For example, the outgoing electron being negatively charged, and the neutrino being neutral, the W must bring in a negative charge to the vertex (or carry away a positive charge). Thus

W must be charged, unlike the photon. Further, since we know of no long range force that is measurable over macroscopic distances other than the electromagnetic and gravitational forces, W must have a mass, so that its range is restricted as in Lecture 4, equation (4.25). At the second order, the interaction (10.1) then leads to a diagram with four fermions, of the form also shown in Fig. 10.1. We can write down the mathematical expression for this very easily, following the rules we have discussed before,

$$\mathcal{A} \sim \frac{(ig)^2}{2}(\bar{e}_L(k)\,\gamma^\mu \nu_{eL}(k'))(\bar{p}_L(q)\,\gamma_\mu n_L(p))\,\frac{i}{(p-q)^2 - M_W^2 + i\epsilon}$$
$$\times (2\pi)^4 \delta^{(4)}(p - q - k - k')$$
$$\approx i\frac{g^2}{2\,M_W^2}(\bar{e}_L(k)\,\gamma^\mu \nu_{eL}(k'))(\bar{p}_L(q)\,\gamma_\mu n_L(p))\,(2\pi)^4\delta^{(4)}(p-q-k-k')$$

$$(10.2)$$

In this expression, we have indicated the momenta carried by the particles in parentheses after the wave functions. In the first line of this equation, we have also done the integration over the coordinates and over the momentum of the propagator using the δ-function, so that the momentum transfer $(p-q)$ is the momentum carried by the propagator. In the second line, we have considered the limit of low energies where the momentum transfer is small compared to the mass of the W. This is quite reasonable for processes like nuclear β-decay, since the transfer momentum for those cases is of the order of MeV's, but the mass of the W is of the order of 80 GeV. (This particular value was identified only many years later, but estimates could be made even in the 1960s.) The second line is then exactly of the form of the $V - A$ interaction, with $2\sqrt{2}\,G_F \sim (g^2/2M_W^2)$. This is in agreement with the dimension of G_F, g being dimensionless. Thus we see that it is possible to have a vertex like the one in (10.1) and recover all the good results of the $V - A$ theory in the low energy limit. At high energies, (10.1) has the possibility of cross sections going to zero as required by unitarity, since g is dimensionless.

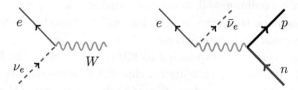

Fig. 10.1: The basic vertex for the electron-neutrino pair with a W and a four-fermion term made of two such vertices

Thus, it is plausible that (10.1) offers a way out of the problem of rising cross sections. However, it is still rather *ad hoc*, we do not know how to write down the vertex for the coupling of the $W_\mu^\pm$ to all the particles which participate in weak interactions, and we do not know if additional new particles have to be postulated. In other words, we do not yet have a principle for this coupling, as we had for electromagnetism. Recall that in that case, we had a simple rule: Start with the Lagrangian of the particles without the photon coupling. Then replace each derivative ∂_μ in the Lagrangian by $\partial_\mu + iqA_\mu$ where q is the charge of the particle. This gave a universal prescription for coupling a point particle to the photon. We must now ask:

> Is there a universal principle by which the coupling of the W's (and any other particle that may be necessary) can be written down?

The universal principle we seek is called the gauge principle. It is an idea which evolved out of Einstein's theory of gravity (or the general theory of relativity). So we will briefly talk about that theory and extract the essence of the gauge principle from it.

Gravity

The fundamental guiding principle behind Einstein's theory of gravity (or the general theory of relativity, as it is often called) is the freedom of coordinate transformations. We are familiar with the fact that in solving physics problems, we can use different coordinate systems, some more convenient than others. For example, in solving the problem of planetary motion in classical mechanics, we can use the Cartesian coordinates if we want, but a spherical polar coordinate system is a bit more convenient because of the spherical symmetry of the potential. We do not expect the laws of physics and the basic results we obtain to depend on the choice of coordinates.

This seems such a simple and obvious statement. After all, we physicists set up coordinate systems for our convenience and different physicists can choose different systems and physics should be independent of the choice. This has been known and accepted by physicists for a long time. However, there is more to the idea of coordinate choices. We can choose coordinate systems in different ways locally. For example, while we use a spherical polar system centered at the position of the Sun, for discussing the motion of, say, Earth around the Sun, we can use a local Cartesian system for the motion of a pendulum at some point on the surface of Earth. The two coordinate systems will have different origins and will be connected by a transformation which expresses one set of coordinates as functions of the other set of coordinates. The point is that we can set up a local coordinate system and do physics in a sensible way without first correlating it with or checking whether it agrees with some more global, cosmologically set up coordinate system.

This is the basic idea behind Einstein's theory: Physics should be invariant under any local nonsingular change of coordinates. (In this context, nonsingular means that the transformation from one set of coordinates to another is invertible.) A law of physics, for example, would be a particular relation among physical quantities such as the metric, electric or magnetic fields, or positions of particles and so on, which we can collectively denote by $\{\alpha\}$. Let us say that physicist A measures these quantities and identifies a law connecting them, expressing it as a relation $f(\alpha_1, \alpha_2, \cdots) = 0$. The quantities α themselves will be different as measured by physicist B who may use another coordinate system, let us denote them by α'. The law obtained by B should read $f(\alpha'_1, \alpha'_2, \cdots) = 0$, *with the same relation f but with the new α's substituted.* In other words, start with $f(\alpha_1, \alpha_2, \cdots) = 0$ and transform each α by the coordinate transformation connecting the two choices of coordinates. The law $f(\alpha_1, \alpha_2, \cdots) = 0$ expressed in terms of α' obtained by the transformation should be the same as $f(\alpha'_1, \alpha'_2, \cdots) = 0$. This is the basic idea.

To develop this idea further, it would be easier if we had a way of expressing the laws which make the invariance under coordinate transformations manifest. Let us discuss this briefly. Consider a scalar function $\phi(x)$ which could be a wave function or a field. The same geometrical point at which ϕ is evaluated can be described by different coordinates, say, x^μ or x'^μ. For example, we may use Cartesian or spherical polar coordinates so that $x^\mu = (t, x_1, x_2, x_3)$ and $x'^\mu = (t', r, \theta, \varphi)$ with a well defined transformation between them,

$$t = t', \quad x_1 = r \sin\theta \cos\varphi, \quad x_2 = r \sin\theta \sin\varphi, \quad x_3 = r \cos\theta \quad (10.3)$$

In other words, x'^μ is a function of x^μ. The value of ϕ does not change since it is evaluated at the same geometric point. Thus we may think of $\phi(x)$ as $\phi(x')$ as well. Consider now a vector $A_\mu(x)$. There are 4 components $A_0(x), A_1(x), A_2(x), A_3(x)$. But it is not adequate to think of these as four functions of x because the components are the projections of the vector along the coordinate directions and if we consider coordinate transformations, the frame of unit vectors at each point may change. So the components may change under a coordinate transformation. To see how this works out, we note that the gradient of a scalar behaves like a vector, so by considering how a gradient changes, we can see how the components of a vector transform. We see from the chain rule of differentiation,

$$\frac{\partial \phi(x)}{\partial x^\mu} = \frac{\partial x'^\alpha}{\partial x^\mu} \frac{\partial \phi(x')}{\partial x'^\alpha} = \mathbf{M}_\mu{}^\alpha \frac{\partial \phi}{\partial x'^\alpha}, \qquad \mathbf{M}_\mu{}^\alpha = \frac{\partial x'^\alpha}{\partial x^\mu} \tag{10.4}$$

(Recall that every time there is a repeated index, there is always a summation over the values of that index. Thus $\mathbf{M}_\mu{}^\alpha \partial_\alpha \phi = \mathbf{M}_\mu{}^0 \partial_0 \phi + \mathbf{M}_\mu{}^1 \partial_1 \phi + \mathbf{M}_\mu{}^2 \partial_2 \phi + \mathbf{M}_\mu{}^3 \partial_3 \phi$.) This shows that we may consider the transformation rule of the derivative operator as

$$\frac{\partial}{\partial x^\mu} = \mathbf{M}_\mu{}^\alpha \frac{\partial}{\partial x'^\alpha} \tag{10.5}$$

Since a vector should transform the same way, we conclude that, for a vector,

$$A_\mu(x) = \mathbf{M}_\mu{}^\alpha (A_\alpha)' \tag{10.6}$$

In a similar way, we can understand the transformation rules for other quantities. For example, the metric or the infinitesimal distance ds between nearby points is defined by

$$ds^2 = g_{\mu\nu}\, dx^\mu\, dx^\nu = g'_{\mu\nu}\, dx'^\mu\, dx'^\nu \tag{10.7}$$

As the physical distance between two points, this should not depend on the coordinates used to measure it. We have indicated this by the second equality in (10.7). From this, we can conclude that

$$g_{\mu\nu} = \mathbf{M}_\mu{}^\alpha \mathbf{M}_\nu{}^\beta\, g'_{\alpha\beta} \tag{10.8}$$

Now the metrical components $g_{\mu\nu}$ can be considered as a matrix and we can take its inverse. (The inverse should exist, otherwise, the spacetime is singular.) Denoting this by superscript indices, $g^{\mu\nu} g_{\nu\lambda} = \delta^\mu{}_\lambda$, we get

$$g^{\mu\nu} = (\mathbf{M}^{-1})^\mu{}_\alpha (\mathbf{M}^{-1})^\nu{}_\beta\, g'^{\alpha\beta} \tag{10.9}$$

Going back to (10.6), we see that combinations like $A_\mu B_\nu g^{\mu\nu}$ are invariant under coordinate transformations. In fact, it is quite easy to make invariants, by suitable combinations of the metric $g_{\mu\nu}$, its inverse $g^{\mu\nu}$ and products of vectors and so on. What helps in this is the homogeneous transformation of the vectors.

The vector transforming as in (10.6) is what is usually referred to as a covariant vector. One can introduce contravariant vectors which transform via $(\mathbf{M}^{-1})^\mu{}_\alpha$. We will follow the standard convention of using subscripts for the covariant indices, superscripts for the contravariant indices, so that a general tensor $T^{\nu_1\nu_2\cdots\nu_m}_{\mu_1\mu_2\cdots\mu_n}$ will transform as

$$T^{\nu_1\nu_2\cdots\nu_m}_{\mu_1\mu_2\cdots\mu_n} = \mathbf{M}_{\mu_1}{}^{\alpha_1}\mathbf{M}_{\mu_2}{}^{\alpha_2}\cdots\mathbf{M}_{\mu_m}{}^{\alpha_m}\,(\mathbf{M}^{-1})^{\nu_1}{}_{\beta_1}(\mathbf{M}^{-1})^{\nu_2}{}_{\beta_2}\cdots(\mathbf{M}^{-1})^{\nu_n}{}_{\beta_n}$$
$$\times (T^{\beta_1\beta_2\cdots\beta_n}_{\alpha_1\alpha_2\cdots\alpha_m})' \tag{10.10}$$

Thus $g_{\mu\nu}$ is a covariant rank-two tensor and $g^{\mu\nu}$ is a contravariant rank-two tensor. From the transformation law for the metric, we can also see that $A^\mu = g^{\mu\nu}A_\nu$ transforms as a contravariant vector if A_ν transforms as a covariant vector. Thus "raising" and "lowering" of indices can be done, using the metric tensor appropriately.

We may now ask, how do we take the derivative of a vector? We will certainly need derivatives to formulate the laws of physics. Direct differentiation of (10.6) gives

$$\frac{\partial A_\mu}{\partial x^\nu} = \mathbf{M}_\mu{}^\alpha\left(\frac{\partial A'_\alpha}{\partial x'^\beta}\cdot\frac{\partial x'^\beta}{\partial x^\nu}\right) + \frac{\partial \mathbf{M}_\mu{}^\alpha}{\partial x^\nu}A'_\alpha(x')$$

$$= \mathbf{M}_\mu{}^\alpha\mathbf{M}_\nu{}^\beta\left(\frac{\partial A'_\alpha}{\partial x'_\beta}\right) + \frac{\partial \mathbf{M}_\mu{}^\alpha}{\partial x^\nu}A'_\alpha(x') \tag{10.11}$$

This formula for the derivative gives us a bit of trouble. While the first term on the right hand side gives a homogeneous transformation, with two factors of $\mathbf{M}$, which we may cancel with suitable products of inverse metric and some other vectors and so on, the last term has the derivative of $\mathbf{M}$ and it is not easy to make invariants out of this or formulate the laws of physics in such a way that it drops out. Basically, derivatives of vectors do not transform into derivatives of vectors, so the homogeneity of the transformation law is not obtained. So we seek a different strategy: Add to the derivative some suitable term as a compensating factor which will eliminate the inhomogeneous part of equation (10.11). In other words, we define a "covariant derivative" as

$$D_\nu A_\mu \equiv \frac{\partial A_\mu}{\partial x^\nu} - \Gamma^\lambda_{\nu\mu}A_\lambda \tag{10.12}$$

By definition or desire, we want this to transform in a homogeneous way so that

$$\left(\frac{\partial A_\mu}{\partial x_\nu} - \Gamma^\lambda_{\nu\mu}A_\lambda\right) = \mathbf{M}_\mu{}^\alpha\mathbf{M}_\nu{}^\beta\left(\frac{\partial A'_\alpha}{\partial x'_\beta} - \Gamma'^\gamma_{\beta\alpha}A'_\gamma\right) \tag{10.13}$$

In other words, $D_\nu A_\mu$ should transform as a covariant rank-two tensor. The quantity $\Gamma^\lambda_{\nu\mu}$, introduced as a compensating factor or field, is defined to have a transformation law which makes the above equation hold. Thus, if we use the explicit formula (10.11), we find

$$\mathbf{M}_\mu{}^\alpha \mathbf{M}_\nu{}^\beta \frac{\partial A'_\alpha}{\partial x'_\beta} + \frac{\partial \mathbf{M}_\mu{}^\alpha}{\partial x^\nu} A'_\alpha - \Gamma^\lambda_{\nu\mu} \mathbf{M}_\lambda{}^\gamma A'_\gamma$$

$$= \mathbf{M}_\mu{}^\alpha \, \mathbf{M}_\nu{}^\beta \frac{\partial A'_\alpha}{\partial x'_\beta} - \mathbf{M}_\mu{}^\alpha \, \mathbf{M}_\nu{}^\beta \Gamma'^\gamma_{\beta\alpha} A'_\gamma \qquad (10.14)$$

After canceling out the common term on both sides and multiplying suitably by the inverse of $\mathbf{M}$, this gives the transformation law for the compensating field $\Gamma^\lambda_{\mu\nu}$ as

$$\Gamma^\lambda_{\nu\mu} = \mathbf{M}_\nu{}^\beta \, \mathbf{M}_\mu{}^\alpha \, (\Gamma'^\gamma_{\beta\alpha}) \, (\mathbf{M}^{-1})_\gamma{}^\lambda + \frac{\partial \mathbf{M}_\mu{}^\gamma}{\partial x^\nu} (\mathbf{M}^{-1})_\gamma{}^\lambda \qquad (10.15)$$

It is acceptable for the field $\Gamma^\lambda_{\nu\mu}$ to depend on the properties of spacetime, on the metric in particular, but it should not depend on the vector A_μ since we want to use the same form for other vectors as well. If we can find a field $\Gamma^\lambda_{\nu\mu}$ with these properties, then we have a covariant derivative as in (10.12) which transforms homogeneously and it is then trivial to make invariants by combining such things suitably with the metric or its inverse. Indeed there is such a $\Gamma^\lambda_{\nu\mu}$; it is called the Christoffel symbol and is given by

$$\Gamma^\lambda_{\nu\mu} = \frac{1}{2} g^{\lambda\sigma} \left(-\frac{\partial g_{\mu\nu}}{\partial x^\sigma} + \frac{\partial g_{\sigma\nu}}{\partial x^\mu} + \frac{\partial g_{\mu\sigma}}{\partial x^\nu} \right) \qquad (10.16)$$

We will not go through the calculations here, but it is not difficult to show that if the metric transforms as in (10.8), then $\Gamma^\lambda_{\nu\mu}$ defined by (10.16) transforms as required, namely, as in (10.15). By using covariant derivatives in place of derivatives for all quantities, we can easily construct quantities which are invariant under coordinate transformations. The laws of physics can then be expressed using such quantities only, so that the principle of invariance under different choices of coordinates is easily realized. (Notice that, from (10.4), the covariant derivative for a scalar function is the same as the ordinary derivative.)

Another useful observation is that the combination $\sqrt{-\det g}\, d^4x$ is invariant under coordinate transformations. For this, let us recall that the transformation of d^4x is via the Jacobian of the transformation matrix,

$$d^4x' = \left| \frac{\partial x'}{\partial x} \right| d^4x = \det \mathbf{M}\, d^4x \qquad (10.17)$$

Taking the determinant of both sides of (10.8), we find

$$\det g' = \det \mathbf{M}^{-2}\, \det g \qquad (10.18)$$

These two equations show the invariance of $\sqrt{-\det g}\, d^4x$. (The minus sign inside the square root is irrelevant for this property; with the signs in the metric appropriate to spacetime, $\det g$ is negative, so to obtain a positive real measure for integration, we use $\sqrt{-\det g}$.)

We are now in a position to state the general principle of covariance or the gauge principle for gravity:

Prop 10.1 (Principle of covariance/Gauge principle for gravity).
Start with the Lorentz invariant action for any theory in flat space. Replace the metric $\eta_{\mu\nu}$ by a general metric $g_{\mu\nu}$, d^4x by $\sqrt{-\det g}\, d^4x$ and the derivatives of fields by covariant derivatives. The resulting action will be invariant under all coordinate transformations and it will describe the dynamics of the field/particle in a gravitational background specified by the choice of $g_{\mu\nu}$.

At the level of fundamental particle interactions, this is also the principle of equivalence. As an example of the application of this principle, consider a spin zero particle for which, in flat space, we wrote the action

$$S = \frac{1}{2} \int d^4x \left[\eta^{\mu\nu} \partial_\mu \phi \, \partial_\nu \phi - m^2 \phi^2 \right] \tag{10.19}$$

By applying the gauge principle, we get

$$S = \frac{1}{2} \int d^4x \sqrt{-\det g} \left[g^{\mu\nu} D_\mu \phi \, D_\nu \phi - m^2 \phi^2 \right]$$
$$= \frac{1}{2} \int d^4x \sqrt{-\det g} \left[g^{\mu\nu} \partial_\mu \phi \, \partial_\nu \phi - m^2 \phi^2 \right] \tag{10.20}$$

(Since the covariant derivative of a scalar function is the same as the ordinary derivative, we have some simplification in the second line.) In a similar way, consider a theory for a vector particle of the form

$$S = \frac{1}{2} \int d^4x \; \eta^{\mu\alpha} \eta^{\nu\beta} \frac{\partial A_\mu}{\partial x^\nu} \frac{\partial A_\alpha}{\partial x^\beta} \tag{10.21}$$

The corresponding generalization of this would be

$$S = \frac{1}{2} \int d^4x \sqrt{-\det g} \; g^{\mu\alpha} g^{\nu\beta} \left(D_\nu A_\mu \right) \left(D_\beta A_\alpha \right) \tag{10.22}$$

Now the covariant derivatives do contain the Christoffel symbols and the action is a bit more involved. The actions (10.20) and (10.22) will describe the dynamics of spin zero particles and spin-1 particles in a gravitational field, as well as in any coordinate system. (The second action (10.22) will turn out not to be completely consistent in the full quantum theory (for reasons not related to invariance under coordinate transformations), so some more modifications will have to be done. We will take this up later.)

We have not addressed the question: How do we know what to choose for $g_{\mu\nu}$ for a given problem? While there is some freedom due to coordinate transformations in the choice of $g_{\mu\nu}$, we must have a way to choose $g_{\mu\nu}$ for a given physical situation, up to equivalence under coordinate transformations. Stated in a way independent of coordinate choices, how do we choose ds^2 for a given physical situation? This is done by Einstein's equations for $g_{\mu\nu}$, which are differential equations determining the metric in terms of the energy-momentum tensor for matter fields. We will not discuss them in any detail here, but once $g_{\mu\nu}$ is chosen by solving the Einstein equations, we can use it (or any coordinate-transformed version of it) to discuss the dynamics of various objects in a gravitational field. The gauge principle is thus a very powerful principle. By a simple rule, it gives us the gravitational interactions of all matter.

We will now turn to developing a gauge principle for interactions other than gravity.

Remark 10.1.
The field equations for gravity

The general theory of relativity identifies gravity as the effect of spacetime curvature on matter. The coupling of particles or fields to gravity is obtained by the gauge principle wherein ordinary derivatives are replaced by spacetime covariant derivatives. For this to be implemented, we need to know the metric we should use in a given physical situation, so that the corresponding Christoffel symbol, and hence the covariant derivative, can be constructed. We have already alluded to this question, mentioning the role of the Einstein field equations for making this choice. Here we will take a brief look at these equations to get a flavor of how it all works out. We will first need the specific mathematical definition of curvature. Such a quantity must be covariant and should be defined entirely in terms of the metric and its derivatives. Notice that the Christoffel symbol does not qualify as it transforms in a noncovariant way. In fact, it was designed to have just the right kind of inhomogeneous terms in its transformation to cancel the lack of covariance in the derivative of a vector. The curvature can be defined in terms of multiple covariant derivatives.

We start by first writing down the covariant derivative for a covariant rank-two tensor which transforms as the product of two vectors. Denoting such a tensor as $W_{\mu\nu}$, the transformation law is

$$W'_{\mu\nu} = \mathbf{M}_\mu{}^\alpha \, \mathbf{M}_\nu{}^\beta \, W_{\alpha\beta} \tag{10.23}$$

When we take the derivative of such a quantity, there will be two terms involving derivatives of the transformation matrix $\mathbf{M}$, so we will need two Christoffel symbols to cancel them to give a covariant derivative. Thus the covariant derivative is given by

$$D_\mu W_{\nu\lambda} = \partial_\mu W_{\nu\lambda} - \Gamma^\alpha_{\mu\nu} \, W_{\alpha\lambda} - \Gamma^\alpha_{\mu\lambda} \, W_{\nu\alpha} \tag{10.24}$$

Notice that the Christoffel symbols always have one index as the index in the derivative, the other being taken from W; the latter has a new index (α here) which is contracted with the upper index of the Christoffel symbol. This pattern can be generalized to tensors of any rank. (By the way, the metric tensor itself is a rank-two tensor, but with the definition of $\Gamma^\alpha_{\mu\nu}$, it is easy to see that $D_\mu g_{\nu\lambda} = 0$.) We can now consider the second covariant derivative of a vector as

$$D_\mu(D_\nu V_\lambda) = \partial_\mu(D_\nu V_\lambda) - \Gamma^\alpha_{\mu\nu}(D_\alpha V_\lambda) - \Gamma^\alpha_{\mu\lambda}(D_\nu V_\alpha) \tag{10.25}$$

If we put in the definition of $D_\nu V_\lambda$ in this expression, we will find second derivatives of V_λ appearing. That term can be canceled out by antisymmetrization. We can then work out the relation

$$[D_\mu, D_\nu] \, V_\lambda = D_\mu \, D_\nu \, V_\lambda - D_\nu \, D_\mu \, V_\lambda$$
$$= - R^\alpha_{\mu\nu\lambda} \, V_\alpha \tag{10.26}$$

where

$$R^\alpha_{\mu\nu\lambda} = \partial_\mu \Gamma^\alpha_{\nu\lambda} - \partial_\nu \Gamma^\alpha_{\mu\lambda} - \Gamma^\sigma_{\mu\lambda} \, \Gamma^\alpha_{\nu\sigma} + \Gamma^\sigma_{\nu\lambda} \, \Gamma^\alpha_{\mu\sigma} \tag{10.27}$$

This is known as the Riemann curvature tensor. Obviously it will transform homogeneously as a tensor because it is obtained via the covariant equation (10.26) and the vector, which is removed to identify $R^\alpha_{\mu\nu\lambda}$, also transforms covariantly. (As written, $R^\alpha_{\mu\nu\lambda}$ transforms contravariantly on the α-index and covariantly on the other indices.) The curvature tensor measures the lack of commutativity of covariant derivatives.

There are two other covariant quantities we can define from $R^\alpha_{\mu\nu\lambda}$ via the use of the metric tensor. These are the Ricci tensor defined by

$$R_{\nu\lambda} = R^\mu_{\mu\nu\lambda} \tag{10.28}$$

and the Ricci scalar defined by

$$R = g^{\nu\lambda} \, R_{\nu\lambda} \tag{10.29}$$

We are now in a position to write down the Einstein field equations for gravity. They are:

$$R_{\mu\nu} - \frac{1}{2} g_{\mu\nu} R + \Lambda g_{\mu\nu} = 8\pi G T_{\mu\nu} \tag{10.30}$$

where Λ is known as the cosmological constant and $T_{\mu\nu}$ is the energy-momentum tensor for matter fields.

The energy-momentum tensor may be obtained as follows. We consider the action for the matter fields in a general curved background, obtained, if you like, by the application of the gauge principle for gravity. Then we can write the variation of the action with respect to the metric, rather with respect to the inverse of the metric, as

$$\delta S = \frac{1}{2} \int d^4 x \sqrt{-\det g} \, \delta g^{\mu\nu} \, T_{\mu\nu} \tag{10.31}$$

This equation defines the energy-momentum tensor $T_{\mu\nu}$; apart from obvious factors, it is defined as the coefficient of the variation $\delta g^{\mu\nu}$ in δS. As an example, consider the scalar field with the action

$$S = \frac{1}{2} \int d^4 x \sqrt{-\det g} \, \left[g^{\mu\nu} \partial_\mu \phi \, \partial_\nu \phi - m^2 \phi^2 \right] \tag{10.32}$$

For the determinant of $g_{\mu\nu}$, we can use the formula $\log \det M = \operatorname{Tr} \log M$ (valid for any diagonalizable matrix M) and obtain

$$\delta \sqrt{-\det g} = -\frac{1}{2} \sqrt{-\det g} \, g_{\mu\nu} \, \delta g^{\mu\nu} \tag{10.33}$$

This leads to

$$\delta S = \frac{1}{2} \int d^4 x \sqrt{-\det g} \, \delta g^{\mu\nu} \left[\partial_\mu \phi \, \partial_\nu \phi - g_{\mu\nu} \frac{1}{2} \left(g^{\alpha\beta} \partial_\alpha \phi \, \partial_\beta \phi - m^2 \phi^2 \right) \right] \tag{10.34}$$

Comparing with (10.31), we identify the energy-momentum tensor for the scalar field with the action (10.32) as

$$T_{\mu\nu} = \left[\partial_\mu \phi \, \partial_\nu \phi - g_{\mu\nu} \frac{1}{2} \left(g^{\alpha\beta} \partial_\alpha \phi \, \partial_\beta \phi - m^2 \phi^2 \right) \right] \tag{10.35}$$

Physically, $T_{\mu\nu}$ is important because T_{00} is the energy density whose integral is the Hamiltonian, T_{0i} is the momentum density, and the other components correspond to various stresses possible in the system. The 00-component of the Einstein equations thus contains the energy density (equivalent to the mass density via the mass energy relation) on the right hand side, similar to how the Poisson equation for the nonrelativistic gravitational potential has the mass density as the source of the potential. In the fully relativistic case, the appropriate generalization would need the whole energy-momentum tensor as the source, as in (10.30).

The field equations (10.30) are quite remarkable in that the left hand side is all about the geometry of spacetime while the right hand side is determined by the matter content. Spacetime itself is molded by the presence of matter whose dynamics, in turn, is affected by the geometry. Classically, the idea is that one should solve the equations of motion for the matter fields, the field ϕ in our example, (obtained as the variational equations for the matter action) along with (10.30), viewing them as coupled equations. Thus matter determines the metric of spacetime and that in turn affects the dynamics of matter. Of course, in practice, approximations have to be made to make predictions. Thus for the solar system, one could solve the Einstein equations with only the energy-momentum tensor of the Sun as the source, ignoring perturbations to the metric due to the planets and use this metric to determine the dynamics of the planets. Systematic approximation schemes for going beyond this (which would be needed for binary star systems, for example) have been developed by now.

As a quantum theory, the Einstein equations have difficulties, both of interpretation and calculation. The unhappy middle way of treating gravity classically while the matter fields are treated quantum mechanically is what is usually done. In this scenario, the right hand side of (10.30) is often interpreted as the expectation value $\langle \Psi | T_{\mu\nu} | \Psi \rangle$ of the energy-momentum operator of the matter fields, where $|\Psi\rangle$ denotes the quantum state for matter. But this is really not satisfactory and the equations (10.30) await a better and more complete embedding in quantum theory.

The cosmological constant Λ in (10.30) was not included in Einstein's original version of the equations. The resulting solutions for the cosmos as a whole seemed to give an expanding universe. Einstein tried to avoid this (not for any physics reason, but for sheer human discomfort with the idea) by putting in the cosmological constant which, for a proper choice of sign, allowed static universes as solutions to the equations. However, a few years after this, the expansion of the universe was discovered, and Einstein considered his introduction of Λ his biggest blunder, since he missed what would have been the most dramatic prediction about the universe ever made. In the late 1990s, astronomers found evidence that the pace of expansion of the universe is increasing, which can be viewed as evidence for a small nonzero cosmological constant, so maybe introducing it into the equations in 1917 was not such a bad idea after all.

Remark 10.2.
The Schwarzschild metric and planetary motion

We will briefly consider the dynamics of a test particle in a gravitational field, i.e., in a given spacetime. A test particle, by definition, is one whose effect on the background geometry can be neglected. In full generality, the Einstein field equations (10.30) and the equations for matter have to be solved as coupled equations, but, in many situations the backreaction of matter on the geometry is small. For example, in the case of planetary motion in the solar system, the geometry is primarily determined by the Sun. The corrections due to the planets are small, so they may be regarded, to a good first approximation, as test particles.

The action for a point-particle of mass m in a general spacetime is given by

$$S = -mc \int ds = -mc \int \sqrt{g_{\mu\nu}dx^\mu dx^\nu} \qquad (10.36)$$

We see that, for a given path, S is proportional to the spacetime distance between the initial and final points obtained by integrating ds along the path. From the variational principle, the classical trajectory is thus the extremum of the spacetime distance between the initial and final points of the particle's trajectory. It is therefore a generalization of the notion of the straight line in flat space which is obtained by minimizing the distance between two points. Such extrema are generally designated as "geodesics". Notice that there is no notion of a Newtonian gravitational force here. The particle moves along what may be considered as a "straight line"; it is the curvature of spacetime which makes the trajectory seem curved. Explicitly, for a general metric $ds^2 = g_{\mu\nu}dx^\mu dx^\nu$, the geodesic equation is

$$\frac{d^2x^\alpha}{ds^2} + \Gamma^\alpha_{\mu\nu}\frac{dx^\mu}{ds}\frac{dx^\nu}{ds} = 0 \qquad (10.37)$$

This can be obtained by extremizing the action (10.36).

The solution of the Einstein equations for the exterior region of a single spherically symmetric gravitating mass M such as the Sun (or for a point mass taken to be at the origin) is given by the Schwarzschild metric

$$ds^2 = \left(1 - \frac{2GM}{c^2 r}\right)c^2 dt^2 - \left(1 - \frac{2GM}{c^2 r}\right)^{-1} dr^2 - r^2 d\theta^2 - r^2 \sin^2\theta \, d\varphi^2 \qquad (10.38)$$

This is written in a coordinate system which reduces to the flat space spherical polar coordinates when $M = 0$. Also, even though generally we use units in which $c = 1$, we have displayed the factors of c here to show how the nonrelativistic limit will emerge. The geodesic equations can be obtained by simplifying (10.37) for the metric (10.38), but, in practice, it is easier to directly use the expression for ds^2 in (10.38) and work out the Euler-Lagrange equations, rather than go through calculating $\Gamma^\alpha_{\mu\nu}$.

Writing $dr = \dot{r}dt$, $d\theta = \dot{\theta}dt$, etc. in (10.36), we find

$$S = -mc^2 \int dt \sqrt{\left(1 - \frac{2GM}{c^2r}\right) - \left(1 - \frac{2GM}{c^2r}\right)^{-1} \frac{\dot{r}^2}{c^2} - \frac{r^2\dot{\theta}^2}{c^2} - \frac{r^2\sin^2\theta\,\dot{\varphi}^2}{c^2}}$$

(10.39)

Since $\dot{r}^2 + r^2\dot{\theta}^2 + r^2\sin^2\theta\,\dot{\varphi}^2$ is the square of the velocity expressed in spherical coordinates, we can simplify the above action, in the limit of small velocities as

$$S \approx -mc^2 \int dt \sqrt{\left(1 - \frac{2GM}{c^2r}\right) - \frac{\dot{r}^2}{c^2} - \frac{r^2\dot{\theta}^2}{c^2} - \frac{r^2\sin^2\theta\,\dot{\varphi}^2}{c^2}}$$

$$\approx -mc^2 \int dt \sqrt{1 - \frac{v^2}{c^2} - \frac{2GM}{c^2r}}$$

$$\approx \int dt \left[-mc^2 + \frac{1}{2}mv^2 + \frac{GMm}{r}\right]$$

(10.40)

In the last line, we have expanded the square root to the first relevant term, i.e., the term without factors of $1/c^2$. Since the constant mc^2 does not affect the equations of motion, the Lagrangian may be taken, in this limit, as

$$L = \frac{1}{2}mv^2 + \frac{GMm}{r} = T - V$$

(10.41)

with $V = -GMm/r$ as the gravitational potential energy. This shows how we can recover all the usual results of planetary motion in the nonrelativistic limit, starting from the invariant expression (10.36) or (10.39). If calculations are done without making the nonrelativistic approximation, then the corrections to the planetary motion due to the general theory of relativity, such as the famous precession of the perihelion of Mercury, can be obtained.

Chapter 11

The Gauge Principle II

Einstein's theory of gravity is the quintessential example of a theory built on invariance under local symmetry transformations. It provides the basic paradigm for the gauge principle which we seek to generalize. Let us start by recalling that the gauge symmetry behind gravity was the symmetry under local coordinate transformations. For example, a vector A_μ transforms under coordinate transformations as

$$A_\nu = \mathbf{M}_\nu{}^\beta A'_\beta \tag{11.1}$$

where $\mathbf{M}_\nu{}^\beta = (\partial x'^\beta / \partial x^\nu)$ is the matrix of the coordinate transformation. The components of the vector transform homogeneously under a coordinate transformation. We then noticed that when we differentiate a vector we do not get a nice homogeneous transformation property,

$$(\partial_\mu A_\nu) \neq \mathbf{M}_\mu{}^\alpha \, \mathbf{M}_\nu{}^\beta \, (\partial'_\alpha A'_\beta) \tag{11.2}$$

Our strategy was to introduce a compensating field which eliminated the inhomogeneous term in the derivative and gave us a covariant derivative

$$D_\mu A_\nu = \partial_\mu A_\nu - \Gamma^\lambda_{\mu\nu} \, A_\lambda \tag{11.3}$$

which has the nice homogeneous transformation property

$$(D_\mu A_\nu) = \mathbf{M}_\mu{}^\alpha \, \mathbf{M}_\nu{}^\beta \, (D_\alpha A_\beta)' \tag{11.4}$$

Interaction of any field with gravity was then contained in the simple replacement $\partial_\mu \to D_\mu$.

We want to interpret the minimal coupling principle for electromagnetic interactions, namely the rule of $\partial_\mu \to \partial_\mu + iqA_\mu$, in a similar way. For gravity, the starting point was the homogeneous transformation law of vectors, $A_\nu = \mathbf{M}_\nu{}^\beta A'_\beta$. Taking inspiration from gravity, we will consider fields which can have some homogeneous transformation acting on them. (*Caution: We are only using gravity as an inspiration here; the transformations considered below are not coordinate transformations.*)

Let us consider a (complex) field which can be used to describe a charged particle, say, of spin zero, for simplicity. The action, without electromagnetic interactions, is of the form

$$S = \int d^4x \ \left[\eta^{\mu\nu}(\partial_\mu\phi)^*(\partial_\nu\phi) - m^2\phi^*\phi\right] \tag{11.5}$$

There is a natural homogeneous transformation $\phi \to \phi' = e^{i\theta}\,\phi$ which leaves the action unchanged, $S[\phi] = S[e^{i\theta}\phi]$, provided θ is independent of x^μ. We now ask the question: Can we make this into a local symmetry by allowing θ to be a function of x^μ? (This is in the spirit of the allowing local coordinate transformations in the general theory of relativity, but, once again, this is not a coordinate transformation.) It is clear that terms in the Lagrangian without derivatives of ϕ, such as $m^2\phi^*\phi$, will remain invariant,

$$\phi^*\phi \to (e^{i\theta}\phi)^*(e^{i\theta}\phi) = \phi^*\phi \tag{11.6}$$

But terms with derivatives of ϕ will fail to remain invariant since

$$\partial_\mu\phi' = \partial_\mu(e^{i\theta}\phi(x)) = e^{i\theta}\partial_\mu\phi + e^{i\theta}(i\,\partial_\mu\theta)\phi \tag{11.7}$$

As in the case of coordinate transformations, we will introduce a compensating term which can eliminate the inhomogeneous term and define a covariant derivative:

$$D_\mu\phi = \partial_\mu\phi - i\,\mathcal{A}_\mu\,\phi \tag{11.8}$$

Since we are trying to eliminate the term with $\partial_\mu\theta$ (which is a vector), it is clear that we need a vector $\mathcal{A}_\mu$ as the compensating field. The transformation of $\mathcal{A}_\mu$ is then defined by the compensation requirement, i.e.,

$$(D_\mu\phi)' = e^{i\theta}\,(D_\mu\phi) \tag{11.9}$$

Using (11.7), this can be written out as

$$\partial_\mu\phi' - i\mathcal{A}'_\mu\phi' = e^{i\theta}(\partial_\mu\phi - i\mathcal{A}_\mu\phi)$$
$$e^{i\theta}(\partial_\mu\phi + i\partial_\mu\theta\,\phi) - i\mathcal{A}'_\mu e^{i\theta}\phi = e^{i\theta}\partial_\mu\phi - e^{i\theta}i\mathcal{A}_\mu\phi \tag{11.10}$$

In this equation, $e^{i\theta}$ cancels out from both sides and so does $\partial_\mu\phi$, so that the required transformation property of $\mathcal{A}_\mu$ is given as

$$i(\partial_\mu\theta - \mathcal{A}'_\mu) = -i\mathcal{A}_\mu, \qquad \text{or}$$
$$\mathcal{A}'_\mu = \mathcal{A}_\mu + \partial_\mu\theta \tag{11.11}$$

In the case of coordinate transformations, the compensating term $\Gamma^{\lambda}_{\mu\nu}$ could be constructed in terms of derivatives of the metric. There is no such possibility here, we simply have to take $\mathcal{A}_{\mu}$ as a new field (or particle) we must have in the theory if we want to have invariance under $\phi \to e^{i\theta}\,\phi$. Of course, not all components of $\mathcal{A}_{\mu}$ are physically relevant. The point is that θ can be chosen in any way we like. So the very fact that the transformation $\phi \to e^{i\theta}\,\phi$, $\mathcal{A}_{\mu} \to \mathcal{A}_{\mu} + \partial_{\mu}\theta$ is an invariance tells us that, if we want to, we can choose θ so as to eliminate some components of $\mathcal{A}_{\mu}$. (In fact, this is how the photon turns out to have only two independent polarization states although it is described by a 4-vector which would suggest 4 independent polarizations.)

Now we can formulate our gauge principle for the electromagnetic interactions as follows. Start with the action for a complex field in the absence of electromagnetic couplings. Replace derivatives by the covariant derivative (11.8) involving $\mathcal{A}_{\mu}$. The resulting action will give the interaction of the field with the photon. The action will also be invariant under the combined transformation $\phi \to e^{i\theta}\,\phi$, $\mathcal{A}_{\mu} \to \mathcal{A}_{\mu} + \partial_{\mu}\theta$. (This transformation is called a *gauge transformation*.)

However, there is one catch in this argument. While every field (or particle) couples to gravity, not all fields couple to photons; only charged particles do. To take care of this explicitly, we modify the transformations slightly, writing,

$$\phi \to e^{-iq\theta}\,\phi, \qquad D_{\mu}\phi = \partial_{\mu}\phi + iqA_{\mu}\phi \qquad (11.12)$$

where q is the charge of the particle described by ϕ. Thus neutral particles with $q = 0$ will have no phase transformation and no coupling to A_{μ}. Notice that the covariant derivative satisfies the covariance requirement $(D_{\mu}\phi)' = e^{-iq\theta}\,(D_{\mu}\phi)$ with $A'_{\mu} = A_{\mu} + \partial_{\mu}\theta$. Basically, we are using $\mathcal{A}_{\mu} \to -qA_{\mu}$. With this slight modification, the gauge principle, as formulated above, will give the coupling of the photons to any fundamental charged particle.

If we apply our gauge principle to the action (11.5), we get

$$S = \int d^4x\ \left[\eta^{\mu\nu}(D_{\mu}\phi)^*(D_{\nu}\phi) - m^2\phi^*\phi\right]$$

$$= \int d^4x\ \left[\eta^{\mu\nu}(\partial_{\mu}\phi + iqA_{\mu}\phi)^*(\partial_{\nu}\phi + iqA_{\nu}\phi) - m^2\phi^*\phi\right] \quad (11.13)$$

This will give the coupling of the particle to the photon. This result is in agreement with what we did in Lecture 7, for particles with $q = e$.

There is one more thing to be done though. We do not yet have an action for the photon itself. Such an action is needed to work out the propagator for the photon, which is, in turn, essential to calculate the amplitudes for various processes. The required action must be at most quadratic in the derivatives of the photon field A_μ and also must respect the symmetry $A_\mu \rightarrow A'_\mu = A_\mu + \partial_\mu\theta$. There is a simple strategy for this. We know that $(D_\mu\phi)' = e^{-iq\theta}(D_\mu\phi)$, so that, since $D_\mu\phi$ transforms the same way as ϕ does under the gauge transformation, we can iterate this and say that $(D_\mu(D_\nu\phi))' = e^{-iq\theta}(D_\mu(D_\nu\phi))$. Multiple applications of D_μ preserve the covariance. Terms involving derivatives of ϕ can be eliminated by taking the commutator, since $(\partial_\mu\partial_\nu - \partial_\nu\partial_\mu)\phi = 0$ for any well-defined function. Thus we can hope to extract something independent of ϕ by considering

$$
\begin{aligned}
D_\mu(D_\nu\phi) - D_\nu(D_\mu\phi) &= (\partial_\mu + iqA_\mu)(\partial_\nu\phi + iqA_\nu\phi) \\
&\quad - (\partial_\nu + iqA_\nu)(\partial_\mu\phi + iqA_\mu\phi) \\
&= \partial_\mu\partial_\nu\phi + iqA_\mu\partial_\nu\phi + iq(\partial_\mu A_\nu)\phi + iqA_\nu\partial_\mu\phi \\
&\quad - q^2 A_\mu A_\nu\phi - \{\mu \leftrightarrow \nu\} \\
&= iq\,(\partial_\mu A_\nu - \partial_\nu A_\mu)\,\phi
\end{aligned}
\tag{11.14}
$$

The transformed version of this equation would read

$$
\begin{aligned}
(D_\mu(D_\nu\phi) - D_\nu(D_\mu\phi))' &= iq(\partial_\mu A'_\nu - \partial_\nu A'_\mu)\,\phi' \\
&= e^{-iq\theta}(D_\mu(D_\nu\phi) - D_\nu(D_\mu\phi)) \\
&= e^{-iq\theta}(iq\,(\partial_\mu A_\nu - \partial_\nu A_\mu)\,\phi) \\
&= iq\,(\partial_\mu A_\nu - \partial_\nu A_\mu)\,(\phi')
\end{aligned}
\tag{11.15}
$$

The first equality in this equation is just (11.14), the second follows from $(D\phi)' = e^{-iq\theta}(D\phi)$, the third again from (11.14). Comparing the first and last lines, we see that $F_{\mu\nu} \equiv \partial_\mu A_\nu - \partial_\nu A_\mu$ must be invariant under the transformation $A_\mu \rightarrow A_\mu + \partial_\mu\theta$. It is easy enough to verify this directly as well.

$$
\begin{aligned}
\partial_\mu(A_\nu)' - \partial_\nu(A_\mu)' &= \partial_\mu(A_\nu + \partial_\nu\theta) - \partial_\nu(A_\mu + \partial_\mu\theta) \\
&= \partial_\mu A_\nu - \partial_\nu A_\mu + \partial_\mu\partial_\nu\theta - \partial_\nu\partial_\mu\theta \\
&= \partial_\mu A_\nu - \partial_\nu A_\mu
\end{aligned}
\tag{11.16}
$$

The quantity

$$
F_{\mu\nu} = \partial_\mu A_\nu - \partial_\nu A_\mu
\tag{11.17}
$$

is the electromagnetic field tensor. Since ϕ is a common factor in equation (11.14) throughout, we could rewrite the definition of $F_{\mu\nu}$ as

$$
[D_\mu, D_\nu] = iq\,F_{\mu\nu}
\tag{11.18}
$$

As in Lecture 5, the components of $F_{\mu\nu}$ can be identified as the electric and magnetic fields,

$$F_{0i} = \partial_0 A_i - \partial_i A_0 = E_i, \qquad F_{ij} = \partial_i A_j - \partial_j A_i = \epsilon_{ijk} B^k \qquad (11.19)$$

(Here it is useful to note that $\epsilon^{123} = 1$ and $\epsilon_{123} = -1$.)

Let us now consider the construction of an action using this quantity. The action must be Lorentz-invariant, so the indices μ, ν, etc. must be contracted with $\eta^{\mu\nu}$. Further, the action must involve two powers of $F_{\mu\nu}$, because there is already one derivative in F and we want at most two powers of the time-derivative in the Lagrangian, so that the equations of motion will be of at most second order in the time-derivatives. Since $F_{\mu\nu}$ is antisymmetric in μ, ν, $\eta^{\mu\nu} F_{\mu\nu} = 0$, so the only quantity to consider is $\eta^{\mu\alpha}\eta^{\nu\beta} F_{\mu\nu} F_{\alpha\beta}$. In terms of the electric and magnetic fields,

$$\eta^{\mu\alpha}\eta^{\nu\beta} F_{\mu\nu} F_{\alpha\beta} = \eta^{00}\eta^{ij}(F_{0i}F_{0j} + F_{i0}F_{j0}) + \eta^{ij}\eta^{kl} F_{ik}F_{jl}$$
$$= -2\, E_i E_i + \epsilon_{ikm}\epsilon_{ikn} B_m B_n$$
$$= -2\, \vec{E}^2 + 2\, \vec{B}^2 \qquad (11.20)$$

Putting in the proper normalization for the term with time-derivatives (namely, we want $\frac{1}{2}\dot{A}^2$), the action for the field can be taken as

$$S = -\frac{1}{4} \int d^4x\, \eta^{\mu\alpha}\eta^{\nu\beta} F_{\mu\nu} F_{\alpha\beta} = \frac{1}{2} \int d^4x\, (\vec{E}^2 - \vec{B}^2) \qquad (11.21)$$

We have indeed recovered the original action for the electromagnetic field (or photons) as discussed in Lecture 7. We see that this is the only action we can write which has invariance under the gauge transformation $A_\mu \to A_\mu + \partial_\mu\theta$, is Lorentz invariant and is quadratic in the time-derivatives of the field A_μ.

Let us rephrase the gauge principle again. We start with the action for a charged particle. The derivatives in this action are replaced by covariant derivatives, $\partial_\mu \to D_\mu = \partial_\mu + iqA_\mu$. Then we construct $F_{\mu\nu}$ by the equation $[D_\mu, D_\nu] = iq\, F_{\mu\nu}$. The full action is then

$$S = -\frac{1}{4} \int d^4x\, \eta^{\mu\alpha}\eta^{\nu\beta} F_{\mu\nu} F_{\alpha\beta} + \Big[S_{\text{other particles}}\Big]_{\partial_\mu \to \partial_\mu + iqA_\mu} \qquad (11.22)$$

(Here "other particles" refers to particles other than the photon. The photon itself is described by the first term in (11.22).) Applying this to the Dirac action $S = \int \bar{\Psi}(i\gamma^\mu \partial_\mu - m)\Psi$, with $q = -e$ for the electron, we get the action for the electron-photon system (or quantum electrodynamics),

$$S = -\frac{1}{4} \int d^4x\, \eta^{\mu\alpha}\eta^{\nu\beta} F_{\mu\nu} F_{\alpha\beta} + \int d^4x\, \bar{\Psi}\Big(i\gamma^\mu(\partial_\mu - ieA_\mu) - m\Big)\Psi \qquad (11.23)$$

This simple principle gives all the interactions of the electron with the electromagnetic field. Since most of atomic physics, all of molecular physics and most of solid state physics are built on this, we can safely say that this simple gauge principle accounts for much of everyday physics and, in principle, all of chemistry.[1]

We now have the tools of gauge transformations at hand, and so we can ask the question: Can they be generalized to matrix transformations? We have not yet talked about whether such a generalization is needed or useful for any kind of interactions in physics (this will come later), but we can certainly entertain this possibility and work out how such a generalization can be done. Again, we take the cue from the case of gravity. The transformation of a vector under coordinate transformations can be written explicitly in terms of components as

$$
\begin{pmatrix} A_0 \\ A_1 \\ A_2 \\ A_3 \end{pmatrix} = \begin{bmatrix} M_0{}^0 & M_0{}^1 & M_0{}^2 & M_0{}^3 \\ M_1{}^0 & M_1{}^1 & .. & .. \\ ... & ... & ... & .. \\ ... & ... & ... & .. \end{bmatrix} \begin{pmatrix} A_0' \\ A_1' \\ A_2' \\ A_3' \end{pmatrix}
\tag{11.24}
$$

This suggests that it makes sense to consider more general transformations than the simple one $\phi \to \phi' = e^{iq\theta} \phi$. We can consider a set of fields ϕ_1, ϕ_2, etc., organized as a column vector and consider a matrix transformation on these. In other words,

$$
\Phi = \begin{pmatrix} \phi_1 \\ \phi_2 \\ . \\ . \\ . \end{pmatrix} \to \Phi' = \begin{pmatrix} \phi_1' \\ \phi_2' \\ . \\ . \\ . \end{pmatrix} = \begin{bmatrix} R_1^1 & R_1^2 & R_1^3 & .. & .. \\ R_2^1 & R_2^2 & .. & .. & .. \\ .. & .. & .. & .. & .. \\ .. & .. & .. & .. & .. \\ .. & .. & .. & .. & .. \end{bmatrix} \begin{pmatrix} \phi_1 \\ \phi_2 \\ . \\ . \\ . \end{pmatrix}
\tag{11.25}
$$

We emphasize that Φ is not a spacetime vector; it is a set of fields which transform in the way indicated, the transformation may be viewed as some internal symmetry transformation. We can write (11.25) more briefly as $\Phi' = R\,\Phi$ in a matrix notation. The properties of R are basically up to us; we may use desirable invariants (needed for the action) as a guide. For example, we might want the invariance of $\Phi^\dagger \Phi$. This would require $(\Phi')^\dagger \Phi' = \Phi^\dagger R^\dagger R\,\Phi = \Phi^\dagger \Phi$, and we see that invariance is possible if $R^\dagger R = \mathbb{1}$; in other words, if R is a unitary matrix. Another possibility would be to take Φ to be real and require invariance of $\Phi^T \Phi$. This would require $R^T R = \mathbb{1}$, or R should be an orthogonal matrix. We see that there are

---

[1]We borrow from Dirac's comment on the Schrödinger equation that "it contains much of physics and, in principle, all of chemistry".

many ways to generalize the transformation $\phi \to e^{iq\theta}\phi$. (This particular case which we started from may be regarded as a 1×1 matrix version of (11.25) with $\mathbf{R}$ being unitary.) For what we want to do, i.e., for physics applications, mostly we need the case of $\mathbf{R}$ being unitary, so we will phrase the arguments to follow in terms of unitary matrices. And, to emphasize this, we will use $\mathbf{U}$ in place of $\mathbf{R}$. Thus the transformation of the field is of the form

$$\Phi' = \mathbf{U}\,\Phi \tag{11.26}$$

Invariants can be naturally constructed from products of Φ and $\Phi^\dagger$, in combinations like $\Phi^\dagger\Phi$. (For example, we could use this for a mass term.) But we must once again deal with the derivative, which does not have a homogeneous transformation property, but instead gives

$$\partial_\mu\Phi' = (\partial_\mu\mathbf{U})\,\Phi + \mathbf{U}\,\partial_\mu\Phi \tag{11.27}$$

As before, we would like to introduce a compensating field to cancel the first term. But notice that $\partial_\mu\mathbf{U}$ is a matrix as well as a vector. So we need a matrix-valued vector to be able to compensate for this term. So let us consider such a quantity

$$\mathcal{A}_\mu = \begin{bmatrix} (\mathcal{A}_\mu)_{11} & (\mathcal{A}_\mu)_{12} & \cdots \\ & \cdots & \\ & & \cdots \end{bmatrix} \tag{11.28}$$

A covariant derivative can now be constructed, in the same way we have done so far, as

$$D_\mu\Phi = \partial_\mu\Phi - i\mathcal{A}_\mu\Phi \tag{11.29}$$

The requirement on $\mathcal{A}_\mu$ is that

$$(D_\mu\Phi)' = \mathbf{U}\,(D_\mu\Phi) \tag{11.30}$$

Using (11.27) we can write this out as

$$\partial_\mu\mathbf{U}\,\Phi + \mathbf{U}\,\partial_\mu\Phi - i\mathcal{A}'_\mu\,\mathbf{U}\,\Phi = \mathbf{U}\,\partial_\mu\Phi - i\mathbf{U}\,\mathcal{A}_\mu\,\Phi \tag{11.31}$$

This reduces to

$$\left(\mathcal{A}'_\mu\,\mathbf{U} - \mathbf{U}\,\mathcal{A}_\mu + i\partial_\mu\mathbf{U}\right)\Phi = 0 \tag{11.32}$$

If this equation is to hold for any Φ, the quantity in brackets must vanish. Multiplying the result by $\mathbf{U}^{-1}$ from the right, we find the required transformation law for $\mathcal{A}_\mu$ as

$$\mathcal{A}'_\mu = \mathbf{U}\,\mathcal{A}_\mu\,\mathbf{U}^{-1} - i\,(\partial_\mu\mathbf{U})\,\mathbf{U}^{-1} \tag{11.33}$$

(The inverse to the matrix $\mathbf{U}$ exists, since it is unitary.) Since $\mathbf{U}$ is unitary, $-i\partial_\mu \mathbf{U} \mathbf{U}^{-1}$ is hermitian, so the minimal choice for $\mathcal{A}_\mu$ is to take it to be a hermitian matrix. Notice also that $\mathbf{U}\mathcal{A}_\mu \mathbf{U}^{-1} = \mathbf{U}\mathcal{A}_\mu \mathbf{U}^\dagger$ is also hermtian, so such a choice of $\mathcal{A}_\mu$ is consistent with (11.33). (Adding nonhermitian terms in $\mathcal{A}_\mu$ would not only be nonminimal, they would also lead to difficulties with positivity of energy, so we will not consider such terms.)

Remark 11.1.
The gauge principle in classical electrodynamics

The gauge principle gives us a way of constructing the electromagnetic interactions of charged particles in the quantum theory, where particles are represented by fields. But how about classical electrodynamics? Does the gauge principle determine the interactions of charged particles classically? As for the action for the electric and magnetic fields, it is obviously gauge invariant, in fact, it is exactly what was given in (11.21). We also talked about minimal coupling in Lecture 5. Let us do that again, in a slightly different way here. First we start with the action for a free particle of mass m. This can be taken as the usual nonrelativistic action with $L = \frac{1}{2}mv^2 - V$, or for the relativistic case, we can write

$$S = -m \int ds \qquad (11.34)$$

where ds is the proper spacetime distance. The equations of motion are obtained by extremizing this with respect to the paths the particle can take from a given starting point (x_{init}) to a given end point (x_{fin}). Thus we are varying the nature of the trajectory in between these two points in carrying out this extremization. Now consider adding to (11.34) a term which depends only on the initial and final points of the trajectory. Since these are kept fixed when looking for the extremum by varying the path in between, we see that such boundary terms in the action have no effect on the equations of motion.

Now consider adding a term involving A_μ to this. Since A_μ undergoes the transformation $A_\mu \to A_\mu + \partial_\mu \theta$, we cannot just add any function of A_μ to (11.34) to get a gauge invariant result. We can add functions of $F_{\mu\nu}$, with some suitable coupling to the dynamical variables x^i, $\dot{x}^i$ for the particle. We may expect such terms to be suppressed in a way similar to what happens in the field theory; this is explained in the next remark. However, there is one other term we can write which is not invariant under gauge transformations, but whose variation under a gauge transformation is just a boundary term. This is acceptable since the equations of motion, which are all we need in the classical theory, will not be affected by the boundary terms. The term we are talking about is the integral of $A_\mu dx^\mu$ along the path, so that the full action is

$$S = -m \int ds - q \int A_\mu \, dx^\mu \qquad (11.35)$$

If we take out a factor of dt, we can bring this to a more familiar form as

$$S = \int dt \left[-m\sqrt{1 - \dot{x}^2} - qA_0 - qA_i \dot{x}^i \right] \qquad (11.36)$$

We can now easily check that this does give the right equations of motion. The two principles which led to this action are relativistic invariance and gauge invariance. Relativity tells us that the first term must be the integral of ds, and that we must have a relativistically invariant coupling of the 4-vector A_μ to the degrees of freedom of the particle. Further we must have gauge invariance. For the coupling in (11.35) this follows from

$$\int_{x_{init}}^{x_{fin}} A_\mu \, dx^\mu \rightarrow \int_{x_{init}}^{x_{fin}} (A_\mu + \partial_\mu \theta) \, dx^\mu = \int_{x_{init}}^{x_{fin}} A_\mu \, dx^\mu + \theta(x_{fin}) - \theta(x_{init})$$
$$(11.37)$$

With the addition of the Maxwell action, the full action for classical electrodynamics is thus

$$S = -\frac{1}{4} \int d^4 x \, \eta^{\mu\alpha} \eta^{\nu\beta} F_{\mu\nu} F_{\alpha\beta} + \int dt \left[-m\sqrt{1 - \dot{x}^2} - qA_0(x) - qA_i(x)\dot{x}^i \right]$$
$$(11.38)$$

In principle, we could add terms of higher dimension involving powers of $F_{\mu\nu}$ and its derivatives and velocities (with coefficients which carry inverse powers of some mass-like parameter) but, as in the field theory, we expect such terms to be less significant than what is given by (11.38), for fields which are slowly varying on the scale of the masses involved. Thus classical electrodynamics for fields which are not rapidly varying is entirely given by (11.38). One can easily generalize to include many particles as well, by writing the matter part of the action as

$$S = \sum_{\alpha=1}^{N} \int dt \left[-m\sqrt{1 - \dot{x}_\alpha^2} - qA_0(x_\alpha) - qA_i(x_\alpha)\dot{x}_\alpha^i \right] \qquad (11.39)$$

where α labels the particle. This allows us to use the action for the classical description of material media as well. It is quite amazing that a whole host of physical phenomena including optics, radiation and diffraction phenomena, behavior of electric and magnetic fields, etc. can be ultimately traced to two key principles: relativity and gauge invariance.

Remark 11.2.
The gauge principle and composite particles

It is useful to reiterate the gauge principle, which is summed up in (11.22) and (11.23). It states that the action should be invariant under the transformations

$$\text{Matter field} \to (\text{Matter field})' = e^{-iq\,\theta}\,(\text{Matter field})$$
$$A_\mu \to A'_\mu = A_\mu + \partial_\mu\theta \tag{11.40}$$

where q is the charge of the matter field under consideration. This leads us to the requirement of replacing derivatives of fields by covariant derivatives and gives the coupling of the photon to any fundamental particle. For a composite particle, the principle applies to every fundamental constituent. From that, we have to extract the coupling to the whole composite particle. This can be more involved. For example, the neutron is neutral, but is made of charged quarks. The result of applying the gauge principle to the charged quarks is that while there is no coupling of the neutron field Ψ to A_μ directly, i.e., there is no term like $q\bar\Psi\gamma^\mu\Psi A_\mu$ since q is zero, one can have more involved couplings, involving higher derivatives of A_μ. The nonzero magnetic moment of the neutron is a classic example. But in all cases, we must and do have invariance under gauge transformations. Thus for example, one could have additional interaction terms in the action of the form

$$S_{add} = \text{constant} \int d^4x \ \bar\Psi\,[\gamma^\mu,\gamma^\nu]\,\Psi\,F_{\mu\nu} \tag{11.41}$$

(This is the term which can describe the magnetic moment interaction of the neutron. As mentioned above, the Dirac action for the neutron field will not lead to such a term since the neutron has zero charge; we have to obtain this from the underlying quark structure of the neutron. For a charged particle, the gyromagnetic ratio g is 2 from the Dirac theory, we do not need an extra term of the form (11.41) for this much. But for anything beyond this value, namely for the $(g-2)$-part, effectively we have a term of the form (11.41). For example, for the proton, which is a spin-$\frac{1}{2}$ composite particle with nonzero charge, $g \neq 2$; the Dirac theory contributes 2 to g and the rest is a term of the form (11.41).)

In general, for a composite particle, there could be many other gauge invariant terms as well, (11.41) is just one example. But notice that in terms of dimension counting, the interaction term (11.41) has a nonzero dimension; in fact, it is equal to 1 in mass units. Thus we need the constant in front to be of dimension $(mass)^{-1}$. For the neutron, it will turn out to have a factor of $1/m$ where m is the neutron mass. If the fields are not very strong, or if they are not rapidly varying with $\vec{x}$ or t, this amounts to a suppression of the interaction. The higher terms with more powers of $F_{\mu\nu}$ or its derivatives will have more suppression factors. In effect, the conclusion is that, even for composite particles, the leading terms in the interaction with the electromagnetic field for slowly varying fields, i.e., the terms which are not suppressed by inverse powers of some mass, are given by the principle of replacing derivatives by covariant derivatives. The neutron has no such term as it has zero charge; the magnetic moment interaction, in this way of counting, is suppressed for slowly varying fields. For the proton, which is also a composite particle of nonzero charge, we will have a nonzero term $-e\bar{\Psi}\gamma^{\mu}A_{\mu}\Psi$, which will be the leading term. There can also be additional terms involving powers of $F_{\mu\nu}$ and its derivatives.

As a curiosity, we might wonder: If the nonminimal couplings such as the magnetic moment term in (11.41) can emerge from summing up the effects of the minimal couplings to the fundamental charged constituent point-particles of a composite particle, then, could we not have a similar situation for the gravitational couplings? Since the quantum description of coupling matter to gravity is somewhat involved, let us first focus on the classical case and ask: While point-particles follow a geodesic as given by (10.36), could the trajectory of a composite bulk mass deviate from a geodesic? The answer is, of course, yes. And in fact, among the most significant of such effects is the deviation of the trajectory of a spinning mass from a geodesic due to a coupling to the Riemann curvature tensor. The equations of motion for a mass m with angular momentum $S_{\mu\nu}$, known as the Mathisson-Papapetrou-Dixon equations, are

$$\frac{d^2 x^\alpha}{ds^2} + \Gamma^\alpha_{\mu\nu} \frac{dx^\mu}{ds} \frac{dx^\nu}{ds} = -\frac{1}{2m} R^\alpha_{\beta\mu\nu} \frac{dx^\beta}{ds} S^{\mu\nu} \qquad (11.42)$$

$$\frac{DS^{\mu\nu}}{ds} + \frac{dx^\mu}{ds} \frac{DS^{\nu\lambda}}{ds} \frac{dx_\lambda}{ds} - \frac{dx^\nu}{ds} \frac{DS^{\mu\lambda}}{ds} \frac{dx_\lambda}{ds} = 0 \qquad (11.43)$$

where

$$\frac{DS^{\mu\nu}}{ds} = \frac{dS^{\mu\nu}}{ds} + \Gamma^\mu_{\alpha\beta} S^{\alpha\nu} \frac{dx^\beta}{ds} + \Gamma^\nu_{\alpha\beta} S^{\mu\alpha} \frac{dx^\beta}{ds} \qquad (11.44)$$

These equations were originally obtained independently by Mathisson and Papapetrou with a more careful derivation given by Dixon.

At the quantum level, a spin-curvature coupling naturally emerges from coupling fields of nonzero spin, such as the electron, to gravitational fields, even in the case of point-particles. The gyrogravitational ratio for intrinsic spin is 2, as compared to 1 for orbital angular momentum, just as it is for the gyromagnetic ratio.

Remark 11.3.
About coupling the photon to gravity

The photon has energy, so it has an effective mass E/c^2. (This is an effective mass, its mass is zero.) So it can respond to gravity. One of the consequences is the bending of light by big gravitating masses such as the Sun. The verification of this effect at the total solar eclipse of 1919 was one of the first triumphs of Einstein's theory of gravity. In this context, we may ask the general question: How does one couple the photon to gravity? The action for the photon in flat space, ignoring other particle species, is given in (11.21); we just repeat it here:

$$S = -\frac{1}{4}\int d^4x\ \eta^{\mu\alpha}\eta^{\nu\beta}F_{\mu\nu}F_{\alpha\beta} \tag{11.45}$$

By the gauge principle for gravity, the action when we couple it to gravity is

$$S = -\frac{1}{4}\int d^4x\sqrt{-\det g}\ g^{\mu\alpha}g^{\nu\beta}\mathcal{F}_{\mu\nu}\mathcal{F}_{\alpha\beta} \tag{11.46}$$

where

$$\begin{aligned}\mathcal{F}_{\mu\nu} &= (\partial_\mu A_\nu - \Gamma^\lambda_{\mu\nu}A_\lambda) - (\partial_\nu A_\mu - \Gamma^\lambda_{\nu\mu}A_\lambda)\\ &= \partial_\mu A_\nu - \partial_\nu A_\mu \end{aligned} \tag{11.47}$$

Here we are somewhat lucky; it so happens that $\Gamma^\lambda_{\mu\nu}$ is symmetric in μ, ν, so that the Γ-terms in (11.47) cancel out. Thus the photon coupled to gravity is described by

$$S = -\frac{1}{4}\int d^4x\sqrt{-\det g}\ g^{\mu\alpha}g^{\nu\beta}F_{\mu\nu}F_{\alpha\beta} \tag{11.48}$$

This theory has two invariances:

1. We have invariance under the gauge transformation $A_\mu \to A_\mu + \partial_\mu\theta$.
2. We have invariance under coordinate transformations $A_\mu \to A'_\mu = (\mathbf{M})_\mu{}^\alpha A_\alpha$, $g^{\mu\nu} \to (g')^{\mu\nu} = (\mathbf{M}^{-1})^\mu{}_\alpha(\mathbf{M}^{-1})^\nu{}_\beta g^{\alpha\beta}$.

If we take the metric to be the Schwarzschild metric given in (10.38), as is appropriate for the metric around the Sun, we can derive the bending of starlight by the gravitational effect of the Sun from this action (11.48). The usual textbook derivations use a simpler analysis by considering the ray optics limit of the photon, so that its trajectory can be described as a particle trajectory, given as a geodesic in the Schwarzschild metric.

Chapter 12

Gauge Symmetry: The Matrix Generalization

In the last lecture, we started the generalization of the idea of gauge symmetry to transformations using matrices rather than just a complex number. The key ideas were the following. We can consider a number of fields together, say, as a column vector with N entries. Let us designate this as Φ. Then a linear transformation of fields is of the form

$$\Phi \rightarrow \Phi' = \mathbf{U}\,\Phi \tag{12.1}$$

We take $\mathbf{U}$ to be a unitary matrix. The idea of gauge symmetry is that we would like the action of the theory to be invariant under this even when $\mathbf{U}$ is an x-dependent (i.e., locally defined) quantity. For example, the action

$$S = \int d^4x \,\left[(\partial_\mu \Phi)^\dagger \, \partial_\mu \Phi - m^2 \Phi^\dagger\, \Phi \right] \tag{12.2}$$

is clearly invariant under the transformation (12.1) if $\mathbf{U}$ is independent of spacetime coordinates. But if $\mathbf{U}$ is a function of spacetime coordinates, the derivatives in (12.2) will spoil the invariance. The strategy is to replace the derivatives by covariant derivatives, replacing the action (12.2) by

$$S = \int d^4x \,\left[(D_\mu \Phi)^\dagger \, D_\mu \Phi - m^2 \Phi^\dagger\, \Phi \right] \tag{12.3}$$

This is invariant by definition, since the covariant derivative transforms exactly as the field itself, namely,

$$(D_\mu \Phi)' = \mathbf{U}\,(D_\mu\,\Phi) \tag{12.4}$$

Explicitly the covariant derivative is given by $D_\mu \Phi = \partial_\mu \Phi - i \mathcal{A}_\mu\, \Phi$, so that the transformation rule (12.4) is consistent if we assign the transformation law

$$\mathcal{A}_\mu \rightarrow \mathcal{A}'_\mu = \mathbf{U}\mathcal{A}_\mu\,\mathbf{U}^{-1} - i\,(\partial_\mu \mathbf{U})\,\mathbf{U}^{-1} \tag{12.5}$$

This transformation also shows that we can take $\mathcal{A}_\mu$ as a hermitian matrix. (The quantity $-i\,\partial_\mu \mathbf{U}\,\mathbf{U}^{-1}$ is hermitian if $\mathbf{U}$ is unitary; hence the hermiticity property of $\mathcal{A}_\mu$ will be preserved under the transformation.)

We also need to construct an action for the dynamics of the gauge field $\mathcal{A}_\mu$ as well. The simplest way to do this is to consider the commutator of two covariant derivatives. Since $D_\mu \Phi$ transforms the same way as Φ does, the process can be repeated. Thus

$$(D_\mu D_\nu \Phi)' = \mathbf{U}\,(D_\mu D_\nu \Phi), \qquad (D_\mu D_\nu D_\alpha \Phi)' = \mathbf{U}\,(D_\mu D_\nu D_\alpha \Phi), \quad \text{etc.} \tag{12.6}$$

If we expand these out, we get terms with multiple (ordinary) derivatives acting on Φ. Thus

$$\begin{aligned}
D_\mu D_\nu \Phi &= (\partial_\mu - i\mathcal{A}_\mu)(\partial_\nu \Phi - i\mathcal{A}_\nu \Phi) \\
&= \partial_\mu \partial_\nu \Phi - i\mathcal{A}_\mu \partial_\nu \Phi - i(\partial_\mu \mathcal{A}_\nu)\Phi - i\mathcal{A}_\nu \partial_\mu \Phi - \mathcal{A}_\mu \mathcal{A}_\nu \Phi
\end{aligned} \tag{12.7}$$

Since derivatives on a function commute, we can eliminate the terms involving derivatives of Φ by considering the commutator of covariant derivatives. We find

$$\begin{aligned}
D_\mu D_\nu \Phi - D_\nu D_\mu \Phi &= -i\left(\partial_\mu \mathcal{A}_\nu - \partial_\nu \mathcal{A}_\mu - i[\mathcal{A}_\mu, \mathcal{A}_\nu]\right)\Phi \\
&\equiv -i\,\mathbf{F}_{\mu\nu}\,\Phi
\end{aligned} \tag{12.8}$$

where

$$\mathbf{F}_{\mu\nu} = \partial_\mu \mathcal{A}_\nu - \partial_\nu \mathcal{A}_\mu - i[\mathcal{A}_\mu, \mathcal{A}_\nu] \tag{12.9}$$

The last term in this equation is the matrix commutator of the fields $\mathcal{A}_\mu$ and $\mathcal{A}_\nu$. $\mathbf{F}_{\mu\nu}$ is a hermitian matrix, in addition to being a function of the coordinates. It is known as the field strength tensor for the gauge field $\mathcal{A}_\mu$. The transformation law (12.6) shows that

$$\begin{aligned}
\left([D_\mu, D_\nu]\Phi\right)' &= -i\,\mathbf{F}'_{\mu\nu}\,\Phi' \\
&= \mathbf{U}\left([D_\mu, D_\nu]\Phi\right) \\
&= -i\,\mathbf{U}\,\mathbf{F}_{\mu\nu}\,\Phi
\end{aligned} \tag{12.10}$$

The first line of these equations is the definition of the field strength tensor applied to the transformed variables, the second line is a rewriting of the left hand side using (12.6) and the third is the use of (12.8) again for the untransformed variables. Equation (12.10) demonstrates that the transformation law for the field strength tensor is

$$\mathbf{F}'_{\mu\nu} = \mathbf{U}\,\mathbf{F}_{\mu\nu}\,\mathbf{U}^{-1} \tag{12.11}$$

The matter of choosing a suitable action is now simple. We know we need two powers of $\mathbf{F}_{\mu\nu}$ since we need two powers of the first derivative of the field. This is further confirmed by the fact that the action for the Maxwell equations is of the form $-\frac{1}{4}\int F_{\mu\nu}F^{\mu\nu}$, where the $F_{\mu\nu}$ has a similar form as $\mathbf{F}_{\mu\nu}$ except that it applies to a 1×1 matrix. Thus we might consider $\mathbf{F}_{\mu\nu}\mathbf{F}^{\mu\nu}$. However, this is not invariant under the transformations with $\mathbf{U}$ since

$$(\mathbf{F}_{\mu\nu}\mathbf{F}^{\mu\nu})' = (\mathbf{U}\,\mathbf{F}_{\mu\nu}\,\mathbf{U}^{-1})\,(\mathbf{U}\,\mathbf{F}^{\mu\nu}\,\mathbf{U}^{-1}) = \mathbf{U}\,\mathbf{F}_{\mu\nu}\mathbf{F}^{\mu\nu}\,\mathbf{U}^{-1} \qquad (12.12)$$

Further, $\mathbf{F}_{\mu\nu}\mathbf{F}^{\mu\nu}$ is still a matrix, but we need a number for the action, not a matrix. The solution is given by taking a trace. The invariance of the trace under cyclic permutations shows that

$$\mathrm{Tr}\,(\mathbf{F}_{\mu\nu}\mathbf{F}^{\mu\nu})' = \mathrm{Tr}\,(\mathbf{F}_{\mu\nu}\mathbf{F}^{\mu\nu}) \qquad (12.13)$$

Thus we have an invariant quantity. The action describing the dynamics of the gauge field $\mathcal{A}_\mu$ will now be taken as

$$S = -\frac{1}{2\,g^2}\int d^4x\;\mathrm{Tr}(\mathbf{F}^{\mu\nu}\mathbf{F}_{\mu\nu}) \qquad (12.14)$$

where g is a constant. This action is known as the Yang-Mills action. The conventional normalization for the matrices is to take $\mathcal{A}_\mu = t_a\mathcal{A}_\mu^a$, where t_a are hermitian matrices with $\mathrm{Tr}(t_a t_b) = \frac{1}{2}\delta_{ab}$. In this case, the action reduces to

$$S = -\frac{1}{4\,g^2}\int d^4x\;\mathrm{Tr}(\mathbf{F}^{a\mu\nu}\mathbf{F}^a_{\mu\nu}) \qquad (12.15)$$

A further redefinition $\mathcal{A}_\mu^a = g\,A_\mu^a$ brings this to a form similar to the action for electrodynamics. This also shows that the constant g is the unit of charge for the Yang-Mills theory.

Remark 12.1.
The trace of a matrix

The trace of a matrix $\mathbf{M}$, denoted by $\mathrm{Tr}\,\mathbf{M}$, is defined as the sum of the diagonal elements of the matrix,

$$\mathrm{Tr}\,\mathbf{M} = \sum_i (\mathbf{M})_{ii} \qquad (12.16)$$

An important immediate property is that the trace of a product of matrices is invariant under cyclic permutations,

$$\mathrm{Tr}\,(\mathbf{MN}) = \sum_i (\mathbf{MN})_{ii} = \sum_i \sum_k \mathbf{M}_{ik}\mathbf{N}_{ki}$$

$$= \sum_k \sum_i \mathbf{N}_{ki} \mathbf{M}_{ik} = \sum_k (\mathbf{NM})_{kk}$$
$$= \mathrm{Tr}\,(\mathbf{NM}) \tag{12.17}$$

The first line of this set of equations follows from the definition of the matrix product, the second from rearranging the order for the ordinary product of the matrix elements and recombining as matrix product again. For a product of three matrices, we can write

$$\mathrm{Tr}\,(\mathbf{MNR}) = \mathrm{Tr}\left((\mathbf{MN})\mathbf{R}\right) = \mathrm{Tr}\left(\mathbf{R(MN)}\right)$$
$$= \mathrm{Tr}\left(\mathbf{RMN}\right) = \mathrm{Tr}\left(\mathbf{NRM}\right) \tag{12.18}$$

The first line follows from (12.17) by viewing $\mathbf{MN}$ as a single matrix. The cyclic symmetry of the trace is clear from (12.18). We also see that this can be obtained recursively for the product of any number of matrices.

This property of cyclic invariance also tells us that the trace is invariant under similarity transformations,

$$\mathrm{Tr}\left(\mathbf{UMU}^{-1}\right) = \mathrm{Tr}\left(\mathbf{U}^{-1}\,\mathbf{UM}\right) = \mathrm{Tr}\,\mathbf{M} \tag{12.19}$$

Another interesting property of the trace is its expression in terms of eigenvalues. Since a hermitian matrix can be diagonalized by a unitary transformation as $\mathbf{M} = \mathbf{S}\,\mathbf{M}_{diag}\,\mathbf{S}^{-1}$, where $\mathbf{M}_{diag}$ is a diagonal matrix with the eigenvalues λ_i of $\mathbf{M}$ as its entries, we see that the trace of $\mathbf{M}$ gives the sum of its eigenvalues,

$$\mathrm{Tr}\,\mathbf{M} = \mathrm{Tr}\,\mathbf{M}_{diag} = \sum_i \lambda_i \tag{12.20}$$

The trace is a number since it is the sum of the diagonal elements or its eigenvalues.

Here we are considering finite dimensional matrices, so that the sums involved in the definition of the trace exist. In the case of infinite-dimensional matrices, these results generalize only for a class of matrices for which the trace can be defined. For our purpose here, we only need finite-dimensional matrices.

Remark 12.2.
The curvature, the field strength tensor and gravity

The field strength tensor arises from the commutator of the covariant derivatives. The Riemann curvature tensor is defined via the commutator of the covariant derivatives needed for the covariance under coordinate transformations. Clearly they are both of the same ilk, except that for the field strength tensor, the symmetry is that of gauge transformations which correspond to some sort of rotations of the field Φ in some internal space, while for the Riemann tensor, we are talking about coordinate transformations in spacetime. To bring out the similarity better, it is useful to think of the Christoffel symbol as a matrix-valued vector Γ_μ interpreting $\Gamma^\alpha_{\mu\lambda} = (\Gamma_\mu)_\lambda{}^\alpha$ as the (λ, α)-matrix element of Γ_μ. The Riemann tensor can then be written as

$$
\begin{aligned}
(R_{\mu\nu})_\lambda{}^\alpha &= \partial_\mu (\Gamma_\nu)_\lambda{}^\alpha - \partial_\nu (\Gamma_\mu)_\lambda{}^\alpha - (\Gamma_\mu)_\lambda{}^\sigma (\Gamma_\nu)_\sigma{}^\alpha + (\Gamma_\nu)_\lambda{}^\sigma (\Gamma_\mu)_\sigma{}^\alpha \\
&= (\partial_\mu \Gamma_\nu - \partial_\nu \Gamma_\mu - [\Gamma_\mu, \Gamma_\nu])_\lambda{}^\alpha
\end{aligned}
\tag{12.21}
$$

This is the field strength tensor if we take Γ_μ as $i\mathcal{A}_\mu$.

The action for the theory of gravity is however not of the Yang-Mills type. This is because the gauge field $\mathcal{A}_\mu$ is the basic dynamical variable for a gauge theory, but the Christoffel symbol is not; it can be written in terms of the derivatives of the metric and the metric is the basic dynamical variable for the theory of gravity. But the transformation properties and the principle behind how the symmetry is implemented are very similar.

There are a couple of contexts in which the similarity can be pushed further. One can consider Einstein gravity on a higher dimensional space where the dimensions beyond the usual temporal and spatial ones are viewed as forming a compact space. The full space is thus of the form Minkowski $\times M$, where M is compact, like a circle, a sphere, etc. In this case, some of the additional components of the metric behave as a gauge field with a part of the coordinate transformations for the space M acting as the usual gauge transformations. The local symmetry is the set of transformations which preserve the metric of the space M, i.e., the so-called isometries of M. This scenario is the Kaluza-Klein approach. The field equations for gravity also include the field equations for the gauge field corresponding to a Yang-Mills type action.

Another way to compare the gauge principle for gravity and Yang-Mills type theories is in terms of frames. It is possible to introduce local frames of vectors, denoted by $\{e^a_\mu\}$, $a = 0, 1, 2, 3$, in terms of which we can write the metric tensor as

$$
g_{\mu\nu} = e^a_\mu e^b_\nu \eta_{ab}
\tag{12.22}
$$

where η_{ab} is the *flat* Minkowski metric. By using the combination $e^a_\mu dx^\mu$ (which is a differential one-form), one can automatically get invariance under coordinate transformations, the transformation on the μ-index of e^a_μ

being compensated by the transformation of dx^μ. In this version, one has local symmetry under Lorentz transformations, so that we truly have a gauge theory of the Lorentz group. The gauge field in this case is called a spin connection. One can recover all the usual results of gravity in this framework as well. It also makes it easier to deal with spinor fields which are defined by their Lorentz transformation properties.

In this picture, beyond the bare spacetime manifold, we have an additional structure given by e^a_μ at each point in spacetime; these provide the frames for vectors, tensors, etc. So a natural extension of this idea is to consider matter fields as an additional similar structure at each point in spacetime. Thus if we are interested in an n-component scalar field ϕ^i, we may think of having an n-component flat space $\mathbb{R}^n$ (or $\mathbb{C}^n$ if ϕ^i are complex) at each point in spacetime with the field $\phi^i(x)$ being a map from spacetime to this $\mathbb{R}^n$ (or $\mathbb{C}^n$). Gauge transformations on the i-index of ϕ^i of the form $\phi^i(x) \rightarrow \phi'^i(x) = \mathbf{U}^i{}_j(x)\,\phi^j(x)$ naturally become x-dependent rotations in $\mathbb{R}^n$ (or $\mathbb{C}^n$), bringing this conceptually closer to gravity. This is the formalism of fiber bundles, which is the appropriate structure for discussing fields from the mathematician's point of view.

Chapter 13

Gauge Symmetry: The Matrix Generalization II

In the last lecture we formulated the matrix generalization of the idea of gauge symmetry, concluding with the definition of the field strength and the Yang-Mills action. It is very useful to see how this all works out for some simple examples.

The simplest case is, of course, that of $U(1)$ symmetry, where the unitary matrix is a 1×1 matrix. In this case, the matrix is just a function, of the form $\mathbf{U} = \exp(-iQ\theta)$, for some constant Q and θ is a real-valued function on spacetime. There is only one generator Q, so to speak, so that the commutation rules (for the Qs) are trivial. Fields, which are now just functions, transform as $\Phi \to \Phi' = e^{-iQ\theta} \Phi$ and the covariant derivative is $D_\mu\Phi = \partial_\mu\Phi + iQA_\mu\Phi$. The field strength is $F_{\mu\nu} = \partial_\mu A_\nu - \partial_\nu A_\mu$, with the commutator term vanishing. This is all familiar, we are just rephrasing the case of electromagnetism. (Here we used Q since we referred to a general $U(1)$ symmetry; for electromagnetism, Q evaluated on any field corresponds to the charge of that field.)

The simplest case, beyond the 1×1 matrices which correspond to the electromagnetic theory, is when $\mathbf{U}$ is a 2×2 unitary matrix. Since $\det(\mathbf{U}_1\mathbf{U}_2) = \det(\mathbf{U}_1)\det(\mathbf{U}_2)$, if both $\mathbf{U}_1$ and $\mathbf{U}_2$ have unit determinant, then the combined transformation, which corresponds to $\mathbf{U}_1\mathbf{U}_2$, will also have unit determinant. For any unitary matrix, we can write $\mathbf{U} = e^{i\theta}\,\tilde{\mathbf{U}}$, where $\tilde{\mathbf{U}}$ has unit determinant. The fact that the matrices of unit determinant preserve that property under multiplication means that we can separately treat the transformations of any field under the $e^{i\theta}$ part and under $\tilde{\mathbf{U}}$. Unitary matrices with determinant equal to 1 are called special unitary matrices. So the simplest case for us to consider, beyond the electromagnetic case, is that of special unitary matrices which are 2×2. They are said to belong to the set (or group) $SU(2)$, in an obvious notation.[1] (We will drop the tilde on the **U**s from now on.)

Any $SU(2)$ matrix can be written as

$$\mathbf{U} = \exp\left(i\frac{\tau_a}{2}\theta_a\right) = \exp\left(i\frac{\tau_1}{2}\theta_1 + i\frac{\tau_2}{2}\theta_2 + i\frac{\tau_3}{2}\theta_3\right) \qquad (13.1)$$

where θ_a are three real parameters and τ_a are the three Pauli matrices,

$$\tau_1 = \begin{pmatrix} 0 & 1 \\ 1 & 0 \end{pmatrix}, \qquad \tau_2 = \begin{pmatrix} 0 & -i \\ i & 0 \end{pmatrix}, \qquad \tau_3 = \begin{pmatrix} 1 & 0 \\ 0 & -1 \end{pmatrix} \qquad (13.2)$$

The symmetry does not correspond to spin, so even though mathematically τ_a are the Pauli matrices, they act on the internal space of the components of a field like Φ and so we use a different letter, τ_a rather than σ_a, to emphasize this. If we consider infinitesimal transformations, i.e., take θ_a to be infinitesimal so that $\mathbf{U} \simeq \mathbb{1} + i(\tau_a/2)\,\theta_a$, then the transformation of a field $\mathcal{A}_\mu$ can be written as

$$\begin{aligned}
\mathcal{A}'_\mu &= \mathbf{U}\mathcal{A}_\mu\mathbf{U}^{-1} - i(\partial_\mu\mathbf{U})\,\mathbf{U}^{-1} \\
&\approx \left(\mathbb{1} + i(\tau_a/2)\,\theta_a\right)\mathcal{A}_\mu\left(\mathbb{1} - i(\tau_i/2)\,\theta_i\right) \\
&\quad -i\partial_\mu(\mathbb{1} + i(\tau_a/2)\,\theta_a)\left(\mathbb{1} - i(\tau_i/2)\,\theta_i\right) \\
&\approx \mathcal{A}_\mu + i\theta_a\left[\frac{\tau_a}{2}, \mathcal{A}_\mu\right] + \frac{\tau_a}{2}\partial_\mu\theta_a
\end{aligned} \qquad (13.3)$$

This equation shows that it is sufficient to take $\mathcal{A}_\mu$ as a matrix which is a linear combination of τ_a. Then, because the commutator of the τ's will give something proportional to the τ's again, the nature of $\mathcal{A}_\mu$ will not change after the transformation. (Recall that any 2×2 matrix can be expanded in terms of the identity matrix and the τ_a. The part of $\mathcal{A}_\mu$ proportional to the identity does not respond to the $SU(2)$ transformations, it is the gauge field for the $U(1)$ transformations $e^{i\theta}$, while the part which is a linear combination of the τ_a is the gauge field for the $SU(2)$ transformations.) Explicitly, if we take $\mathcal{A}_\mu = \mathcal{A}_\mu^a\,(\tau_a/2)$, (13.3) becomes

$$\begin{aligned}
\mathcal{A}'_\mu &\approx \mathcal{A}_\mu + i\theta_a\left[\frac{\tau_a}{2}, \frac{\tau_b}{2}\right]\mathcal{A}_\mu^b + \frac{\tau_a}{2}\partial_\mu\theta_a \\
&\approx \mathcal{A}_\mu - \theta_a\epsilon_{abc}\frac{\tau_c}{2}\mathcal{A}_\mu^b + \frac{\tau_a}{2}\partial_\mu\theta_a
\end{aligned}$$

---

[1]The transformations given by the set of unitary matrices form a group. We can combine them via matrix multiplication, which is associative. Further, the product of two unitary matrices is also unitary, we have the identity matrix $\mathbb{1}$, and we have the inverse since $\mathbf{U}^\dagger\mathbf{U} = \mathbb{1}$. Thus we see that the four requirements for a group, namely closure under composition, associativity, existence of identity and inverse are satisfied by the set of unitary matrices of a fixed dimension. Gauge symmetry can be defined for any Lie group, although we will mainly use special unitary groups.

$$\approx \mathcal{A}_\mu + \frac{\tau_a}{2}\left(\partial_\mu\theta_a + \epsilon_{abc}\mathcal{A}_\mu^b\theta_c\right) \tag{13.4}$$

We see that the change is indeed proportional to a combination of the τ's. In fact, we may write the infinitesimal transformation law as[2]

$$(\mathcal{A}_\mu^a)' \approx \mathcal{A}_\mu^a + \left(\partial_\mu\theta^a + \epsilon^{abc}\mathcal{A}_\mu^b\theta^c\right) \tag{13.5}$$

Even though we have shown that it is consistent to consider $\mathcal{A}_\mu$ of the form $\mathcal{A}_\mu = (\tau_a/2)\,\mathcal{A}_\mu^a$ only for transformations by unitary matrices which are infinitesimally different from the identity, the result holds in general since any unitary transformation for any θ^a can be built up by successive infinitesimal transformations.

We can also calculate $\mathbf{F}_{\mu\nu}$ as follows.

$$\begin{aligned}
\mathbf{F}_{\mu\nu} &= \frac{\tau_a}{2}\partial_\mu\mathcal{A}_\nu^a - \frac{\tau_a}{2}\partial_\nu\mathcal{A}_\mu^a - i\left[\frac{\tau_b}{2},\frac{\tau_c}{2}\right]\mathcal{A}_\mu^b\mathcal{A}_\nu^c \\
&= \frac{\tau_a}{2}\left(\partial_\mu\mathcal{A}_\nu^a - \partial_\nu\mathcal{A}_\mu^a + \epsilon_{abc}\,\mathcal{A}_\mu^b\mathcal{A}_\nu^c\right) \\
&= \frac{\tau_a}{2}\,F_{\mu\nu}^a
\end{aligned} \tag{13.6}$$

$$F_{\mu\nu}^a = \partial_\mu\mathcal{A}_\nu^a - \partial_\nu\mathcal{A}_\mu^a + \epsilon_{abc}\,\mathcal{A}_\mu^b\mathcal{A}_\nu^c \tag{13.7}$$

The Yang-Mills action thus becomes

$$S = -\frac{1}{4g^2}\int F^{a\mu\nu}F_{\mu\nu}^a \tag{13.8}$$

where we used the fact that $\mathrm{Tr}(\tau_a\tau_b) = 2\,\delta_{ab}$. It is also convenient to make a change in the definition of the field by writing $\mathcal{A}_\mu = g\,\mathbf{A}_\mu$ (or $\mathcal{A}_\mu^a = g\,A_\mu^a$) and redefine $\mathbf{F}_{\mu\nu}$ by dividing by g so that

$$D_\mu\Phi = \partial_\mu\Phi - ig\,\mathbf{A}_\mu\Phi$$
$$\mathbf{F}_{\mu\nu} \equiv \partial_\mu\mathbf{A}_\nu - \partial_\nu\mathbf{A}_\mu - ig\left[\mathbf{A}_\mu,\mathbf{A}_\nu\right]$$
$$S = -\frac{1}{2}\int\mathrm{Tr}\left(\mathbf{F}^{\mu\nu}\mathbf{F}_{\mu\nu}\right) \tag{13.9}$$

The constant g is now seen to be a coupling constant, the same for coupling of the field A_μ to the matter fields Φ and to itself via the nonlinear term in $\mathbf{F}_{\mu\nu}$.

There is another fascinating property as well which shows that the algebra of the matrices is really what matters. For example, consider 3×3 matrices of the form

$$\mathbf{U} = \exp\left(iK_1\theta_1 + iK_2\theta_2 + iK_3\theta_3\right)$$

---

[2]Sometimes we write the indices on the θs as superscripts, sometimes as subscripts, for typographical clarity. There is really no difference, raising and lowering of indices for the internal symmetry groups of interest to us will be done with δ_b^a.

$$K_1 = \begin{pmatrix} 0 & 0 & 0 \\ 0 & 0 & -i \\ 0 & i & 0 \end{pmatrix}, \qquad K_2 = \begin{pmatrix} 0 & 0 & i \\ 0 & 0 & 0 \\ -i & 0 & 0 \end{pmatrix}, \qquad K_3 = \begin{pmatrix} 0 & -i & 0 \\ i & 0 & 0 \\ 0 & 0 & 0 \end{pmatrix} \qquad (13.10)$$

One can check directly that

$$\left[K_a, K_b\right] = i\epsilon_{abc}\, K_c \qquad (13.11)$$

In other words, the K's obey the same commutation rules as the $\frac{\tau_a}{2}$. For this reason, the composition of **U**'s of the form $e^{iK\cdot\theta}$ leads to matrices of the same form. Of course, such **U**'s are not the most general unitary matrices which are 3×3. Nevertheless, one can restrict attention consistently to these. It is easily verified that if we write $\mathcal{A}_\mu = K_a\, \mathcal{A}_\mu^a$ then the expressions for the field strength is the same as in (13.7); we get the same expression because the constants ϵ_{abc} are the same for both cases. This allows for a certain universality in how we couple particles. For example, consider two particle species, Φ which has two components, and Ψ, which has 3 components, transforming as

$$\Phi' = \exp\left(i\frac{\tau_i}{2}\theta_i\right)\Phi, \qquad \Psi' = \exp\left(iK_i\theta_i\right)\Psi \qquad (13.12)$$

The commutator algebra of the matrices which implement the transformation is the same, so are the parameters θ_i. The covariant derivatives for these fields can be defined by

$$D_\mu\Phi = \partial_\mu\Phi - i\mathcal{A}_\mu^a\frac{\tau_a}{2}\,\Phi, \qquad D_\mu\Psi = \partial_\mu\Psi - i\mathcal{A}_\mu^a K_a\,\Psi \qquad (13.13)$$

Because the algebra is the same, we need only one set of fields $\mathcal{A}_\mu^a$ to obtain the covariant derivative for both Φ and Ψ, even though they are multiplied by different matrices in the expressions for the covariant derivatives for the two different fields. We may think of the matrices $\frac{\tau_a}{2}$ and K_a as charge matrices for the two fields, a generalization of the Q we had for the electromagnetic case.

One worry might be about $F_{\mu\nu}^a$ and the action. We can use $\mathcal{A}_\mu = \mathcal{A}_\mu^a\frac{\tau_a}{2}$ to obtain the expression (13.7), but what happens if we use $\mathcal{A}_\mu = \mathcal{A}_\mu^a K_a$, following the cue from the covariant derivative for Ψ? This would give

$$\begin{aligned} \mathbf{F}_{\mu\nu} &= K_a\partial_\mu\mathcal{A}_\nu^a - K_a\partial_\nu\mathcal{A}_\mu^a - i\left[K_b, K_c\right]\mathcal{A}_\mu^b\mathcal{A}_\nu^c \\ &= K_a\left(\partial_\mu\mathcal{A}_\nu^a - \partial_\nu\mathcal{A}_\mu^a + \epsilon_{abc}\mathcal{A}_\mu^b\mathcal{A}_\nu^c\right) \end{aligned} \qquad (13.14)$$

This shows that the components $F_{\mu\nu}^a$ and hence the Yang-Mills action (as in (13.8)) are the same. We see that the dynamics of $\mathcal{A}_\mu$ depends only on the algebra (via the appearance of ϵ_{abc}), and not on the specific realization or representation used for the covariant derivative for different matter fields.

Analysis starting from symmetry

Since we claim that symmetry and its algebra are the key, let us rephrase the analysis starting from the symmetry point of view. This means that we start by specifying the type of transformations which we want to implement as a local symmetry for the theory. We will set up the analysis as a sequence of steps.

First step

We start with the definition of the set of unitary matrices we need. For example, if the symmetry is $SU(N)$, this means that it is defined as the set of $N \times N$ unitary matrices with determinant equal to one. We can write these unitary matrices as $\mathbf{U} = \exp(it_a\theta_a)$, where θ_a are a set of real parameters and $\{t_a\}$ are a set of linearly independent $N \times N$ hermitian matrices. In this parametrization, the set of matrices $\{t_a\}$ which generate the unitary matrix are called the generators.

Second step

We then construct the commutator algebra of the t_a. It will be of the form

$$\left[t_a, t_b\right] = if_{abc}\, t_c \tag{13.15}$$

where f_{abc} are a set of constants which can be worked out from the choice of the $\{t_a\}$. We may worry about the question: How do we know that the commutator of t_a and t_b should be proportional to another t? The reason is that the composition of two symmetry transformations must be a symmetry of the same type. Thus if we consider $\mathbf{U}_1 = \exp(it_a\theta_a)$ and $\mathbf{U}_2 = \exp(it_b\alpha_b)$ for some angles θ_a and α_b, then the transformation first by $\mathbf{U}_2$ and then by $\mathbf{U}_1$ is equivalent to the transformation $\mathbf{U}_1\mathbf{U}_2$. This is given by

$$
\begin{aligned}
\mathbf{U}_1\mathbf{U}_2 &= \exp(it_a\theta_a)\,\exp(it_b\alpha_b) \\
&= \exp\left(it_a(\theta_a + \alpha_a) - \frac{1}{2}\left[t_a, t_b\right]\theta_a\alpha_b\right. \\
&\qquad\left. -\frac{i}{12}\left[t_c, \left[t_a, t_b\right]\right](\theta_c - \alpha_c)\theta_a\alpha_b + \cdots\right)
\end{aligned}
\tag{13.16}
$$

where we used the Baker-Campbell-Hausdorff formula for combining exponentials of matrices,

$$e^X e^Y = \exp\left(X + Y + \frac{1}{2}[X, Y] + \frac{1}{12}[X - Y, [X, Y]] + \cdots\right) \tag{13.17}$$

The exponent is made of commutators, so if the commutator algebra gives t_a back again, the combined transformation has the same form (with different parameters). For a symmetry we need this property of closure, so by definition, if we say we have a symmetry, we can take the commutator algebra to close; otherwise the transformations do not form a symmetry.

Third step

Having obtained the algebra (13.15), we then consider the abstract algebra

$$[T_a, T_b] = i f_{abc} T_c \tag{13.18}$$

We can interpret the first set of matrices $\{t_a\}$ used to define the symmetry as a particular realization or representation of this abstract algebra (13.18). We can then look for other representations which may be matrices of different dimensions but realizing the same set of commutation rules (13.18). For example, for the case of $SU(2)$, the algebra is given by $[T_a, T_b] = i \epsilon_{abc} T_c$. This is similar to the angular momentum commutation rules familiar from elementary quantum mechanics, so we can borrow results from there to see that there are representations of this algebra where T_a are $(2s+1) \times (2s+1)$ matrices, with

$$(T_3)_{mn} = (n - s - 1) \delta_{mn}$$
$$(T_1 + iT_2)_{mn} = \sqrt{s(s+1) - (n-s)(n-s-1)}\ \delta_{m,n+1}$$
$$(T_1 - iT_2)_{mn} = \sqrt{s(s+1) - (n-s-1)(n-s-2)}\ \delta_{m,n-1} \tag{13.19}$$

where $m, n = 1, 2, \cdots, (2s+1)$. The possible values of $2s$ are positive integers. $s = \frac{1}{2}$ will give $\tau_a/2$, and $s = 1$ will give the matrices K_a in (13.10), after a similarity transformation. Although it is a bit more involved, representations for $SU(N)$, $N > 2$ can also be worked out in a similar way as for $SU(2)$.

The importance of the existence of various representations is that they will give us the possible ways particles or fields can transform under the chosen symmetry. We can have different fields which transform under different representations; for example,

$$\Phi' = \mathbf{U}^{(r_1)}\, \Phi, \qquad \chi' = \mathbf{U}^{(r_2)}\, \chi, \qquad \Psi' = \mathbf{U}^{(r_3)}\, \Psi, \quad \text{etc.} \tag{13.20}$$

where we have used a superscript to indicate that the $\mathbf{U}$'s are the same transformation (same parameters θ_a) but in different representations. For each of these, we can write the covariant derivative,

$$D_\mu \Phi = \partial_\mu \Phi - i\, T_a^{(r_1)}\, \mathcal{A}_\mu^a\, \Phi, \qquad D_\mu \chi = \partial_\mu \chi - i\, T_a^{(r_2)}\, \mathcal{A}_\mu^a\, \chi,$$

$$D_\mu \Psi = \partial_\mu \Psi - i T_a^{(r_3)} \mathcal{A}_\mu^a \Psi, \quad \text{etc.} \tag{13.21}$$

Notice that the potential $\mathcal{A}_\mu^a$ is the same for all particles which respond to the same symmetry, although they are multiplied by matrices of the appropriate representation in each case.

Fourth step

In the action for the matter fields Φ, χ, Ψ, etc., we must replace the derivatives by the covariant derivatives, i.e, the action is

$$S_{\text{matter}} = \Big[S_{\text{matter}}(\Phi, \chi, \Psi, ...) \Big]_{\partial_\mu \Phi \to D_\mu \Phi,\, \partial_\mu \chi \to D_\mu \chi,\, \text{etc.}} \tag{13.22}$$

For this to give an invariant action, the starting action, before the replacement $\partial_\mu \to D_\mu$, must be invariant with respect to similar transformations for constant (spacetime-independent) **U**s.

The dynamics for the gauge field $\mathcal{A}_\mu^a$ is then given by

$$S = -\frac{1}{4g^2} \int d^4x \; F^{a\mu\nu} F_{\mu\nu}^a \tag{13.23}$$

where

$$F_{\mu\nu}^a = \partial_\mu \mathcal{A}_\nu^a - \partial_\nu \mathcal{A}_\mu^a + f^{abc} \mathcal{A}_\mu^b \mathcal{A}_\nu^c \tag{13.24}$$

Fifth step

Conventionally, we introduce a unit of charge by the scaling $\mathcal{A} = g\, A$. The covariant derivatives become

$$D_\mu \Phi = \partial_\mu \Phi - ig\, T_a^{(r_1)} A_\mu^a \Phi, \quad D_\mu \chi = \partial_\mu \chi - ig\, T_a^{(r_2)} A_\mu^a \chi,$$
$$D_\mu \Psi = \partial_\mu \Psi - ig\, T_a^{(r_3)} A_\mu^a \Psi, \quad \text{etc.} \tag{13.25}$$

We also divide out a factor of g in $F_{\mu\nu}^a$, so that we use

$$F_{\mu\nu}^a = \partial_\mu A_\nu^a - \partial_\nu A_\mu^a + g\, f^{abc} A_\mu^b A_\nu^c \tag{13.26}$$

The action can then be rewritten as

$$S = -\frac{1}{4} \int d^4x \; F^{a\mu\nu} F_{\mu\nu}^a$$
$$+ \Big[S_{\text{matter}}(\Phi, \chi, \Psi, ...) \Big]_{\partial_\mu \Phi \to D_\mu \Phi,\, \partial_\mu \chi \to D_\mu \chi,\, \text{etc.}} \tag{13.27}$$

Remarks

There are several remarkable things about the gauge principle which is the name for the procedure we have outlined.

(1) The first and foremost thing is that symmetry is central. For each symmetry which we want to implement locally, we have a gauge field. The symmetry algebra, namely, (13.18), also tells us how the matter fields can respond to the symmetry transformation. The representations of the algebra lead to the possible ways matter fields can transform, as in (13.20). The coupling of the fields to the gauge field is thus completely determined by this property.

(2) There is universality. The gauge field $\mathcal{A}_\mu^a$ couples the same way to all matter fields which respond to the same symmetry transformation, apart from the charge matrices $T_a^{(r)}$, which are specific to the matter field.

(3) Finally, the only way to introduce couplings of vector particles is via the gauge principle. This is the only way consistent with the general principles of quantum field theory such as the unitarity of time-evolution, or equivalently, the conservation of probability, if it is to be taken as being valid to arbitrarily high energies. (The proof of this statement requires many results from quantum field theory and can be found in books on that subject; here we will simply accept this result and go on.)

The primacy of symmetry and universality make the gauge principle a very powerful starting point for the formulation of all interactions. Nevertheless, it is still a very general statement; it provides a general mathematical framework. It does not tell us which set of matter fields transform according to which representation of what symmetry. Should we use unitary matrices which are 2×2, or do we need 3×3 matrices, should we group matter fields into column vectors with 2 entries, 3 entries or even more entries? Or should we use some combinations of these? This is to be determined by experiment. But before we take up this question, we will work out a few examples starting by specifying the symmetry.

Examples

$SU(2)$

$SU(2)$ is the set of all unitary 2×2 matrices which have unit determinant, the letters standing for *special, unitary* and 2×2. This is the case we have already discussed. So we will move on to another example.

$SU(3)$

This is the set of all special unitary 3×3 matrices. Let us start by construct-ing a general element of this group. Any unitary matrix can be written as e^{ih} where h is hermitian. Further, we know that $\det(e^A) = e^{\operatorname{Tr}A}$. Thus the condition $\det \mathbf{U} = 1$ gives $\operatorname{Tr} h = 0$. Therefore to get the most general such matrix, we need to write down the general 3×3 hermitian matrix which is traceless. Any 3×3 matrix can be expanded in terms of a basis of 9 linearly independent matrices, since there are 9 slots or matrix elements in the matrix. One of them is the identity $\mathbb{1}$ which is not traceless. Dropping this, we can write

$$h = \sum_1^8 \frac{\lambda_a}{2} \theta_a \equiv t_a \theta_a \tag{13.28}$$

where λ_a are the basis matrices and θ_a are real numbers, eventually real-valued functions of the spacetime coordinates for a local symmetry. The index a takes values from 1 to 8, so there are 8 independent λ-matrices and 8 independent parameters. Such transformations will thus involve 8 different types of "rotations" in some internal space.

There are many ways to choose the basis matrices; a conventional choice is given by

$$\lambda_1 = \begin{pmatrix} 0 & 1 & 0 \\ 1 & 0 & 0 \\ 0 & 0 & 0 \end{pmatrix} \quad \lambda_2 = \begin{pmatrix} 0 & -i & 0 \\ i & 0 & 0 \\ 0 & 0 & 0 \end{pmatrix} \quad \lambda_3 = \begin{pmatrix} 1 & 0 & 0 \\ 0 & -1 & 0 \\ 0 & 0 & 0 \end{pmatrix}$$

$$\lambda_4 = \begin{pmatrix} 0 & 0 & 1 \\ 0 & 0 & 0 \\ 1 & 0 & 0 \end{pmatrix} \quad \lambda_5 = \begin{pmatrix} 0 & 0 & -i \\ 0 & 0 & 0 \\ i & 0 & 0 \end{pmatrix} \quad \lambda_6 = \begin{pmatrix} 0 & 0 & 0 \\ 0 & 0 & 1 \\ 0 & 1 & 0 \end{pmatrix}$$

$$\lambda_7 = \begin{pmatrix} 0 & 0 & 0 \\ 0 & 0 & -i \\ 0 & i & 0 \end{pmatrix} \quad \lambda_8 = \frac{1}{\sqrt{3}} \begin{pmatrix} 1 & 0 & 0 \\ 0 & 1 & 0 \\ 0 & 0 & -2 \end{pmatrix}. \tag{13.29}$$

These matrices are often referred to as the Gell-Mann matrices. Once we have them, we can calculate the commutator algebra

$$\left[t_a, t_b\right] = i f_{abc} t_c \tag{13.30}$$

The constants f_{abc} (usually called the structure constants of $SU(3)$) can be calculated explicitly. These are completely antisymmetric under the permutation of any two indices, so many of them are zero. The nonzero constants, up to permutations, are given in Table 13.1. The abstract $SU(3)$ algebra is thus given by

$$[T_a, T_b] = i\, f_{abc}\, T_c \tag{13.31}$$

with the same f_{abc} as listed in the table. The choice $T_a = \frac{1}{2}\lambda_a = t_a$ gives one (3-dimensional) representation of this algebra. Now we can ask the next question: Are there other representations of the same algebra? The answer, of course, is yes. There are infinite representations possible, they are not as simple as in the case of $SU(2)$. The representations are labeled by two integers p and q, with the dimension of the corresponding matrices given by

$$\dim(p, q) = \frac{(p+1)(q+1)(p+q+2)}{2} \tag{13.32}$$

The 3-dimensional representation we started with corresponds to $(p, q) = (1, 0)$. There is another distinct 3-dimensional representation usually denoted as $\mathbf{3^*}$, for which the t_a are given in terms of the transpose of the matrices for the 3-dimensional representation given above, i.e.,

$$(t_a)_{\mathbf{3^*}} = -(t_a)_{\mathbf{3}}^T \tag{13.33}$$

(The superscript T denotes the transpose of the matrix.) This corresponds to $(p, q) = (0, 1)$. Some of the other low dimensional representations have dimensions 6, 8 (which is $(1, 1)$ in the (p, q) notation), 10, 15, etc. We will not need to deal with most of these, but, just to give another example, the 8×8 matrices corresponding to the T_a are given by the f_{abc}'s themselves, i.e., T_a are taken as K_a given by $(K_a)_{bc} = -i f_{abc}$. These 8×8 matrices

Table 13.1: Structure constants of $SU(3)$

a b c	f_{abc}	a b c	f_{abc}	a b c	f_{abc}
1 2 3	1	2 4 6	$\frac{1}{2}$	3 6 7	$-\frac{1}{2}$
1 4 7	$\frac{1}{2}$	2 5 7	$\frac{1}{2}$	4 5 8	$\sqrt{3}/2$
1 5 6	$-\frac{1}{2}$	3 4 5	$\frac{1}{2}$	6 7 8	$\sqrt{3}/2$

are cumbersome to write down in full, but as an example, from the table of values for f_{abc}, we find

$$K_1 = -if_{1bc} = \begin{bmatrix} 0 & 0 & 0 & 0 & 0 & 0 & 0 & 0 \\ 0 & 0 & -i & 0 & 0 & 0 & 0 & 0 \\ 0 & i & 0 & 0 & 0 & 0 & 0 & 0 \\ 0 & 0 & 0 & 0 & 0 & 0 & -\frac{i}{2} & 0 \\ 0 & 0 & 0 & 0 & 0 & -\frac{i}{2} & 0 & 0 \\ 0 & 0 & 0 & 0 & \frac{i}{2} & 0 & 0 & 0 \\ 0 & 0 & 0 & \frac{i}{2} & 0 & 0 & 0 & 0 \\ 0 & 0 & 0 & 0 & 0 & 0 & 0 & 0 \end{bmatrix} \qquad (13.34)$$

Imagine now that we have two fields Φ and χ transforming as the 3-dimensional and 8-dimensional representations of $SU(3)$, respectively. By this we mean that Φ is a column vector with 3 entries, and χ can be thought of as a column vector with 8 entries. Thus the transformations we are interested in are

$$\Phi' = \left[\exp(i(\lambda_a/2)\theta_a)\right]\Phi, \qquad \chi' = \left[\exp(i(K_a\theta_a)\right]\chi \qquad (13.35)$$

We can now write down the covariant derivatives and the field strength. There are 8 types of vector gauge particles $\mathcal{A}_\mu^a$, corresponding to $a = 1, 2, \cdots, 8$. The expressions for the covariant derivatives are similar to what we have given before, except that we should use the specific forms of the matrices $\lambda_a/2$, K_a and the constants f_{abc}.

Remark 13.1.
A useful identity

Here is the basic identity we used,

$$\det\left(\exp(\mathbf{M})\right) = \exp\left(\mathrm{Tr}\,\mathbf{M}\right) \qquad (13.36)$$

We are interested in this identity for the case when $\mathbf{M}$ is diagonalizable. This is clearly the case when $\mathbf{M}$ is hermitian or i times a hermitian matrix, since any hermitian matrix can be diagonalized by a unitary transformation Λ as $\mathbf{M} = \Lambda\,\mathbf{M}_{diag}\,\Lambda^{-1}$, where $\mathbf{M}_{diag}$ is diagonal. Further $\mathrm{Tr}\,\Lambda\,\mathbf{M}_{diag}\,\Lambda^{-1} = \mathrm{Tr}\,\mathbf{M}_{diag}$ and also $\det(\Lambda\,\mathbf{M}_{diag}\,\Lambda^{-1}) = (\det\Lambda)(\det\mathbf{M}_{diag})(\det\Lambda^{-1}) = \det\mathbf{M}_{diag}$ using the rule $\det\mathbf{MN} = \det\mathbf{M}\det\mathbf{N}$ for two matrices $\mathbf{M}$, $\mathbf{N}$. Thus the identity (13.36) needs to be proved only for the case of diagonal matrices, the general result would then follow. If $\mathbf{M}$ is diagonal,

$$\mathbf{M}_{diag} = \begin{bmatrix} m_1 & 0 & 0... & ... \\ 0 & m_2 & 0 & ... \\ 0 & 0 & m_3 & ... \\ ... & ... & ... & ... \end{bmatrix}, \quad \exp(\mathbf{M}_{diag}) == \begin{bmatrix} e^{m_1} & 0 & 0... & ... \\ 0 & e^{m_2} & 0 & ... \\ 0 & 0 & e^{m_3} & ... \\ ... & ... & ... & ... \end{bmatrix} \quad (13.37)$$

We find trivially

$$\det \exp(\mathbf{M}_{diag}) = e^{m_1} e^{m_2} \cdots = \exp(\sum_i m_i), \qquad \mathrm{Tr}\, \mathbf{M}_{diag} = \sum_i m_i$$

$$(13.38)$$

thus proving the identity.

Remark 13.2.
Groups and physics

Groups are the basic mathematical structure for discussing symmetries in physics. A group G is defined as a set of elements with a composition law or multiplication law which obeys the following four requirements:

(1) Closure: If a, $b \in G$, then their composition $a\,b$ is also an element of G, i.e., $a\,b \in G$.

(2) Identity: There is an element of G, denoted by e, such that

$$e\,a = a\,e = a, \quad \text{for all } a \in G$$

(3) Inverse: For every $a \in G$, there is an element, denoted by a^{-1}, such that

$$a^{-1} a = a\,a^{-1} = e$$

(4) Associativity: The composition law is associative; i.e.,

$$a\,(b\,c) = (a\,b)\,c, \quad \text{for all } a, b, c \in G$$

Notice that we do not require commutativity; in general we can have $a\,b \neq b\,a$.

Let us concretize the notion of a group by looking at a couple of examples of groups. The set of elements $\mathbb{Z}_N = \{e^{2\pi i a/N}, a = 0, 1, \cdots, (N-1)\}$ forms a group under the standard multiplication law,

$$e^{2\pi i a/N}\, e^{2\pi i b/N} = e^{2\pi i (a+b)/N} \quad (13.39)$$

There are N distinct elements for this group; it is easy to verify that all requirements for a group are satisfied. $\mathbb{Z}_N$ is the cyclic group of order N. Another example is given by the set of matrices $\{\mathbf{M}(\theta), 0 \leq \theta < 2\pi\}$, with

$$\mathbf{M}(\theta) = \begin{bmatrix} \cos\theta & \sin\theta \\ -\sin\theta & \cos\theta \end{bmatrix} \tag{13.40}$$

(The point $\theta = 2\pi$ is identified with $\theta = 0$, since $\mathbf{M}$ has this periodicity.) The composition law is matrix multiplication. We can easily check by elementary trigonometric identities that

$$\mathbf{M}(\theta_1)\,\mathbf{M}(\theta_2) = \mathbf{M}(\theta_1 + \theta_2) \tag{13.41}$$

With $\mathbf{M}(0) = \mathbf{M}(2\pi) = \mathbb{1}$ (the identity matrix), we can check all the requirements for a group. Since a vector $\vec{v}$ in two dimensions transforms under rotations as

$$\begin{pmatrix} v_1' \\ v_2' \end{pmatrix} = \begin{bmatrix} \cos\theta & \sin\theta \\ -\sin\theta & \cos\theta \end{bmatrix} \begin{pmatrix} v_1 \\ v_2 \end{pmatrix} \tag{13.42}$$

where θ is the angle of rotation, we see that the set of rotations in two dimensions form a group. Rotations in higher dimensions also form a group. For an n-dimensional vector $\vec{v}$, we can write the transformation under rotations as

$$\vec{v}' = \mathbf{R}\,\vec{v} \tag{13.43}$$

where $\mathbf{R}$ is an $n \times n$ real matrix, and $\vec{v}$ is viewed as a column vector in (13.43). Since the length of a vector is preserved under rotations, the possible matrices $\mathbf{R}$ should obey the condition

$$\mathbf{R}^T\,\mathbf{R} = \mathbb{1} \tag{13.44}$$

where the superscript T denotes the transpose of the matrix. This says that $\mathbf{R}$ is a real orthogonal matrix. $\mathbf{M}(\theta)$ given in (13.40) is easily seen to be an orthogonal matrix. The property (13.41) shows that the multiplication of $\mathbf{M}(\theta)$ for different values of θ is commutative. But this property will not hold in higher dimensions in general. It is possible to parametrize $\mathbf{R}$ in terms of $n(n-1)/2$ angles, but generally for different values of parameters

$$\mathbf{R}(\{\theta\})\,\mathbf{R}(\{\theta'\}) \neq \mathbf{R}(\{\theta'\})\,\mathbf{R}(\{\theta\}) \tag{13.45}$$

Thus, while rotations in n dimensions form a group, it is not a commutative group.

Going back to $\mathbb{Z}_N$, notice that it has a discrete set of elements, while the group of rotations in any dimension has an infinite number of elements, with the elements parametrized by angles which can take on continuous values in some real interval. This shows by example that it is possible to have discrete groups and continuous groups. Generally the elements of the latter are parametrized by continuous parameters. The composition law takes the form

$$g_1(\{\theta\}) \, g_2(\{\theta'\}) = g(\{\alpha\}) \tag{13.46}$$

where g_1, g_2, $g \in G$ and parameters $\alpha = \alpha(\theta, \theta')$ are functions of the parameters θ, θ'.

There is a particular set of continuous groups which are important for us in physics. These are the so-called Lie groups. These are continuous groups which satisfy the additional conditions given below:

(1) The parameters $\alpha(\theta, \theta')$ are real analytic functions of $\{\theta\}$, $\{\theta'\}$.
(2) The parameters $\tilde{\theta}$ corresponding to the inverse, i.e., $\tilde{\theta}$ defined by $g(\{\tilde{\theta}\}) \, g(\{\theta\}) = \mathbb{1}$, are real analytic functions of $\{\theta\}$.

Because of these analyticity properties, both the algebraic and geometrical properties of Lie groups can be analyzed in great detail. The set of real orthogonal matrices in n dimensions (or the rotation group in n dimensions) is an example of a Lie group. Other examples include the set of $n \times n$ unitary matrices, the set of $2n \times 2n$ symplectic matrices, the five exceptional groups G_2, F_4, E_6, E_7, E_8. There are also variants obtained by complex continuations of the parameters; the set of Lorentz (velocity boost) transformations and the set of spatial rotations in n dimensions together form a group corresponding to a particular continuation of the rotation group in $(n + 1)$ dimensions. The whole subject is by now very mature and a large number of interesting and useful results have been obtained. We will not dwell on this further here, but rather, we shall conclude with some comments on the role of groups in physics.

Why are groups important for physics? Observables in physics are responses of the system under observation to physical transformations. We have already seen this in Lecture 3, where observables such as momentum, angular momentum, etc. correspond to translations, rotations, etc. These transformations do have a composition law (since many transformations can be done in sequence), the notion of the identity (equivalent to carrying out no transformation at all) and an inverse (taking us back to the original system). Further, in the quantum theory, all transformations are unitary transformations on the Hilbert space of states. Such linear transformations are associative. All conditions for a group are thus satisfied. In fact, we have a bit more: Every physically implementable transformation must be a unitary transformation,[3] which means that not only do we have the group structure, but we need a unitary representation of the action of the group. This is equivalent to saying that for every transformation we have a unitary operator which tells us how the Hilbert space responds to the transformation. We see from these observations that groups, both discrete and continuous, are central to physics. Examples of discrete groups include parity, charge conjugation, symmetry groups of crystals, molecules, etc. Continuous symmetries of physical interest include the Lorentz and Poincaré groups and internal symmetry groups, both global and local.

---

[3]The only exception is time-reversal, which is an anti-unitary transformation involving complex conjugation of the wave function. This can be treated as a special case in its own right.

Chapter 14

Back to Particles and the Strong Nuclear Force

We are now in a position to return to the discussion about particles and their interactions. Once again the fundamental particles, as we know them to date, are as listed in Table 1.1, which is reproduced here, as Table 14.1, for convenience. We should now consider the basic forces, all of which will be described by a gauge theory. In other words, we need to specify the type of symmetry transformations and what particles respond to them in what way. The forces of interest, putting aside gravity, are the electromagnetic forces, the strong nuclear force and the weak force. Of these, we have discussed the electromagnetic force to some extent and the weak force using the $V - A$ theory, although we know from the problem of rising cross sections that the $V - A$ theory has to be superseded by some more fundamental theory. The latter will turn out to have the Yang-Mills structure. The strong nuclear force, which will also be of the Yang-Mills type, is the simplest to formulate (although the hardest to analyze), so we will start with it.

The basic gauge symmetry of the strong nuclear force will be given by the set of 3×3 unitary matrices which are also special, i.e., have unit determinant. In other words, the gauge symmetry of strong nuclear forces is $SU(3)$. This is not something one can *a priori* arrive at by pure thought, it is the result of a lot of experimentation and correlation of experimental results. We will talk about some of these a little later. However, the moment we say that we have an $SU(3)$ symmetry, the dynamics can be readily constructed. From what we have discussed before, it is almost entirely algorithmic. Thus we can say that the unitary matrix $\mathbf{U}$ of such a transformation can be written in terms of the λ-matrices we introduced before,

$$\mathbf{U}(x) = \exp\left(it_a\theta_a(x)\right), \qquad t_a = \frac{\lambda_a}{2} \tag{14.1}$$

Further, the commutation rules are of the form $[t_a, t_b] = i f_{abc} t_c$, with f_{abc} given in the last lecture. Also, we can immediately say that the force must be mediated by a set of vector particles A_μ^a, with $a = 1, 2, \cdots, 8$, so that there are 8 types of these particles. They are called gluons, a somewhat unimaginative word derived from "glue", since they are the force carriers responsible for binding quarks together to form the proton, neutron, etc., i.e, they are the glue holding nuclei together. The field strength for the field A_μ^a is given by

$$F_{\mu\nu}^a = \partial_\mu A_\nu^a - \partial_\nu A_\mu^a + g_s f_{abc} A_\mu^b A_\nu^c \tag{14.2}$$

where g_s is a constant, the coupling constant, which has a role similar to what e, the charge of the electron, plays in electrodynamics. It is the basic unit in which we measure the "charge" or quantum number corresponding to the strong nuclear forces. The dynamics of the field A_μ^a is given by the Yang-Mills action

$$
\begin{aligned}
S = -\frac{1}{4} &\int d^4x \; F_{\mu\nu}^a F^{a\,\mu\nu} \\
= -\frac{1}{4} &\int d^4x \; \Big[(\partial_\mu A_\nu^a - \partial_\nu A_\mu^a)(\partial^\mu A^{a\nu} - \partial^\nu A^{a\mu}) \\
&+ 2\, g_s f_{abc}(\partial_\mu A_\nu^a - \partial_\nu A_\mu^a) A^{b\mu} A^{c\nu} \\
&+ g_s^2 f_{abc} f_{amn} A_\mu^b A_\nu^c A^{m\mu} A^{n\nu} \Big]
\end{aligned}
\tag{14.3}
$$

Notice that the first set of terms which are quadratic in A_μ^a and involve the square of $(\partial_\mu A_\nu^a - \partial_\nu A_\mu^a)$ is like the Maxwell action, except that there are 8 copies of it (and, in terms of the physics, A_μ^a is not the electromagnetic field). So from our experience with the Maxwell action, we can expect the propagator for the gluons to be

$$D_{\mu\nu}^{ab}(x, y) = -\delta^{ab} \eta_{\mu\nu} \int \frac{d^4k}{(2\pi)^4} e^{-ik(x-y)} \frac{i}{k^2 + i\epsilon} \tag{14.4}$$

The cubic and quartic terms in (14.3) show that, unlike the photons, the gluons can directly interact with themselves. There is a basic cubic vertex and a quartic vertex which may be represented as shown in the diagram, Fig. 14.1. Higher order processes can be constructed, as usual, by combining vertices and making internal gluon lines by replacing two A's by the propagator.

Next we turn to the matter fields. One important fact is that, at the fundamental level, the leptons do not respond to strong nuclear forces. In other words, the leptons or the fields corresponding to them do not change under a gauge transformation corresponding to the strong nuclear force.

Table 14.1: List of fundamental particles

Type	Species			Spin	Electric charge
Leptons	e	μ	τ	$\frac{1}{2}$	-1
	ν_e	ν_μ	ν_τ	$\frac{1}{2}$	0
Quarks	u	c	t	$\frac{1}{2}$	$\frac{2}{3}$
	d	s	b	$\frac{1}{2}$	$-\frac{1}{3}$
Force Carriers	γ (Photon)			1	0
	$W^\pm$			1	±1
	Z^0			1	0
	g (Gluons, 8 types)			1	0
	Graviton			2	0
Condensate	H (Higgs)			0	0

So if ℓ represents any one of the leptons, $\ell \to \ell$ when we make such a gauge transformation. This means that we do not have to write a covariant derivative for the leptons involving the A^a_μ for the strong interactions.

The quarks, however, do respond to strong nuclear forces. Each quark has 3 internal states which can be rotated or transformed into each other by the gauge transformation of strong nuclear forces, i.e., by a transformation of the type (14.1). In addition, recall that quarks are spin-$\frac{1}{2}$ particles, so their wave functions (or fields) are given as Dirac spinors, a column vector with 4 entries, on which the γ-matrices act by matrix multiplication. Thus we may represent the field of an up-quark by the symbol $u^i_r(x)$, where

Fig. 14.1: The basic vertices for gluon-gluon interaction

$i = 1, 2, 3$ and $r = 1, 2, 3, 4$. The label i counts the internal states for the strong nuclear force while r denotes the spinor element. The internal quantum number for strong forces is called "color". (It has nothing at all to do with color as we observe everyday; it is just a name.) For this reason, the theory of strong nuclear forces is often referred to as quantum chromodynamics or QCD for short. (In a similar strain of naming things, the different species of quarks are called different "flavors". Thus the up-quark and the down-quark and the strange-quark and so on are different flavors of the quark.) The gauge transformation on the up-quark can be written as

$$u_r^i(x) \rightarrow (u_r^i)'(x) = \mathbf{U}^i{}_j(x)\, u_r^j(x) \tag{14.5}$$

Notice that the spinor label is not touched by this. This transformation means that we have to use covariant derivatives in place of ordinary derivatives for the up-quark. This is given by

$$(D_\mu u)_r^i = \partial_\mu u_r^i - i g_s\, A_\mu^a\, (t_a)^i{}_j\, u_r^j, \qquad t_a = \frac{\lambda_a}{2} \tag{14.6}$$

Thus in place of the usual Dirac action $\bar{u}(i\gamma^\mu \partial_\mu)u$, we must use the action

$$
\begin{aligned}
S_{up} &= \int d^4x\; \bar{u}_r^i\, i\, (\gamma^\mu)_{rs} \left(\partial_\mu u_s^i - i g_s\, A_\mu^a (t_a)^i{}_j\, u_s^j \right) \\
&= \int d^4x\; \bar{u}\, (i\gamma^\mu \partial_\mu)\, u + g_s \int d^4x\; (\bar{u}\, \gamma^\mu\, t_a\, u)\, A_\mu^a
\end{aligned} \tag{14.7}
$$

We have ignored the mass of the up-quark for now. The first term shows that the propagator and wave functions for the free up-quark are as before, see Lecture 10. The second term shows that the basic quark-gluon interaction is represented by the vertex shown in Fig. 14.2. The vertex carries a factor of g_s, a γ-matrix and a factor of t_a. The situation for all species of quarks (or for all "flavors" of quarks), is the same. The strong forces do not distinguish between different flavors of quarks. Thus for the down-quark we may write

$$S_{down} = \int d^4x\; \bar{d}\, (i\gamma^\mu \partial_\mu)\, d + g_s \int d^4x\; (\bar{d}\, \gamma^\mu\, t_a\, d)\, A_\mu^a \tag{14.8}$$

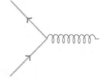

Fig. 14.2: The basic vertex for quark-gluon interaction

There is a similar term for the strange-quark, the charm-quark and so on.

It is also useful to write down the classical equations of motion for the gauge field. Combining the quark part of the action with the Yang-Mills action in (14.3), and carrying out the variation of $A^{a\nu}$, we find

$$\partial^\mu F_{a\mu\nu} + g_s f_{abc} A^{b\mu} F^c_{\mu\nu} + g_s \sum_\alpha \bar{Q}^\alpha \gamma_\nu t_a Q_\alpha = 0 \qquad (14.9)$$

where the summation over α indicates the sum over all flavors of quarks, with $Q_1 = u$, $Q_2 = d$, etc. The time-component of this equation is the QCD analogue of the Gauss law and reads

$$\partial^i F_{ai0} + g_s f_{abc} A^{bi} F^c_{i0} + g_s \sum_\alpha \bar{Q}^\alpha \gamma_0 t_a Q_\alpha = 0 \qquad (14.10)$$

F_{i0} is part of the initial data needed for solving the equations of motion. So the Gauss law is not a true Heisenberg equation of motion since it lacks the time-derivative of the dynamical variables at a given time, i.e., the initial data. It must be understood as a condition which the initial data must satisfy. However, a classical analysis is inadequate for QCD, since the quantum corrections are significant. This is highlighted by the property of asymptotic freedom which is our next topic.

Asymptotic freedom and the confinement of quarks

Quantum Chromodynamics, the theory given by the actions (14.3, 14.7, 14.8, etc.) looks very similar, at least at the level of the action, to electrodynamics, apart from some complications due to matrices. But the interactions play out in a very different way and the physical consequences are dramatically different. First of all, as we noted earlier, there is direct gluon-gluon interaction, unlike the case with photons. (While photons can scatter against photons, this requires either a material medium or if it occurs in the vacuum, it is a higher order quantum process mediated by virtual charged particle pairs.) This means that if we consider the scattering of two quarks via the gluon exchange, diagrammatically shown by the first term in Fig. 14.3, there are corrections of the type shown in the subsequent terms. Some of these subsequent terms, involving loops of quarks, are similar to what happens in electrodynamics but the diagrams involving direct gluon loops are the new ones for QCD. The mathematical expression for the first term in Fig. 14.3 can be read off from the diagram and the expression for the gluon propagator as

$$\mathcal{A} = -(2\pi)^4 \delta^{(4)}(q + k - q')\, \bar{u}(p - k)\gamma^\mu t_a u(p) \left[\frac{i\, g_s^2}{k^2 + i\epsilon} \right] \bar{u}(q')\gamma_\mu t_a u(q)$$

$$(14.11)$$

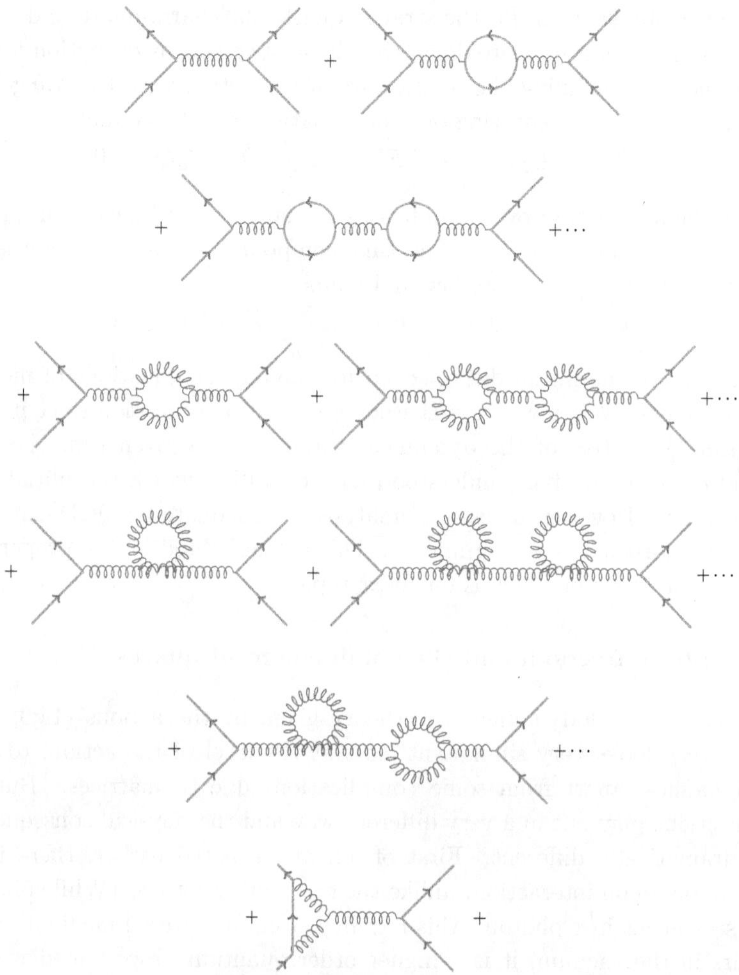

Fig. 14.3: Some of the diagrams contributing to quark-quark scattering

where we take incoming quarks of momenta p, q and outgoing quarks of momenta $p' = p - k$ and q'; so k is the momentum transferred by the gluon from one quark to the other. The higher order terms can also be written down in a similar way, although the algebraic complexity increases quite rapidly.

As mentioned above, some of the diagrams for the higher order corrections are similar to the ones contributing to the analogous process in electrodynamics, say, electron-electron scattering. These are shown in Fig. 14.4. In that case, we have argued that the higher corrections are small because they have additional factors of e^2 from the extra vertices and $(e^2/4\pi) \approx (1/137)$. So, by a similar reasoning, the question of whether the higher terms in QCD are small depends on the value of $g_s^2/4\pi$. Now, one can sum up a particular infinite sequence of higher order corrections, basically the ones shown in Fig. 14.3. (There is a particular kinematic regime of the last diagram (and a sequence related to it) which mimic a propagator correction; this has to be included as well.) The result may be expressed as follows. The amplitude has the same form as in (14.11), but we replace g_s^2 by a k-dependent factor (which is the result of the summation of the series of diagrams). In other words,

$$\mathcal{A} = -(2\pi)^4 \delta^{(4)}(q + k - q') \, \bar{u}(p - k)\gamma^\mu t_a u(p) \left[\frac{i \, g_s^2(k)}{k^2 + i\epsilon} \right] \bar{u}(q')\gamma_\mu t_a u(q)$$

$$(14.12)$$

where

$$\alpha_s(k) \equiv \frac{g_s^2(k)}{4\pi} = \frac{12\,\pi}{(33 - 2N_f) \log(k^2/\Lambda_{QCD}^2)} \tag{14.13}$$

Here Λ_{QCD} is a constant with the dimensions of mass; it is approximately 150 MeV from experimental data. N_f is the number of flavors of quarks with masses much less than k. Since the quark masses are approximately $m_u \approx 3\,\text{MeV}$, $m_d \approx 4\,\text{MeV}$, $m_s \simeq 130\,\text{MeV}$, $m_c \simeq 1.2\,\text{GeV}$, $m_b \simeq 5\,\text{GeV}$ and $m_t \simeq 175\,\text{GeV}$, this means that for momentum transfers of the order of 100 GeV, $N_f = 5$.

The formula (14.13) shows that, for the scattering, it is as if we can neglect the higher corrections to the scattering, calculate the lowest order

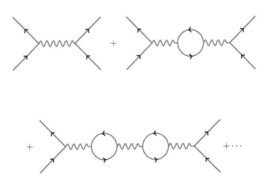

Fig. 14.4: Some of the diagrams contributing to electron-electron scattering

result, but use an effective (k-dependent) coupling $g_s(k)$ instead of just g_s. This reorganizes the discussion of various terms into a simpler framework. It should be kept in mind that $g_s(k)$ is a shorthand notation for a k-dependent factor. Nevertheless, this quantity $g_s^2(k)$ is often referred to by the oxymoronic name "running coupling constant". (The truly constant coupling constant g_s has been absorbed into the parameter Λ_{QCD} in (14.13).) This result is very important. It shows that if we consider processes at higher and higher values of energy or momentum transfer, the logarithm in the denominator becomes larger and larger and hence the effective value of the coupling becomes smaller. Thus for processes at high momenta, we can use perturbation theory and restrict ourselves to a small set of diagrams. It is in this way, by doing scattering experiments at very high momentum transfers and comparing against the predictions of the theory, that we believe that QCD, as given by the actions (14.3, 14.7, 14.8, etc.), is the correct theory for strong nuclear forces. The result (14.13) says that we approach an almost free theory at very high energies, with the effective coupling constant going to zero, although the approach is very slow because it is only logarithmic. Hence the result (14.13) is referred to as asymptotic freedom. Its discovery in 1973 independently by Gross and Wilczek, and by Politzer was the key to the modern theory of nuclear forces.

The formula for the effective coupling (14.13) has been verified in a number of experiments. Since the formula is valid at high energies where perturbation theory can be used, it can be checked in high energy scattering experiments. The result for the cross section can be fit into the formula predicted by perturbative QCD. One can then extract the effective coupling. The result is shown in the graph (Fig. 14.6).

The contrast with quantum electrodynamics (QED) is also very useful.

Fig. 14.5: The single diagram equivalent to the series of diagrams shown in Fig. 14.3. The shaded circle indicates that the vertex carries a k-dependent function $g_s(k)$ rather than just g_s. The γ^μ factor and the t_a are as before.

If we consider the diagrams in Fig. 14.4 and sum them up in a similar way, we can express that result also in terms of a running coupling constant. We find

$$\mathcal{A} = -(2\pi)^4 \delta^{(4)}(q + k - q')\, \bar{e}(p - k)\gamma^\mu e(p) \left[\frac{i\, e^2(k)}{k^2 + i\epsilon}\right] \bar{e}(q')\gamma_\mu e(q) \quad (14.14)$$

where

$$\frac{e^2(k)}{4\pi} = \frac{\alpha_e}{1 - (\alpha_e/3\pi)\,\log(k^2/m_e^2)} \quad (14.15)$$

with $\alpha_e = e^2/4\pi \approx (1/137)$ and m_e is the mass of the electron. In this case, as k increases, the denominator becomes small, and the effective coupling increases, exactly the opposite behavior to QCD. (There is a singularity at $k = m_e \exp(3\pi/2\alpha_e) \approx m_e \times 10^{280}$, but QED is superseded by a more comprehensive theory, namely, the Standard Model, long before we get to such energy scales, so we do not need to worry about the singularity.)

There is an obverse side to asymptotic freedom. Starting from a high value of k^2, if we consider smaller and smaller values of the momentum

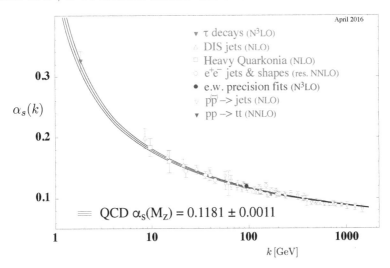

Fig. 14.6: The graph of the effective coupling $\alpha_s(k)$ as a function of the momentum transfer k, from various experiments. Depending on the process, the theoretical calculations used to extract α_s include, in addition to the lowest (or leading) order results, higher order corrections to the next-to-leading order (NLO), to the next-to-next-to leading order (NNLO), etc. Note that the scale for k is logarithmic. Quoted from: C. Patrignani *et al.* (Particle Data Group), Chin. Phys. C, **40**, 100001 (2016).

transfer, the coupling constant becomes larger and larger, eventually becoming infinite at $k^2 = \Lambda^2_{QCD}$. Of course, long before we get to that, we have to abandon (14.13), since we would no longer be within the regime of validity for expansion in powers of the coupling constant. So the possibility of understanding the low energy structure of QCD by perturbation theory is quashed by this. The interaction between quarks becomes stronger at low energies.

We can also rephrase this in terms of the separation between the quarks. Since momenta and distances are in reciprocal relationship (via the uncertainty principle), asymptotic freedom means that the interquark potential at very short separations is well approximated by a Coulomb-like $1/r$ potential. (This is, after all, the result to the lowest order in perturbation theory where all gluon-gluon interactions can be ignored, so the theory looks very much like electrodynamics.) As we increase the distance between the quarks, the effective coupling grows and the Coulombic form is no longer obtained. We cannot, from perturbation theory, say anything definite about what the potential might look like, but there are indications that it becomes linearly increasing. Strictly speaking, even the description in terms of potentials is not sensible for the light quarks since they tend to have large kinetic energies compared to their mass. But for the heavy quarks this statement makes sense. For such cases, one can approximate the potential energy between a quark and an antiquark by

$$V(r) = -\frac{4}{3}\frac{\alpha_s}{r} + \sigma r \tag{14.16}$$

where α_s is given by (14.13) with $k^2 \approx m_q^2$. (The factor of 4/3 arises from the charge matrices $\lambda_a/2$ for the quarks.) The long distance behavior is dominated by the term proportional to the separation r; the coefficient of the linear term, namely σ, is known as the string tension, because a string at a fixed tension σ would have energy proportional to its length. Pictorially, we can visualize this as a string (or a strand of lines of force of the gluonic field) stretching between the quark and the antiquark, not spreading out as in electrodynamics but collimated into a narrow strand, as illustrated in Fig. 14.7.

One consequence of this behavior is the *confinement of quarks*. Consider, for example, a quark-antiquark pair interacting via gluon exchange, say, forming a bound state. Imagine that we want to isolate a single quark and we try to do so by pulling one particle away from the other, a process schematically illustrated in Fig. 14.8. This means giving energy to the $q\bar{q}$

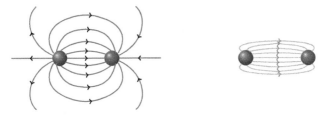

Fig. 14.7: The lines of force for a pair of equal and opposite electric charges is shown on the left. In QCD, the lines of force are squeezed into almost a linear bundle connecting the quark and the antiquark, as shown on the right.

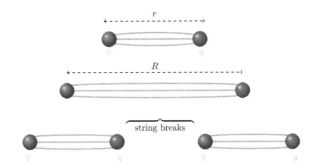

Fig. 14.8: Schematic representation of the attempt to isolate a single quark by pulling off one particle from a $q\bar{q}$ bound state, which leads to the stretching of the strand of lines of force, with the string breaking by pair creation.

system in some fashion, since we need to supply the extra potential energy needed to keep the particles at a larger separation. As we keep on doing this, the potential energy stored in the system increases with separation and there comes a point when this potential energy becomes greater than the energy required to create a $q\bar{q}$ pair spontaneously. This would happen at some separation R such that $V(R) \gtrsim 2\,m_q$. Then, by quantum fluctuations, a $q\bar{q}$ pair can be created, with the potential energy converted to the masses of the quarks. The "string" breaks and we have two sets of $q\bar{q}$ combinations. (In fact this would be the energetically preferred state compared to a single $q\bar{q}$ pair at a separation larger than R.) Our attempt to isolate a single quark would thus fail. Quarks are permanently in bound states with antiquarks (or some combination of quarks), a single isolated quark is not obtainable in any simple way.

There is one possibility of getting beyond this though. At a finite nonzero temperature, the strings connecting the quark and the antiquark, become weaker. The string tension becomes a function of temperature and can go to zero at some high enough temperature, liberating the quarks. The required temperature is of the order of Λ_{QCD}, around 150 MeV or so. This is not obtained even in the core of stars, but was possible at the very early stages of the universe, shortly after the Big Bang. It is also possible to obtain such temperatures for a very short time, in a very small region, in high energy collisions of heavy nuclei. This has been achieved at the Relativistic Heavy Ion Collider (RHIC) at Brookhaven. The resulting plasma of quarks and gluons, a new phase of matter, has been an interesting and important object of study.

Chapter 15

More on Quantum Chromodynamics (QCD)

We have talked about QCD, the theory of strong nuclear forces and its property of asymptotic freedom with the effective coupling decreasing at high energies or short separations, in contrast to quantum electrodynamics. We also discussed the notion of quark confinement which is crucial in understanding the bound states of quarks such as mesons and baryons. It also explains why we do not see free quarks, despite long and careful searches carried out in the 1960s and 1970s. The theory is described by an $SU(3)$ symmetry. Thus there are 8 types of "gluons" interacting with the quarks, each species (or flavor) of quark having 3 colors or internal states. The action for the quarks is obtained from the Dirac action by the gauge principle, specifically using $SU(3)$ symmetry. For example, for the up-quark, the action is

$$S_{\text{up}} = \int d^4x \; \bar{u}_p^i \, i \, (\gamma^\mu)_{pr} \left(\partial_\mu u_r^i - i g_s \, A_\mu^a (t_a)^i_{\ j} \, u_r^j \right)$$

$$= \int d^4x \; \bar{u} \, (i\gamma^\mu \partial_\mu) \, u + g_s \int d^4x \; (\bar{u} \, \gamma^\mu \, t_a \, u) \, A_\mu^a \qquad (15.1)$$

where the index i, j take values $1, 2, 3$, corresponding to the 3 color states of the up-quark, $p, r \; (= 1, \cdots, 4)$ denote spinor labels and A_μ^a, $a = 1, 2, \cdots, 8$, represent the gluons, and $t_a = \lambda_a/2$. (The λ-matrices were given in (13.29) in Lecture 13.)

We must now elaborate on the dynamics of quarks to see how bound states are built up. We know that we cannot have free quarks, so they must get bound in some fashion, forming composite particles. For analyzing this, we first augment the action (15.1) with the other quarks to obtain

$$S_{\text{quark}} = \int d^4x \; \left[\bar{u} \, (i\gamma^\mu \partial_\mu) \, u + \bar{d} \, (i\gamma^\mu \partial_\mu) \, d + \bar{s} \, (i\gamma^\mu \partial_\mu) \, s \right.$$

$$\left. + \bar{c} \, (i\gamma^\mu \partial_\mu) \, c + \bar{b} \, (i\gamma^\mu \partial_\mu) \, b + \bar{t} \, (i\gamma^\mu \partial_\mu) \, t \right]$$

$$+ g_s \int d^4x \left[\bar{u} \gamma^\mu t_a u + \bar{d} \gamma^\mu t_a d + \bar{s} \gamma^\mu t_a s \right.$$

$$\left. + \bar{c} \gamma^\mu t_a c + \bar{b} \gamma^\mu t_a b + \bar{t} \gamma^\mu t_a t \right] A_\mu^a$$

$$- \int d^4x \left[m_u \bar{u}u + m_d \bar{d}d + m_s \bar{s}s + m_c \bar{c}c + m_b \bar{b}b + m_t \bar{t}t \right]$$

$$(15.2)$$

We have also put in the quark mass terms. The quark mass terms arise from weak interactions, as we will see in later lectures, but, for now, we just add them in. Notice also that the coupling of the gluons to the quarks is insensitive to the flavor of the quark; all flavors (u, d, s, c, b, t) couple the same way with the same coupling constant.

This may be a good place to bring up an issue we have alluded to before. What is the evidence for three color states for each quark? There are several pieces of evidence. One is related to the decay process of the neutral pion, $\pi^0 \to 2\gamma$, another is related to the existence of the Ω^- baryon which we will consider briefly later. A third piece of evidence is related to the so-called R-ratio. For any strong interaction process we consider, there will be complications due to gluon interactions which are hard to calculate. A part of the theory where these are not important would involve weak and electromagnetic processes, so they may be a good way to probe for certain properties of the quarks. Quarks have electric charge, so they can be pair-produced in e^+e^- collisions. This is an electromagnetic process, the basic diagram is what is shown in Fig. 15.1. The vertices give a factor of the electric charges of the electron and the quark, so that the amplitude is proportional to q_f, the charge of the particular flavor of quark being considered. The cross section will depend on q_f^2. There are kinematic factors involving masses and so on, but if we take the ratio

$$R = \frac{\sigma(e^+e^- \to q\bar{q})}{\sigma(e^+e^- \to \mu^+\mu^-)} \qquad (15.3)$$

the kinematic factors will cancel out at energies much higher than the quark and muon masses. The total cross section will depend on how many quarks we have. Thus

$$R = \sum_f q_f^2 \qquad (15.4)$$

The idea is to consider this as a function of the center of mass energy of the e^+e^-. As we increase the energy, we pass the threshold for producing each type of quark. Thus for relatively low energies we will find $R =$

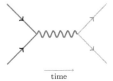

time

Fig. 15.1: The production of a $q\bar{q}$ pair from e^+e^- annihilation

$q_u^2 + q_d^2 = 5/9$, then as we go above the strange quark mass, we will find $R = q_u^2 + q_d^2 + q_s^2 = 6/9$ and then $R = q_u^2 + q_d^2 + q_s^2 + q_c^2 = 10/9$. There will be some variations for some energies due to resonances, due to the fact that we cannot really neglect mass effects near where we cross the threshold for each quark, and so on, but the average values of R at energies significantly above thresholds should be these values. When it is experimentally measured we find 3 times the values given here, namely, 5/3, 6/3, 10/3. If there are 3 internal states (the 3 color states) for each quark, this is naturally explained.

Returning to the main line of reasoning, we can now restate the concept of quark confinement in a more precise fashion as follows.

Prop 15.1 (Color Confinement). All physical states of quarks and gluons are invariant under the $SU(3)$ color transformations.[1]

This is actually a result we would like to prove. After all, we claim we have the correct theory, the action for which is given by (15.2) with the addition of the action for A_μ^a given in (14.3). Thus quark confinement should be a derivable result. Having said that, no one has succeeded in doing so, to date. The theory is strongly coupled at low momentum transfers between particles and therefore not susceptible to perturbation theory; this is the price of asymptotic freedom, as we have already seen. And it is precisely for low momentum transfers, which corresponds to large separations, where

---

[1]Here we mean *all* color transformations, including those transformations which are constant in space-time. The principle of gauge invariance as implemented on the states in the quantum theory guarantees that all physical states are invariant under color transformations which become the identity transformation at infinity. This is because the physically admissible wave functions Ψ can be shown to satisfy the gauge invariance (or Gauss law, see (14.10)) requirement

$$\exp\left[i \int d^3x \left(-\partial^i\theta^a \, F_{ai0} + g_s f_{abc}\theta^a A_i^b F_{i0}^c + g_s\theta^a \sum \bar{Q}^\alpha \gamma_0 t_a Q_\alpha\right)\right] \Psi = \Psi,$$

for parameters $\theta^a(x)$ which vanish at spatial infinity. The statement of confinement goes beyond that- the states must be invariant even for parameters θ^a which do not vanish at spatial infinity.

one could contemplate separating particles far from each other to obtain isolated quarks. So this is the kinematic regime relevant for the question of confinement. And for this, we do not have a clean-cut answer. (This problem, or a slight restatement of it, is one of the millennium problems put forward by the Clay Mathematics Institute, with a prize of $1000000. It also appears on the physicists' list of millennium problems.)

In the absence of any simple solution, physicists have tried a number of different approaches, primarily taking confinement as a working ansatz and analyzing the properties of the strongly interacting particles obtained as bound states of quarks and gluons. Nevertheless, it is a highly nonperturbative problem and approximation methods are necessary. For a first level of understanding, the simplest strategy is to use symmetry for the low mass quarks and the Schrödinger equation for the higher mass quarks. The masses of the quarks are approximately $m_u \approx 3\,\text{MeV}$, $m_d \approx 4\,\text{MeV}$, $m_s \simeq 100\,\text{MeV}$, $m_c \simeq 1.2\,\text{GeV}$, $m_b \simeq 5\,\text{GeV}$ and $m_t \simeq 175\,\text{GeV}$. The mass of a baryon, say, the proton which is made of three quarks, is about 1 GeV, so that the binding energy, which is related to the kinetic energy of the bound quarks is about $300\,\text{MeV}$ per quark. Thus the motion of the up, down and strange quarks in a bound state is relativistic. In bound states, the charm, bottom and top quarks may be considered as nonrelativistic. Therefore, for the bound states of the c, b and t quarks, we can use a potential model, a far from perfect but reasonable description; the potential for this may be taken as the Coulomb plus linear form given in (14.16),

$$V(r) = -\frac{4}{3}\frac{\alpha_s}{r} + \sigma r \qquad (15.5)$$

A Schrödinger equation can be used since the quarks are nonrelativistic and the concept of potential makes sense nonrelativistically. Thus the bound state spectrum of c and $\bar{c}$ may be found by solving

$$\left[-\frac{\nabla^2}{2\,\mu_c} - \frac{4}{3}\frac{\alpha_s}{r} + \sigma r\right]\psi = E\,\psi \qquad (15.6)$$

with the mass of the bound state as $M = 2\,m_c + E$. ($\mu_c = [m_c m_c/(m_c + m_c)] = \frac{1}{2}m_c$ is the reduced mass of the quark-antiquark system.) The $c\bar{c}$ bound states generally are designated as the ψ particle (or as the J/ψ because the two groups which found it used the two names J and ψ.) Being bound states with a spherically symmetric potential, the states are classified by angular momentum; thus there are $\psi(1S)$, $\psi(2S)$, $\chi_{c1}(1P)$, etc. For the bottom quark, the bound states are called the Υ states. (The letter is capital upsilon of the Greek alphabet.) A lot of research on the energy levels (or masses) of these states and on the transitions between them has been done. The spectroscopy of the $c\bar{c}$ and $b\bar{b}$ bound states is quite well understood by now. However, we will not discus the bound states of the heavier quarks in any more detail in these lectures.

For relativistic particle motion, which is needed for the light quarks, the concept of a potential does not make sense, something we have talked about before. Retardation effects, vectorial nature of the interactions, etc., are important. There is a theoretical framework for relativistic bound states, but it becomes too complicated because corrections from higher order effects are also crucial. We cannot use a perturbative formula for the various propagators involved. So the workable approach has been to use symmetries again. We will discuss this shortly.

There are also bound states with one heavy quark and one light quark. These go by the names D-mesons ($D^0 \sim c\bar{u}$, $D^+ \sim c\bar{d}$, $D_s^+ \sim c\bar{s}$), B-mesons ($B^0 \sim d\bar{b}$, $B^+ \sim u\bar{b}$), etc. These are problematic because the light quark has relativistic motion. Again, a potential description is not adequate and the analysis goes through a combination of symmetry and bound state technology. These too, we will not discuss further.

Another approach to QCD uses the so-called lattice gauge theory. The idea here is to approximate spacetime by a lattice of points, finite in number, say, N. The lattice can be taken to be hypercubic (4-dimensional cubic lattice) for simplicity, with a spacing between them given by some distance a. We can then formulate the theory on such a lattice. The problem now reduces to a finite number of degrees of freedom and numerical calculations on a computer can be done. In the limit of $N \to \infty$ and the lattice spacing $a \to 0$, we can recover continuous space-time. The real issue is how large N should be and how small a should be to get a sensible or believable approximation. With the best supercomputers of the day running over a reasonable amount of time, we can do a lattice which is approximately of size $(64)^4$ (64 points in each direction), with some leeway in how the points are split between the temporal and spatial directions. (This can help to optimize certain calculations.) This is hardly the infinity we need, but for certain quantities, by clever use of statistical techniques, we can extrapolate to the limit. For example, for some quantities, the lattice spacing can be reduced to the equivalent of 0.09×10^{-15} m, which is remarkably small. The method has been very successful, in terms of calculating the masses of various low mass mesons and baryons. It has also been possible to calculate some of the transition matrix elements for decay processes for mesons. Even so, the large majority of quantities are still being calculated. In the long run, this may end up as the most reliable way to get numbers. But to formulate the problem on the lattice and understand which combinations of fields one must use for which calculation, we still need to develop the concepts as we do later in this lecture and the next.

There is also a large body of literature attempting direct analytical calculations. These include:

- summing up large numbers of Feynman diagrams, via nonlinear coupled equations for fully nonperturbative propagators and vertices (Schwinger-Dyson equations)

- calculating properties of the infinite dimensional space of field configurations

- comparing to other simpler theories such as supersymmetric theories which have more fields but are simpler to analyze because of the larger symmetries (and which we hope still have features similar to QCD).

Another interesting technique is to consider QCD with an arbitrary number, say N_c, of colors and study the large N_c limit. There are convincing arguments that the theory will simplify in this limit, although solving the limit theory has so far been unsuccessful. Nevertheless, some properties of the large N_c limit seem to hold in real QCD with $N_c = 3$, so one can use the limit theory as a guide to making simpler models which apply in certain kinematic regimes and for particular observables.

These techniques are beyond the scope of these lectures.

The bound states of the light quarks

Let us now talk about the light quarks and how we might get some idea of their bound states using symmetry arguments. For the u, d, s quarks, the action becomes

$$S_{u,d,s} = \int d^4x \left[\bar{u} \left(i\gamma^\mu \partial_\mu \right) u + \bar{d} \left(i\gamma^\mu \partial_\mu \right) d + \bar{s} \left(i\gamma^\mu \partial_\mu \right) s \right]$$

$$+ g_s \int d^4x \left[\bar{u} \gamma^\mu t_a u + \bar{d} \gamma^\mu t_a d + \bar{s} \gamma^\mu t_a s \right] A_\mu^a$$

$$- \int d^4x \left[m_u \bar{u}u + m_d \bar{d}d + m_s \bar{s}s \right] \tag{15.7}$$

Our first observation is that we can write this down as

$$S_{u,d,s} = \int d^4x \left(\mathcal{L}_1 + \mathcal{L}_2 \right)$$

$$\mathcal{L}_1 = \begin{pmatrix} \bar{u} & \bar{d} & \bar{s} \end{pmatrix} \begin{bmatrix} i\gamma^\mu D_\mu & 0 & 0 \\ 0 & i\gamma^\mu D_\mu & 0 \\ 0 & 0 & i\gamma^\mu D_\mu \end{bmatrix} \begin{pmatrix} u \\ d \\ s \end{pmatrix}$$

$$\mathcal{L}_2 = - \begin{pmatrix} \bar{u} & \bar{d} & \bar{s} \end{pmatrix} \begin{bmatrix} m_u & 0 & 0 \\ 0 & m_d & 0 \\ 0 & 0 & m_s \end{bmatrix} \begin{pmatrix} u \\ d \\ s \end{pmatrix} \qquad (15.8)$$

where $D_\mu = \partial_\mu - ig_s A_\mu^a t_a$. Notice that each entry in the square matrix is a 12×12 matrix. For $\gamma^\mu \partial_\mu$ we have the product of the 4×4 γ-matrices and the 3×3 identity for color, for $\gamma^\mu A_\mu^a t_a$ we have the γ's with the t_a and for the mass terms we have a 12×12 identity matrix for each entry in the square matrix. We can make the expressions more compact and show a new approximate symmetry by introducing the notation Q_α, $\alpha = 1, 2, 3$, with $Q_1 = u$, $Q_2 = d$, $Q_3 = s$, thus considering the three flavors as components of a single quark field Q. The terms in (15.8) become

$$\mathcal{L}_1 + \mathcal{L}_2 = \bar{Q}^\alpha (i\gamma^\mu D_\mu) Q_\alpha - \bar{Q}^\alpha M_\alpha^{\ \beta} Q_\beta$$

$$M = \begin{bmatrix} m_u & 0 & 0 \\ 0 & m_d & 0 \\ 0 & 0 & m_s \end{bmatrix} \qquad (15.9)$$

The key point is that the covariant derivative $D_\mu = \partial_\mu - ig_s A_\mu^a t_a$ contains all the interactions due to the gluon field A_μ^a in it; these interactions are all admittedly strong, but they are flavor-blind. We have the same interaction (due to A_μ^a) for each flavor of $\bar{Q}$ and Q in the first term. The masses, however, do depend on the flavor.

Let us neglect the mass term for the moment and look at the first term in (15.9). The flavor independence of the interaction with the gluon tells us that there is symmetry under a transformation which mixes flavors. For example, we can consider the transformation

$$\begin{pmatrix} u \\ d \\ s \end{pmatrix} \rightarrow \begin{pmatrix} u' \\ d' \\ s' \end{pmatrix} = \mathbf{U} \begin{pmatrix} u \\ d \\ s \end{pmatrix} \qquad (15.10)$$

where $\mathbf{U}$ is a unitary matrix. In terms of matrix elements, this equation reads $Q'_\alpha = \mathbf{U}_\alpha^{\ \beta} Q_\beta$. If $\mathbf{U}$ is independent of the spacetime coordinates, then the first term in (15.9) is unchanged since $\mathbf{U}^\dagger \mathbf{U} = \mathbb{1}$. More explicitly,

$$\bar{Q}'^\alpha (i\gamma^\mu D_\mu) Q'_\alpha = \bar{Q}^\beta (\mathbf{U}^*)_\beta^{\ \alpha} (i\gamma^\mu D_\mu) \mathbf{U}_\alpha^{\ \gamma} Q_\gamma = \bar{Q}^\beta ((\mathbf{U}^*)_\beta^{\ \alpha} \mathbf{U}_\alpha^{\ \gamma}) (i\gamma^\mu D_\mu) Q_\gamma$$

$$= \bar{Q}^\beta (\mathbf{U}^\dagger \mathbf{U})_\beta^{\ \gamma} (i\gamma^\mu D_\mu) Q_\gamma = \bar{Q}^\alpha (i\gamma^\mu D_\mu) Q_\alpha \qquad (15.11)$$

If $\mathbf{U}$ depends on x^μ, this is not the case because of the derivatives acting on $\mathbf{U}$. Should we try to introduce covariant derivatives for this too? The answer is no; we already have the action and have no reason to introduce additional fields to make this a gauge symmetry. So we will just leave it as it is; the symmetry we have is thus only a global symmetry, valid for constant $\mathbf{U}$'s. Anyway, this symmetry emerges from the way we have grouped three flavors of quarks together, and only when we neglect the masses. There is no deep reason for the symmetry beyond the fact that the gluon interactions are flavor-blind, and it is not obtained if we retain the mass terms. It is only an approximate symmetry and its validity rests on the fact that the mass differences are small compared to the strength of the gluonic interactions.

Now any unitary matrix can be written as $\mathbf{U} = e^{i\theta}\,\tilde{\mathbf{U}}$ where $\tilde{\mathbf{U}}$ has unit determinant. (Thus $e^{i3\theta}$ is the determinant for the 3×3 matrix we have.) The phase does not play much of a role in what we want to do, so we shall ignore it for now. We may thus state that the theory given by the first term in (15.9) has a global $SU(3)$ symmetry. *This is not to be confused with the color symmetry which is also $SU(3)$. That is a symmetry with x-dependent $\mathbf{U}$'s. The present one has nothing to do with color, it transforms one flavor of quark to another and it involves matrices which do not depend on space-time coordinates. To emphasize this we will write this as $SU(3)_f$.* The relevant matrix will be denoted by $\mathbf{U}_f$. (We drop the tilde; from now on we only consider matrices of unit determinant.)

Now we can use a simple but wonderful theorem from quantum mechanics, namely, that if a theory has a certain global symmetry, then states which are connected by the symmetry will have the same energy. Energy being mass, in our case, we can conclude that bound states of quarks which are connected by the symmetry transformation will have the same mass. In this case, we must conclude that states which are connected by the $SU(3)_f$ transformation will have the same mass. In reality, the symmetry is not perfect due to the mass term in (15.9). Notice that, under the $SU(3)_f$-transformation,

$$\bar{Q}^\alpha\,M_\alpha{}^\beta\,Q_\beta \to \bar{Q}'^\alpha\,M_\alpha{}^\beta\,Q'_\beta = \bar{Q}^\gamma\mathbf{U}^\dagger{}_\gamma{}^\alpha\,M_\alpha{}^\beta\,\mathbf{U}_\beta{}^\delta Q_\delta$$
$$= \bar{Q}^\gamma\big(\mathbf{U}^\dagger M\,\mathbf{U}\big)_\gamma{}^\delta Q_\delta \qquad (15.12)$$

The result is not equal to the second term in (15.9) since M and $\mathbf{U}$ do not commute in general due to the mass differences of the quarks. Thus from the symmetry $SU(3)_f$, we can only expect approximately equal masses. What is interesting is that we can actually include some effects due to the quark mass differences as a small symmetry-breaking effect and get some (limited) predictions about the actual masses. This will be taken up in the next lecture.

Remark 15.1.
A theorem in quantum mechanics

Consider a state $|a\rangle$ which is an eigenstate of the Hamiltonian for a quantum system. We then have

$$H |a\rangle = E_a |a\rangle \tag{15.13}$$

Let G be an operator which takes $|a\rangle$ to some other state, say, $|b\rangle$. Assume that G is a symmetry of the system which means that

$$[G, H] = 0 \tag{15.14}$$

This says that the transformation leaves the Hamiltonian unchanged, which is what we mean by symmetry. We now have the following sequence of equations:

$$
\begin{aligned}
G H |a\rangle = G E_a |a\rangle = E_a (G |a\rangle) = E_a |b\rangle, \qquad & \text{from (15.13)} \\
= H G |a\rangle, \qquad & \text{from (15.14)} \\
= H |b\rangle & \tag{15.15}
\end{aligned}
$$

From the first and last lines, we get $H |b\rangle = E_a |b\rangle$. Thus the state $|b\rangle$ obtained from $|a\rangle$ by a symmetry transformation is also an eigenstate of the Hamiltonian with the same eigenvalue, the same energy, as the state $|a\rangle$. In other words, we have the "theorem",

Theorem 15.1. *States which are connected by a symmetry transformation are degenerate.*

This is the basic theorem, generally attributed to Wigner. A better way to state this is in terms of irreducible representations of the symmetry group, but we will not do that here. Further there is an exception possible if we have an infinite number of degrees of freedom, as in the case of field theory. It may then turn out that the state $G|a\rangle$ is not normalizable and so the argument for $G|a\rangle$ being an eigenstate can break down. This exception includes the case of spontaneous breaking of a symmetry. We will need some ideas of this very interesting topic for our discussion of weak interactions (and strong interactions), and we will take this up a little later, but let us shelve it for now.

Consequences of Wigner's theorem are familiar from elementary quantum mechanics. For example, the Hamiltonian for the Hydrogen atom is

$$H = \frac{\vec{p}^2}{2\,m} - \frac{e^2}{r} \tag{15.16}$$

This is evidently invariant under rotations, since it involves only the square of the magnitude of $\vec{p}$ and the radial distance r, both of which are unchanged under rotations. We also know that rotations are implemented in quantum mechanics by the angular momentum operators L_i, $i = 1, 2, 3$. The change of the Hamiltonian under an infinitesimal rotation is given by $\delta H = i\,[L_i, H]\,\theta^i$, so that the rotational invariance of (15.16) tells us that $[L_i, H] = 0$. The states of the Hydrogen atom, familiar from elementary quantum mechanics, are of the form $|n, l, m\rangle$ where n is the principal quantum number, l gives the square of the total angular momentum via $L_i L_i |n, l, m\rangle = l(l + 1)|n, l, m\rangle$ and m is the azimuthal quantum number corresponding to the eigenvalue of L_3. From standard angular momentum theory, we know that $L_+ = L_1 + iL_2$ increases the m-value by one and $L_- = L_1 - iL_2$ decreases it by one. Thus all states of the same l-value (but different L_3-values) are connected by repeated $L_\pm$ action. So from the theorem, we can conclude that eigenstates of the Hamiltonian fall into groups of states which correspond to the angular momentum eigenstates. We should expect all states of the same n-value and l-value to be degenerate, the different states in a degenerate group corresponding to different m-values. In other words, the energy eigenvalues must be independent of m, the azimuthal quantum number.

The Hamiltonian (15.16) has another symmetry which is not obvious; this extra symmetry is special just for the $1/r$-potential and is related to the conservation of the Runge-Lenz vector. Because of this, there are further degeneracies; thus $|n = 2, l = 0\rangle$ and the three states of $|n = 2, l = 1\rangle$ are degenerate. (There are similar statements for the higher values of n as well.) However, this is special; if we have any perturbation, such as an additional term $\sim r^{-2}$ in the potential, or relativistic corrections with a $\sim (\vec{p}^2)^2$-term, we still have spherical symmetry but the second symmetry is lost. Then the degeneracy of the states $|n = 2, l = 0\rangle$ and $|n = 2, l = 1\rangle$ is lifted.

The Runge-Lenz vector may be viewed classically as the vector from the center to the periapsis for a particle orbiting a central body. The fact that there is no precession of the periapsis for the $1/r$-potential leads to the conservation of the Runge-Lenz vector. This symmetry persists in the quantum theory as well.

Chapter 16

Mesons and Baryons

In the last lecture, we talked about how we might be able to use symmetry for understanding the bound states of quarks. The key ingredients are the notion of color (or quark) confinement (which tells us that physical states must be invariant under the color transformations), the idea that there is a flavor $SU(3)_f$ symmetry and the fact that quarks are fermions, so we must take account of the Pauli exclusion principle when we have identical fermions. With these concepts, we can get quite a bit of useful information on the bound states.

Let us consider bound states involving a quark and an antiquark. Such states are called mesons. We can write the wave function for this (or the field representing this) as $\bar{Q}^i_{\alpha,r} Q^j_{\beta,s}$ where i, j refer to the color, $r, s = 1, 2, 3, 4$ give the spin states and α, β are the flavor labels telling us which flavor of quarks (u, d or s) we are considering. For invariance under color, we have to take $i = j$ and sum. Then the color transformation $Q_{\alpha,r} \rightarrow Q'^i_{\alpha,r} = \mathbf{U}^{ij} Q^j_{\alpha,r}$ gives

$$
\begin{aligned}
\bar{Q}^i_{\alpha,r} Q^i_{\beta,s} \rightarrow \bar{Q}'^i_{\alpha,r} Q'^i_{\beta,s} &= \mathbf{U}^{*ij} \mathbf{U}^{ik} \bar{Q}^j_{\alpha,r} Q^k_{\beta,s} \\
&= (\mathbf{U}^\dagger)^{ji} \mathbf{U}^{ik} \bar{Q}^j_{\alpha,r} Q^k_{\beta,s} \\
&= (\mathbf{U}^\dagger \mathbf{U})^{jk} \bar{Q}^j_{\alpha,r} Q^k_{\beta,s} \\
&= \delta^{jk} \bar{Q}^j_{\alpha,r} Q^k_{\beta,s} \\
&= \bar{Q}^i_{\alpha,r} Q^i_{\beta,s}
\end{aligned}
\tag{16.1}
$$

We see that the combination we have is indeed invariant under the color transformation.

Now let us look at the flavor properties. The indices α, β take values $1, 2, 3$, so that there are 9 possible combinations in $\bar{Q}^i_{\alpha,r} Q^i_{\beta,s}$ for the flavor choices. One of these is invariant under flavor $SU(3)_f$ transformations, easily seen in a way similar to what we did in (16.1). Thus under the flavor transformation $Q_\alpha \to (\mathbf{U}_f)_{\alpha\beta} Q_\beta$, we find

$$\bar{Q}_\alpha Q_\alpha \to (\mathbf{U}_f^*)_{\alpha\beta} (\mathbf{U}_f)_{\alpha\gamma} \bar{Q}_\beta Q_\gamma = (\mathbf{U}_f^\dagger \mathbf{U}_f)_{\beta\gamma} \bar{Q}_\beta Q_\gamma = \bar{Q}_\alpha Q_\alpha \qquad (16.2)$$

So one combination out of the 9 is invariant under $SU(3)_f$. The other 8 get mixed among themselves by $SU(3)_f$. Therefore, from the theorem on implementation of symmetries in quantum mechanics, we expect that we will have 8 particles which are approximately degenerate in mass and then one which can have a significantly different mass. (The degeneracy for the 8 mesons is only approximate because the symmetry is only approximate due to the fact that the quark masses are different for the different flavors.)

Let us now look at the spin. The quark and the antiquark are both spin-$\frac{1}{2}$ particles, so the combination will have the combined spin angular momentum of $\frac{1}{2}$ with $\frac{1}{2}$. Recall the rules of angular momentum. When we combine two spins s_1 and s_2, we get $s_1 + s_2$, $s_1 + s_2 - 1$, $\cdots$, $|s_1 - s_2|$ as the possible spin values. In our case, this means that we get spin 1 and spin zero. The relativistically invariant way to phrase this is as follows. The possible $\bar{Q}Q$ combinations with arbitrary spinor labels can be rearranged into the combinations $\bar{Q}_\alpha \Gamma Q_\beta$, where Γ is the set given in (9.2) which gives a basis for 4×4 matrices,

$$\Gamma = \{\mathbb{1}, \gamma^5, \gamma^\mu, \gamma^\mu \gamma^5, \gamma^{\mu\nu}\} \qquad (16.3)$$

We can take these combinations as representing the field for the mesons in terms of their composite structure. Of these, $\mathbb{1}$ will give a scalar, γ^5 will give pseudoscalar (since $\bar{Q}\gamma^5 Q$ is odd under parity), γ^μ will give a vector, $\gamma^\mu \gamma^5$ will give an axial vector and $\gamma^{\mu\nu}$ will give a tensor (still with spin ≤ 1 because of the antisymmetry of μ, ν).

The conclusion from this argument is thus: We expect 8 mesons of a particular spin-parity-type corresponding to a particular choice of Γ, with approximately the same mass, one meson of the same spin-parity-type but with a different mass, If we look at the experimental data, we find that there are indeed such groupings of mesons. The low mass ones, corresponding to the pseudoscalars and vectors, are given in Table 16.1. (The higher mass ones are less well-defined because the symmetry is not perfect and because they have larger decay widths.) The masses are not very close to each other, but remember that we neglected the quark mass terms which are there in the action, as in (15.9). Of those masses, the strange quark has a mass of about 100 to 130 MeV, so an error of this magnitude is very likely. The hope is that we can put in these effects and explain the mass differences among the members of each meson multiplet.

We can understand the quark content of the mesons as follows. The combination which does not mix with the 8 mesons, namely $\bar{Q}_\alpha Q_\alpha$ is evidently, upon writing out the summation, given by

$$\bar{Q}_\alpha Q_\alpha = \bar{u}u + \bar{d}d + \bar{s}s \tag{16.4}$$

As a state, we may write this as

$$|\text{singlet}\rangle = |\bar{u}u\rangle + |\bar{d}d\rangle + |\bar{s}s\rangle \tag{16.5}$$

For each particle, we have the normalization $\langle u|u \rangle = 1$, $\langle d|d \rangle = 1$, $\langle u|d \rangle = 0$, $\langle u|\bar{u} \rangle = 0$, etc. Thus

$$\langle \text{singlet}|\text{singlet}\rangle = \langle \bar{u}u|\bar{u}u\rangle + \langle \bar{d}d|\bar{d}d\rangle + \langle \bar{s}s|\bar{s}s\rangle = 3 \tag{16.6}$$

The correctly normalized state, which can be identified, say, as the η', should thus be taken as

$$|\eta'\rangle = \frac{1}{\sqrt{3}} \left(|\bar{u}u\rangle + |\bar{d}d\rangle + |\bar{s}s\rangle \right) \tag{16.7}$$

This does not show the spin content. The η' is a spin zero combination, so if we include the spin labels, the state is given by

$$|\eta'\rangle = \frac{1}{\sqrt{3}} \left(\frac{1}{\sqrt{2}} \left(|\bar{u} \uparrow u \downarrow \rangle - |\bar{u} \downarrow u \uparrow \rangle \right) + \frac{1}{\sqrt{2}} \left(|\bar{d} \uparrow d \downarrow \rangle - |\bar{d} \downarrow d \uparrow \rangle \right) \right.$$
$$\left. + \frac{1}{\sqrt{2}} \left(|\bar{s} \uparrow s \downarrow \rangle - |\bar{s} \downarrow s \uparrow \rangle \right) \right) \tag{16.8}$$

Table 16.1: Spin zero and spin-1 mesons with the lowest masses

	Spin 0	Mass (MeV)	Spin 1	Mass (MeV)	Quark content
Singlet	η'	958	ω	783	$(\bar{u}u + \bar{d}d + \bar{s}s)/\sqrt{3}$
	π^0	135	ρ^0	775	$(\bar{u}u - \bar{d}d)/\sqrt{2}$
	π^+	140	ρ^+	775	$\bar{d}u$
	π^-	140	ρ^-	775	$\bar{u}d$
Octet	K^+	494	K^{*+}	892	$\bar{s}u$
	K^-	494	K^{*-}	892	$\bar{u}s$
	K^0	498	K^{*0}	896	$\bar{s}d$
	$\bar{K}^0$	498	$\bar{K}^{*0}$	896	$\bar{d}s$
	η	548	φ	1019	$(\bar{u}u + \bar{d}d - 2\bar{s}s)/\sqrt{6}$

In a similar way, the spin-1 meson of similar quark content, the ω, will have three spin states corresponding to $S_3 = 1, 0, -1$. They are given by

$$|\omega\rangle = \begin{cases} \frac{1}{\sqrt{3}}\left(|\bar{u}\uparrow u\uparrow\rangle + |\bar{d}\uparrow d\uparrow\rangle + |\bar{s}\uparrow s\uparrow\rangle\right) \\ \frac{1}{\sqrt{3}}\left(\frac{1}{\sqrt{2}}\left(|\bar{u}\uparrow u\downarrow\rangle + |\bar{u}\downarrow u\uparrow\rangle\right) + \frac{1}{\sqrt{2}}\left(|\bar{d}\uparrow d\downarrow\rangle + |\bar{d}\downarrow d\uparrow\rangle\right) \\ \qquad + \frac{1}{\sqrt{2}}\left(|\bar{s}\uparrow s\downarrow\rangle + |\bar{s}\downarrow s\uparrow\rangle\right)\right) \\ \frac{1}{\sqrt{3}}\left(|\bar{u}\downarrow u\downarrow\rangle + |\bar{d}\downarrow d\downarrow\rangle + |\bar{s}\downarrow s\downarrow\rangle\right) \end{cases}$$

$$(16.9)$$

Focusing just on the quark content again, we have three states $|\bar{u}u\rangle$, $|\bar{d}d\rangle$, $|\bar{s}s\rangle$, of which we have made one combination given in (16.7). So we must have two orthogonal combinations. These are easily verified to be

$$\frac{1}{\sqrt{2}}\left(|\bar{u}u\rangle - |\bar{d}d\rangle\right), \qquad \frac{1}{\sqrt{6}}\left(|\bar{u}u\rangle + |\bar{d}d\rangle - 2|\bar{s}s\rangle\right) \qquad (16.10)$$

The remaining possibilities involve a quark and an antiquark of different flavors and they are easily seen to constitute an orthonormal set,

$$|\bar{d}u\rangle, \qquad |\bar{u}d\rangle, \qquad |\bar{s}u\rangle, \qquad |\bar{u}s\rangle, \qquad |\bar{s}d\rangle, \qquad |\bar{d}s\rangle \qquad (16.11)$$

These states (16.10), (16.11) give the quark content of the octet of mesons. A convenient way to display these mesons is as a 3×3 matrix

$$\mathbf{M} = \begin{bmatrix} \frac{\pi^0}{\sqrt{2}} + \frac{\eta}{\sqrt{6}} & \pi^+ & K^+ \\ \pi^- & -\frac{\pi^0}{\sqrt{2}} + \frac{\eta}{\sqrt{6}} & K^0 \\ K^- & \bar{K}^0 & -\frac{2}{\sqrt{6}}\eta \end{bmatrix} \qquad (16.12)$$

We have shown the fields for the pseudoscalar mesons. In terms of the matrix elements of $\mathbf{M}$, these fields can be related to the quark content via

$$i\bar{Q}_\alpha\gamma^5 Q_\beta = \mathbf{M}_{\beta\alpha} + \delta_{\beta\alpha}\frac{1}{\sqrt{3}}\eta' \qquad (16.13)$$

The individual meson fields ϕ_a are related to $\mathbf{M}$ by $\phi_a(\lambda_a/\sqrt{2}) = \mathbf{M}$. From the identification in (16.13), we can also see that, under an $SU(3)_f$ transformation $Q_\alpha \rightarrow \mathbf{U}_{\alpha\beta}Q_\beta$, $\mathbf{M} \rightarrow \mathbf{U}\mathbf{M}\mathbf{U}^{-1}$. A matrix similar to (16.12) can be made for the vectors as well.

We have focused mostly on the pseudoscalar and vector mesons, corresponding to $\Gamma = \gamma^5, \gamma^\mu$ from (16.3), as these are well-defined resonances and are the lowest lying in terms of the masses. But other choices for Γ will give scalar mesons, axial vector mesons, etc. There can also be mesons which are excitations which involve nonzero orbital angular momentum; thus they will correspond to composites like $\bar{Q}\partial_\mu Q$, $\bar{Q}\partial_\mu\partial_\nu Q$, etc. The expectation is that these will have higher masses. A complete treatment requires going beyond the symmetry-based classification.

Also, the mesons cannot be the whole story since we need to have particles like the proton and the neutron. So we must look for other combinations which are color-invariant. We can see that such combinations can be made from three quarks. This is based on the following property. Since the color transformation matrices have unit determinant, we have $\epsilon_{pqr} = \epsilon^{ijk} \mathbf{U}_{ip} \mathbf{U}_{jq} \mathbf{U}_{kr}$. Thus the combination $Q^i Q^j Q^k \epsilon^{ijk}$ is unchanged under color transformations,

$$Q^i Q^j Q^k \epsilon_{ijk} \rightarrow Q'^i Q'^j Q'^k \epsilon_{ijk} = \mathbf{U}^{ip} \mathbf{U}^{jq} \mathbf{U}^{kr} \epsilon_{ijk} Q^p Q^q Q^r$$
$$= \epsilon_{pqr} Q^p Q^q Q^r \qquad (16.14)$$

We see that the combination $Q^p Q^q Q^r \epsilon_{pqr}$ qualifies as a color-invariant combination and we may expect bound states of this nature. Such states are called baryons. We can now work out the flavor and spin content of these states.

Quarks are fermions, so we need the full wave function to be antisymmetric. It is already antisymmetric in color, so it should be symmetric under combined flavor and spin exchanges. So one possibility is to consider states which are symmetric under flavor and symmetric under spin. The totally symmetric combination of 3 spin-$\frac{1}{2}$ particles will have spin $= \frac{3}{2}$. Further, symmetry under flavor exchanges tells us that there are 10 states possible. So we expect a decuplet of spin-$\frac{3}{2}$ baryons (and corresponding antibaryons from the $\bar{Q}\bar{Q}\bar{Q}$ combination). These are shown in the diagram Fig. 16.1. (The particular way they are displayed is not for artistic reasons; this arrangement is an isospin-hypercharge diagram. It has a specific group-theoretic meaning as the weight diagram of the 10-dimensional representation of $SU(3)$.)

Another possibility is to have mixed symmetry for flavor where two out of the three quarks are antisymmetrized; in this case, we must also have

Table 16.2: The octet of spin-$\frac{1}{2}$ baryons with the lowest masses (The masses are in MeV.)

Baryon	p	n	Λ	Σ^+	Σ^0	Σ^-
Mass	938	940	1116	1189	1193	1197
Baryon	Ξ^-	Ξ^0				
Mass	1315	1322				

a suitable antisymmetrization of the spin states of the two quarks, so that overall (including color) we have antisymmetry in accordance with the Pauli exclusion principle. We can do the flavor antisymmetrization by considering $\epsilon^{\alpha\beta\delta}Q_\alpha Q_\beta Q_\gamma$ which gives something that has two flavor indices left over, γ, δ in this case. This is now similar to the meson case. If we contract γ and δ, the result is totally antisymmetric in flavor. This combination has antisymmetry for color and flavor, so to be acceptable according to the Pauli principle, we must have total antisymmetry in spin; that is not possible for 3 spin-$\frac{1}{2}$ particles. So the flavor invariant combination is ruled out. Thus, out of $B_\gamma^\delta = \epsilon^{\alpha\beta\delta}Q_\alpha Q_\beta Q_\gamma$ we can only get the 8 states as we found for mesons. The spin in this case should be the combination of spin zero (from the two antisymmetrized flavors) with the spin $\frac{1}{2}$ of the remaining quark; overall spin is thus $\frac{1}{2}$. The conclusion is that we can also have an octet of baryons which are spin-$\frac{1}{2}$ particles. These are identified as the familiar proton (p) and the neutron (n) and 6 other particles as shown in Table 16.2.

These particles, since they form an octet, can be put in the form of a

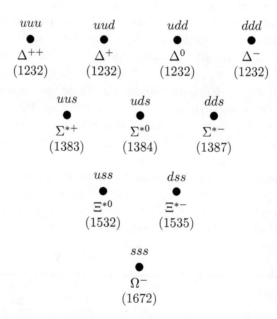

Fig. 16.1: The decuplet of spin-$\frac{3}{2}$ baryons. Masses in MeV are given in brackets.

baryon matrix just as we did for the mesons; it is given by

$$\mathbf{B} = \begin{bmatrix} \frac{\Sigma^0}{\sqrt{2}} + \frac{\Lambda}{\sqrt{6}} & \Sigma^+ & p \\ \Sigma^- & -\frac{\Sigma^0}{\sqrt{2}} + \frac{\Lambda}{\sqrt{6}} & n \\ \Xi^- & \Xi^0 & -\frac{2}{\sqrt{6}}\Lambda \end{bmatrix} \tag{16.15}$$

We can also write down a $\bar{\mathbf{B}}$ matrix given by the hermitian conjugate

$$\bar{\mathbf{B}} = \begin{bmatrix} \frac{\bar{\Sigma}^0}{\sqrt{2}} + \frac{\bar{\Lambda}}{\sqrt{6}} & \overline{\Sigma^-} & \overline{\Xi^-} \\ \overline{\Sigma^+} & -\frac{\bar{\Sigma}^0}{\sqrt{2}} + \frac{\bar{\Lambda}}{\sqrt{6}} & \overline{\Xi^0} \\ \bar{p} & \bar{n} & -\frac{2}{\sqrt{6}}\bar{\Lambda} \end{bmatrix} \tag{16.16}$$

Under the $SU(3)_f$ transformation, these also transform as $\mathbf{B} \to \mathbf{B}' = \mathbf{U}\mathbf{B}\mathbf{U}^{-1}$, $\bar{\mathbf{B}} \to \bar{\mathbf{B}}' = \mathbf{U}\bar{\mathbf{B}}\mathbf{U}^{-1}$.

Because the lowest mass baryons and mesons come as octets, (or more to the point because all these particles (including the decuplet) fall into multiplets obtained from products of the 8-dimensional representation of $SU(3)$ with itself), the classification scheme based on $SU(3)_f$ flavor symmetry was named the "Eightfold Way" by Gell-Mann. (The scheme was independently proposed by Gell-Mann and Ne'eman in 1961. The name was a take on the Eightfold Way in Buddhism whereby we are all encouraged to follow the eight noble truths of the Buddha.)

Masses and interactions

The idea of using the $SU(3)_f$ symmetry tells us that the masses of all members of the meson octet should be the same. Likewise all members of the octet of baryons should have the same mass, all members of the decuplet of baryons should have the same mass. This is clearly not true, although the variance in the masses is not very large. The lack of degeneracy is not surprising since we have neglected the quark masses and not all quarks have the same mass. Thus, the symmetry we talk about is not perfect. We can try to improve on matters by asking whether we can get some idea of the variation in masses by including the mass differences among the quarks. Of the three quarks we are considering, namely, the u, d and s, the up and down quarks have roughly the same mass; in any case their masses are very small, so at the next level of approximation, we may still neglect them. The strange quark has a mass around 100 to 130 MeV, so it is not to be totally neglected. Can this account for the mass differences we see for the baryons and the mesons? The simplest case for which we can try this out is for the decuplet. We notice that, as we go down the levels in the decuplet, we are replacing u or d by s. Thus, we may expect that the mass difference between the Ξ^*'s and the Δ's would be twice that between the Σ^*'s and the Δ's since we have two s quarks for the Ξ^*'s compared to one for the Σ^*'s. This suggests an "equal spacing rule":

$$M_{\Omega^-} - M_{\Xi^*} = M_{\Xi^*} - M_{\Sigma^*} = M_{\Sigma^*} - M_\Delta \qquad (16.17)$$

The three entries in this equation are all approximately 150 MeV, so this idea does seem to be borne out. In fact, at the time this classification scheme was worked out (in 1961), the Ω^- was not known. The Eightfold Way not only predicted the existence of the Ω^-, but the equal spacing rule gave its mass (as approximately 1675 MeV). The subsequent discovery (in 1964) of the Ω^- with a mass of 1672 MeV was one of the early successes of this scheme. To this order, we are also predicting equal masses for the baryons along the same horizontal line in Fig. 16.1. Thus we may take $M_{\Sigma^{*+}} \approx M_{\Sigma^{*0}}$ and other similar relations as another success of this scheme. (A symmetry for the strong nuclear interactions of the up and down quarks and the near equality of their masses (which will give these relations) is an idea that can be traced to Heisenberg in 1932.)

It is also possible to get a formula for the masses of the octets of baryons and mesons. This requires somewhat more sophisticated techniques, the derivation is outlined in one of the remarks given later. Examples of such mass formulae are:

$$2\left(M_p + M_\Xi\right) = M_\Sigma + 3\,M_\Lambda$$
$$2\left(M_K^2 + M_{K^0}^2\right) = M_\pi^2 + 3\,M_\eta^2 \qquad (16.18)$$

It is easily verified that these relations hold to the expected degree within the approximations involved. One can also consider formulae like $M_p \approx M_n$, $M_{\Sigma^+} \approx M_{\Sigma^-} \approx M_{\Sigma^0}$ as symmetry-based predictions of the theory. All these formulae collectively are known as the Gell-Mann-Okubo mass formulae. (Gell-Mann obtained most of them, Okubo gave a firm group-theoretic derivation for them.)

One can go further and derive relations for other particle properties such as the magnetic moments. (They are called the Coleman-Glashow relations.) Symmetry also makes predictions about interactions. If we think of representing the dynamics of mesons and baryons in terms of an action, an "effective action" derived from the fundamental action in terms of quarks and gluons, the statement of symmetry is that the effective action will have the same symmetries, in this case $SU(3)_f$, as the fundamental theory.

For example, let us consider the baryon-baryon-meson interactions for the octets of baryons and mesons. *A priori*, a *B-B-M* interaction can have different amplitudes for each choice of the baryons and the mesons, 8^3 in all. Some of them are obviously ruled out by charge conservation and so on, but there is still a large number of unknowns. But based on $SU(3)_f$ symmetry, we can show that there are only two basic couplings (at energies below the threshold for probing the substructure of the particles) given by

$$S_{int} = \int d^4x \, [g_1 \text{Tr}(\bar{\mathbf{B}}\gamma^5 \, \mathbf{B} \, \mathbf{M}) + g_2 \text{Tr}(\bar{\mathbf{B}}\gamma^5 \, \mathbf{M} \, \mathbf{B})] \tag{16.19}$$

We have included a factor of γ^5 for balance of parity since the simplest case to which we can apply this reasoning is to the pseudoscalar mesons of (16.12).

The way to interpret the formula (16.19) is that we can use it to identify the vertices involved in a calculation of scatterings or decays. The coefficients g_1 and g_2 are, in principle, calculable from the fundamental theory, but as we mentioned earlier, that is a difficult computation; perhaps with improved numerical algorithms and better computers we can do it within the framework of lattice gauge theory. But, even without such a calculation, we see how powerful symmetry can be. With just two unknowns, which can be measured in two appropriate scatterings, we can predict the (approximate) strength of a whole host of scatterings. As an example, consider the pion-nucleon coupling given by this. For this we need only the p, n terms of the baryon matrix and the pion terms of the meson matrix. The result is

$$S_{int} = \int d^4x \, g_1 \text{Tr} \left(\begin{bmatrix} 0 & 0 & 0 \\ 0 & 0 & 0 \\ \bar{p}\gamma^5 & \bar{n}\gamma^5 & 0 \end{bmatrix} \begin{bmatrix} 0 & 0 & p \\ 0 & 0 & n \\ 0 & 0 & 0 \end{bmatrix} \begin{bmatrix} \frac{\pi^0}{\sqrt{2}} & \pi^+ & 0 \\ \pi^- & -\frac{\pi^0}{\sqrt{2}} & 0 \\ 0 & 0 & 0 \end{bmatrix} \right)$$

$$+ \int d^4x \, g_2 \text{Tr} \left(\begin{bmatrix} 0 & 0 & 0 \\ 0 & 0 & 0 \\ \bar{p}\gamma^5 & \bar{n}\gamma^5 & 0 \end{bmatrix} \begin{bmatrix} \frac{\pi^0}{\sqrt{2}} & \pi^+ & 0 \\ \pi^- & -\frac{\pi^0}{\sqrt{2}} & 0 \\ 0 & 0 & 0 \end{bmatrix} \begin{bmatrix} 0 & 0 & p \\ 0 & 0 & n \\ 0 & 0 & 0 \end{bmatrix} \right)$$

$$= g_2 \int d^4x \, \left[\frac{\pi^0}{\sqrt{2}} (\bar{p}\gamma^5 p - \bar{n}\gamma^5 n) + \bar{n}\gamma^5 p \, \pi^- + \bar{p}\gamma^5 n \, \pi^+ \right] \tag{16.20}$$

Notice that the coupling of the π^+, π^0 and π^- are all related, but it is not just a trivial statement that they are all equal. Instead, we have specific relations, such as the factor of $1/\sqrt{2}$. One can look at other couplings given by (16.19) and see that there are many relations among the couplings.

The expression (16.19) assumes strict $SU(3)_f$ symmetry and so predictions made from it have limitations similar to the case with the masses. The fact that $SU(3)_f$ is not a perfect symmetry does affect the predictions for the rates for various processes. Even with the given $SU(3)_f$ symmetric vertices, the actual rates have differences due to the mass differences which show up in the integrations over final states in any process. Also there are additional symmetry-breaking terms one could add to (16.19). In the end, the symmetry is not perfect, we have limitations, but overall we get a good picture of what the physics is without detailed (and, up to now, not possible) calculations.

Remark 16.1.
The determinant of a 3 × 3 matrix

If we consider a 3×3 matrix, say, $\mathbf{N}$, then the determinant is given by

$$\epsilon^{ijk} N_{ip} N_{jq} N_{kr} = (\det N)\, \epsilon_{pqr} \tag{16.21}$$

We can verify this directly. Let us take $p = 1$, $q = 2$ and $r = 3$, so that $\epsilon_{pqr} = \epsilon_{123} = 1$. Then the above equation becomes

$$\epsilon^{ijk} N_{i1} N_{j2} N_{k3} = (\det N) \tag{16.22}$$

Now i can take values $1, 2, 3$, so let us take each value in turn in the sum. Because of ϵ^{ijk}, if $i = 1$, the possibilities are $j = 2, k = 3$ and $j = 3, k = 2$. Writing out the sum in (16.22) explicitly, the left hand side is given by

$$\begin{aligned}
\epsilon^{ijk} N_{i1} N_{j2} N_{k3} = N_{11} \left(N_{22}N_{33} - N_{32}N_{23}\right) &- N_{21} \left(N_{12}N_{33} - N_{32}N_{13}\right) \\
&+ N_{31} \left(N_{12}N_{23} - N_{22}N_{13}\right)
\end{aligned} \tag{16.23}$$

This is the standard definition of the determinant, thus verifying the formula (16.21). (The other choices of indices in (16.21) can also be directly verified.)

Remark 16.2.
Reverse engineering the color symmetry

The theory of strong interactions, as we have outlined it, is the story today, with the full benefit of hindsight. The development of the theory came pretty much in reverse order to the sequence we have followed. The large number of "elementary particles" which were known by the 1960s presented a very difficult problem. The interactions among them had to be sorted out carefully in many, many experiments and then a pattern had to be constructed. Out of this, the Eightfold Way and, later, the quark model emerged. It took another decade of work, both on the experimental and theoretical side, before the idea of color was proposed and the description of strong nuclear forces via an $SU(3)$ gauge theory was formulated. It is a long story, we cannot discuss it in detail here, except for a couple of remarks.

We talked about the R-ratio as a way of identifying the number of colors a quark may have. But the threshold for the charm quark was passed only around 1974. So conclusive evidence from that argument was missing until then. We also mentioned another piece of evidence, namely, the decay of the π^0-meson into two photons. The process could be visualized as due to the initial pion disintegrating into a virtual quark-antiquark pair which then annihilate into two photons, the latter being a purely electromagnetic process. The decay rate must then be proportional to the number of intermediate channels. The calculated rate matches with the observed decay rate if we allow for a multiplicity factor of 3 due to the three colors.

Yet another piece of evidence came from the Ω^-, which is a state with 3 s-quarks, which are all completely identical fermions. Further, the spin of Ω^- is $\frac{3}{2}$, so we know that the spin state is a completely symmetric one. But for fermions, we need an antisymmetric wave function to satisfy the Pauli exclusion principle, so we should expect some internal state for the quark to take care of this. And we need at least three possibilities for this internal quantum number to get the three-quark state to be antisymmetric. Thus we are led (almost) to the idea of three colors.

But it is never that simple. Could we not have orbital excitation states of the quarks in their bound situation, so that antisymmetry is achieved by using different orbital states? How did we establish that quarks are indeed spin-$\frac{1}{2}$ particles? If they are not, there is more wiggle room, more hypotheses possible. Historically, all these variants had to be sorted out, ruled out by experiment, or by a concatenation of theoretical arguments. And many brilliant hypotheses and alternatives, which seemed viable for a time when the data were not very clear, did not work out.

Remark 16.3.

Think symmetry: Mass formulae for baryons

We talked about mass formulae and how one could get some idea of the baryon and meson masses just based on symmetry. If the flavor $SU(3)_f$

symmetry were perfect, the masses of all members of the same multiplet of baryons (or mesons) would be the same. Thus we should expect the proton, the neutron, the Λ, etc. to have the same mass. But the $SU(3)_f$ symmetry is not perfect and there are mass differences, leading to mass formulae such as (16.18). Although we will not derive them in great detail, it is not too difficult to see how such formulae emerge from symmetry. In fact, it is a good example of putting together ideas from field theory and symmetry.

Recall that the mass term in the Lagrangian for a fermion field is of the form $\bar{\Psi}\Psi$. In our case, the baryon fields, say of the octet, are grouped together to form the matrix $\mathbf{B}$ and its conjugate $\bar{\mathbf{B}}$. Under the flavor $SU(3)_f$ they transform as $\mathbf{B} \to \mathbf{B}' = \mathbf{U}\mathbf{B}\mathbf{U}^{-1}$. Since the trace of a product of matrices is invariant under cyclic permutation, we see that $\mathrm{Tr}(\bar{\mathbf{B}}\mathbf{B})$ is an $SU(3)_f$ invariant (where we trace over the flavor indices only). Written out, this means that $\sum_{\alpha,\beta} \bar{\mathbf{B}}_{\alpha\beta}\mathbf{B}_{\beta\alpha}$ is invariant. Thus if $SU(3)_f$ were a perfect symmetry, we could take the mass term of the action for the octet of baryons as

$$S_{\text{mass}} = m_0 \int d^4x \ \bar{\mathbf{B}}_{\alpha\beta}\mathbf{B}_{\beta\alpha}$$

$$= m_0 \int d^4x \ \left(\bar{p}p + \bar{n}n + \overline{\Sigma^-}\Sigma^- + \overline{\Sigma^+}\Sigma^+ + \overline{\Sigma^0}\Sigma^0 \right.$$

$$\left. + \overline{\Xi^-}\Xi^- + \overline{\Xi^0}\Xi^0 + \overline{\Lambda}\Lambda \right) \qquad (16.24)$$

where m_0 is some parameter, which can be calculated if we can really solve the theory, but is not determined by symmetry alone. We see that the masses for all members of the octet are equal, each equal to m_0.

Now let us think about the sources for the breaking of this nice symmetry. The quark masses for the three flavors u, d, s are different, so that is definitely a source for mass differences among the baryons. The vertices for the electroweak interactions also break this symmetry. Actually, we will see shortly that the quark masses themselves arise out of the electroweak theory, so we could lump all sources of breaking of the symmetry among the three flavors of quarks as the electroweak interactions. Nevertheless, the quark masses turn out to be the dominant effect, so we can try to get a mass formula using just the quark masses. Of course, one cannot just directly use the quark masses as there are many strong interaction effects, but we may expect the pattern of symmetry breaking to be controlled by the pattern of how the quark masses are. The mass term for the quarks can be written as

$$S_{\text{mass}} = \int d^4x \ \bar{Q}^i_\alpha \, M_{\alpha\beta} \, Q_{i\beta} \qquad (16.25)$$

where $M_{\alpha\beta}$ is a matrix of the form

$$M_{\alpha\beta} = \begin{pmatrix} m_u & 0 & 0 \\ 0 & m_d & 0 \\ 0 & 0 & m_s \end{pmatrix} \tag{16.26}$$

Since the difference between m_u and m_d is small, let us ignore that for a first pass at a mass formula, and so take $M_{\alpha\beta}$ as

$$M_{\alpha\beta} = m_u \delta_{\alpha\beta} + (m_s - m_u) \delta_{\alpha 3} \delta_{\beta 3} \tag{16.27}$$

This has the structure of a term which preserves the $SU(3)_f$ flavor symmetry, namely, the first term on the right hand side proportional to $\delta_{\alpha\beta}$, and a term which gives a different value for the M_{33} element. So the third component corresponding to the strange quark, is being singled out.

Let us now consider a general mass term for the baryons. This should be a bilinear of $\mathbf{B}$ and $\bar{\mathbf{B}}$, so we can take it to be of the form

$$S_{\text{mass}} = \int d^4x \, \left(M^{(1)}_{\delta\alpha} \bar{\mathbf{B}}_{\alpha\beta} M^{(2)}_{\beta\gamma} \mathbf{B}_{\gamma\delta} \right) \tag{16.28}$$

If the matrices $M^{(1)}_{\alpha\beta}$ and $M^{(2)}_{\alpha\beta}$ are both proportional to $\delta_{\alpha\beta}$, then there is no symmetry breaking, we get a term like (16.24). We can now build in the expected pattern of symmetry breaking by taking

$$M^{(1)}_{\alpha\beta} = a \, \delta_{\alpha\beta} + b \, \delta_{\alpha 3} \delta_{\beta 3}$$
$$M^{(2)}_{\alpha\beta} = a' \, \delta_{\alpha\beta} + c \, \delta_{\alpha 3} \delta_{\beta 3} \tag{16.29}$$

where a, a', b and c are arbitrary constants. If we could solve QCD and calculate the bound state masses, all these constants would be obtained from the theory. But since that task is next to impossible, we simply take these as arbitrary. So now we have a mass formula for the baryons. Written out, this mass term becomes

$$S_{\text{mass}} = m_0 \int d^4x \, \left[\bar{\mathbf{B}}_{\alpha\beta} \mathbf{B}_{\beta\alpha} + \tilde{b} \, \bar{\mathbf{B}}_{3\alpha} \mathbf{B}_{\alpha 3} + \tilde{c} \, \bar{\mathbf{B}}_{\alpha 3} \mathbf{B}_{3\alpha} + \tilde{b}\tilde{c} \, \bar{\mathbf{B}}_{33} \mathbf{B}_{33} \right] \tag{16.30}$$

where $m_0 = aa'$, $\tilde{b} = b/a$ and $\tilde{c} = c/a'$ in terms of parameters in (16.29). The explicit identification of the baryons in (16.15, 16.16) gives

$$\bar{\mathbf{B}}_{3\alpha} \mathbf{B}_{\alpha 3} = \bar{p}p + \bar{n}n + \frac{2}{3} \bar{\Lambda}\Lambda$$
$$\bar{\mathbf{B}}_{\alpha 3} \mathbf{B}_{3\alpha} = \overline{\Xi^-} \Xi^- + \overline{\Xi^0} \Xi^0 + \frac{2}{3} \bar{\Lambda}\Lambda \tag{16.31}$$

Using these, we can now read off the masses from (16.30) as

$$M_p = M_n = m_0(1 + \tilde{b})$$

$$M_{\Sigma^0} = M_{\Sigma^+} = M_{\Sigma^-} = m_0$$

$$M_{\Xi^0} = M_{\Xi^-} = m_0(1 + \tilde{c})$$

$$M_\Lambda = m_0(1 + \frac{2}{3}(\tilde{b} + \tilde{c}) + \frac{2}{3}\tilde{b}\tilde{c}) \qquad (16.32)$$

Since there are 3 unknown constants, we get the mass relations

$$M_p = M_n, \quad M_{\Sigma^0} = M_{\Sigma^+} = M_{\Sigma^-}, \quad M_{\Xi^0} = M_{\Xi^-}$$

$$2(M_p + M_{\Xi^0}) = M_{\Sigma^0} + 3M_\Lambda + 2\,M_{\Sigma^0}\left(\frac{M_{\Sigma^0} - M_p}{M_{\Sigma^0}}\right)\left(\frac{M_{\Xi^0} - M_{\Sigma^0}}{M_{\Sigma^0}}\right)$$

$$(16.33)$$

The last term involving the ratios of masses is small ($\sim 4\%$), we have not systematically kept all terms of this order, so dropping it, we get the mass relation

$$2(M_p + M_{\Xi^0}) = M_{\Sigma^0} + 3M_\Lambda \qquad (16.34)$$

In comparing these mass formulae with the actual masses, the first three mass relations in (16.33) are seen to be valid within an error of 0.2%, 0.7% and 0.5% respectively. The last relation (16.34) is seen to hold to within 0.6%, or to within 1.6% if we include the neglected terms involving the mass ratios in (16.33). Simple symmetry-based arguments, even in a situation where the symmetry is not perfect, have given remarkable agreement with data.

We can try a similar game with the meson masses as well, but recall that the action for (pseudo)scalar particles involves the square of the masses. Thus the effective action for the mesons must have terms of the form

$$S = \int d^4x \left[\frac{1}{2}(\partial\phi)^2 - \frac{M^2}{2}\phi^2 + \cdots\right] \qquad (16.35)$$

This shows that the mass formulae should be phrased in terms of M^2, rather than M, leading to

$$2(M_K^2 + M_{K^0}^2) = M_\pi^2 + 3\,M_\eta^2 \qquad (16.36)$$

This is seen to hold to about 7% accuracy, not as good as the previous ones, but still quite good for a simple symmetry-based analysis.

Remark 16.4.
Imperfect symmetry and mixing

Since $SU(3)_f$ symmetry is imperfect, we might expect that the classification of mesons and baryons into multiplets is somewhat suspect. In other words, the separation of different multiplets (of the same spin and parity content) cannot be rigidly maintained. The effect of symmetry breaking is small, but we might expect that states from different multiplets can mix as well, in addition to the mass differences among the members of a given multiplet. So the assignment of the quark content to the physical meson states in Table 16.1 is only approximate, although it is a very good approximation. There are many examples of mixings between members of the octets and the singlet. Let us consider two quark-antiquark fields denoted by

$$\phi_0 = \frac{1}{\sqrt{3}} (\bar{u}u + \bar{d}d + \bar{s}s)$$

$$\phi_8 = \frac{1}{\sqrt{6}} (\bar{u}u + \bar{d}d - 2\,\bar{s}s) \tag{16.37}$$

The physical η and η' states are then given by

$$\eta = \cos\theta\, \phi_8 - \sin\theta\, \phi_0, \qquad \eta' = \sin\theta\, \phi_8 + \cos\theta\, \phi_0 \tag{16.38}$$

The mixing angle θ is approximately -11.5°, so the identification of the η with ϕ_8 and η' with ϕ_0 as in Table 16.1 is quite good, although the mixing is observationally not negligible. There are similar results for the vector and scalar mesons.

Chapter 17

Spontaneous Symmetry Breaking

In this lecture, we will start considering the ingredients for a theory of weak interactions. The key point we have made so far is that the theory at low energies is described by the $V - A$ theory with an interaction term of the form

$$S_{int} = \frac{G_F}{\sqrt{2}} \int d^4x \ \bar{e}\gamma_\mu(1 - \gamma^5)\nu_e \ \bar{\nu}_\mu \gamma^\mu(1 - \gamma^5)\mu \qquad (17.1)$$

with similar expressions for the other cases such as the decay of the neutron. This form leads, by a simple dimensional analysis, to scattering cross sections which rise with energy as $G_F^2 s$ where $s = (p + p')^2$ is the Lorentz-invariant quantity $(E + E')^2 - (\vec{p} + \vec{p}')^2$ for the two incoming particles. This continual rise of the cross section is unacceptable from the point of view of quantum mechanics since there is a bound on the cross sections due to the bound on probabilities (namely that the probability for any process cannot exceed 1). We have discussed how the inclusion of a mediating particle $W_\mu^\pm$ could improve this since we can obtain (17.1) from a vertex of the form

$$S_{int} = \frac{g}{2\sqrt{2}} \int d^4x \ \left[\bar{e}\gamma^\mu(1 - \gamma^5)\nu_e \ W_\mu^- + \bar{\nu}_\mu \gamma^\nu(1 - \gamma^5)\mu \ W_\nu^+ \right] \qquad (17.2)$$

However, while this does improve matters, it still does not resolve the issue completely. This is because the $W^\pm$ have to be massive to account for the short range nature of the interaction and the propagator for a massive vector particle is of the form

$$D_{\mu\nu}(x, y) = -\int \frac{d^4p}{(2\pi)^4} e^{-ip(x-y)} \frac{i}{p^2 - M^2 + i\epsilon} \left(\eta_{\mu\nu} - \frac{p_\mu p_\nu}{M^2} \right) \qquad (17.3)$$

We have discussed similar propagators for the photon, for which $M^2 = 0$ and we do not get the last term $p_\mu p_\nu / M^2$. In that case, the large p behavior of the propagator goes like p^{-2}. This helps with the large momentum behavior, cutting off growing cross sections for processes involving the photon exchange and leading to the $1/s$ fall-off mentioned in Lectures 7 and 8. The importance of the p^{-2}-behavior in the cross section is also apparent from the explicit calculation in Lecture 7. In the present case, the $p_\mu p_\nu / M^2$-term shows that at large p, we have a term of the order of unity, since $p_\mu p_\nu / p^2 \sim 1$. Thus just postulating a massive vector particle like the $W^\pm$ is not adequate to resolve the issue of the cross sections. (The $p_\mu p_\nu / M^2$-term was not included in our discussion in Lecture 10, equation (10.2), since we were focusing on low momentum transfer.)

The solution to this problem is to use spontaneous symmetry breaking as the basic mechanism for masses. This idea, which was enunciated and explored in the 1960s and early 1970s, provides the only formalism for massive vector particles which is consistent with the general principles of standard quantum field theory. So it plays a very important role in the Standard Model. But before we get to the specifics of how this is implemented for weak interactions, we will need to discuss spontaneous symmetry breaking in some detail.

So what is spontaneous symmetry breaking? This arises when the lowest energy state of a system is degenerate and the entire dynamics which governs the system is symmetric in the sense that it does not discriminate among the various possible ground states. In other words, there is a symmetry transformation which can transform these ground states into one another and the dynamics is invariant under this symmetry. Consider then trying to put the system in the ground state, by cooling it, for example. At some point, the system makes a transition to one of the possible ground states, thereby breaking the symmetry among the ground states. This is called *spontaneous symmetry breaking*. The key point here is that the dynamics (action, Hamiltonian, etc.) preserves the symmetry, but the choice of the ground state breaks it. That is why it is called *spontaneous*, as opposed to explicit symmetry breaking which may happen when we have additional perturbations in the Hamiltonian which are not symmetric. (An example of the latter would be when we have an external electric field for the Hydrogen atom which breaks the rotational symmetry of the Hamiltonian by the perturbation $e\vec{E} \cdot \vec{x}$. The breaking of the $SU(3)_f$ flavor symmetry for the light quarks due to quark masses or weak interaction effects, which we have already discussed, is another example.) In the case of spontaneous symmetry breaking, we can start with one particular ground state and build up the excited states. The probability of transitions between the possible ground states is negligible ($\sim \exp(-cN^\alpha)$) for some positive power α where

N is the number of degrees of freedom in the system) and is zero in the limit of large number of degrees of freedom, in other words, in the thermodynamic limit. (*A priori*, it may seem that the system can choose to be in a mixture of the possible ground states, but the vanishing transition probability between the different ground states in the large N limit shows that this is not possible. Over each ground state, we can construct a complete set of states (a full Hilbert space) with time-evolution restricted entirely to that Hilbert space, and consistent with the conservation of probability.)

Let us take a specific example of a continuous symmetry being broken spontaneously. We will consider a spin-zero field with the action given by

$$S = \int d^4x \left[\partial_\mu \phi^* \, \partial^\mu \phi - \lambda (\phi^* \phi - a)^2 \right] \tag{17.4}$$

We have included an interaction term $\lambda(\phi^*\phi)^2$ (with $\lambda > 0$) and also left the "mass term" $-2\lambda a \, \phi^* \phi$ with an arbitrary sign for now. This theory has a $U(1)$ symmetry. If we replace ϕ by $e^{i\theta}\phi$, where θ is independent of spacetime coordinates, the action is unchanged and we have $S(e^{i\theta}\phi) = S(\phi)$. This is the meaning of symmetry. In this case it is a global $U(1)$ symmetry. It is $U(1)$ because $e^{i\theta}$ may be considered as an element of the set of all 1×1 unitary matrices (which forms $U(1)$) and it is global because θ is independent of the coordinates, so the same transformation is being made globally over all of spacetime. Since $\partial_\mu \phi^* \partial^\mu \phi = |\partial_0 \phi|^2 - |\nabla \phi|^2$, we can identify a kinetic energy and a potential energy, with S having the structure

$$S = \int d^4x \left[|\partial_0 \phi|^2 - |\nabla \phi|^2 - \lambda(\phi^*\phi - a)^2 \right] \equiv \int dt \, (T - V) \tag{17.5}$$

$$T = \int d^3x \, |\partial_0 \phi|^2$$

$$V = \int d^3x \left[|\nabla \phi|^2 + \lambda(\phi^*\phi - a)^2 \right]$$

The energy or the Hamiltonian may be immediately written down as

$$\mathcal{E} = \int d^3x \left[|\partial_0 \phi|^2 + |\nabla \phi|^2 + \lambda(\phi^*\phi - a)^2 - \lambda a^2 \right] \tag{17.6}$$

This is $T + V$, but we have added a constant as well, whose interpretation will be clear soon.

We can now analyze the ground state structure of the theory. This is a relatively easy task, at least classically.

Case when $a < 0$

First consider the case of the parameter a being negative. We can write out the terms in $\mathcal{E}$ as

$$\mathcal{E} = \int d^3x \; \left[|\partial_0\phi|^2 + |\nabla\phi|^2 + 2\lambda|a| \, \phi^*\phi + \lambda(\phi^*\phi)^2 \right] \tag{17.7}$$

All the terms in the integrand are positive, so clearly the ground state has to have zero values for all these. Thus it is characterized by

$$\partial_0\phi = 0, \quad \nabla\phi = 0, \quad \phi = 0 \tag{17.8}$$

In other words, the ground state is such that the field ϕ has the value zero in that state. The constant term $-\lambda a^2$ was added in (17.6) so that the ground state energy (in this phase when $a < 0$) is zero.

One can also look at excited states by considering deviations from the ground state. So we write

$$\phi = \text{ground state value} + \text{deviation}$$
$$= 0 + \phi = \phi \tag{17.9}$$

We substitute this expression for the field into the action to see what the excitations look like. Evidently, we see that the excitations must be interpreted as spin zero particles of mass $m = \sqrt{2\lambda|a|}$, with an interaction vertex given by $\lambda(\phi^*\phi)^2$. There are two spin zero particles of equal mass, represented by the real and imaginary parts of the field ϕ.

Case when $a > 0$

Now let us consider the case when $a > 0$. In this case, we leave the energy expression as it is in (17.6). Apart from the constant term, the other terms are positive and hence minimizing this value for the ground state gives

$$\partial_0\phi = 0, \quad \nabla\phi = 0, \quad \phi^*\phi = a \tag{17.10}$$

This shows that we can take ϕ to be independent of the spacetime coordinates in the ground state and further, it should have a nonzero value equal to, say,

$$\phi = \sqrt{a} \tag{17.11}$$

(There is a phase choice which is not determined by (17.10), but we take this phase to be zero.) Notice that the nonzero value (17.11) breaks the symmetry, since the right hand side in (17.11) is fixed; hence if we transform ϕ as $\phi \to e^{i\theta}\phi$, the equation (17.11) is not preserved. Thus we have

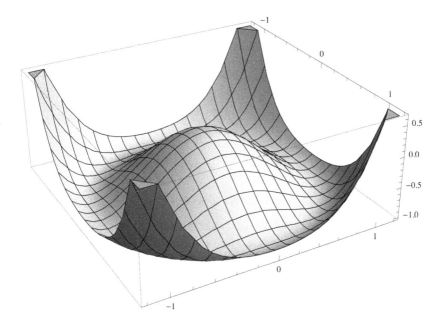

Fig. 17.1: The potential energy of the field ϕ for the case $a > 0$. The axes correspond to the real and imaginary parts of ϕ. There is a circle of minima (the circular valley in the picture) which are all degenerate. One has to choose one of these values as the value of ϕ for the ground state.

spontaneous symmetry breaking. It is also useful to visualize this graphically. Since ϕ is independent of spacetime in the ground state, the potential in (17.6) may be displayed as shown in Fig. 17.1. Notice that there is a circle of minima which correspond to an infinity of degenerate ground states labeled by the azimuthal angle of the circle. We have to make a choice for the value of ϕ in the ground state. No matter what choice we make, the symmetry is lost, since we have to pick one point on the circle of minima as the value of ϕ for the ground state. (The physics of the problem does not depend on which specific point on the circle of minima is chosen, or in other words, which value of the phase α we choose for $\phi = \sqrt{a}\, e^{i\alpha}$ in the ground state; in (17.11) we have chosen $\alpha = 0$.)

Let us now look at the excited states. In this case, we write

$$\phi = \text{ground state value} + \text{deviation}$$
$$= \sqrt{a} + (\eta_1 + i\,\eta_2)/\sqrt{2} \tag{17.12}$$

where we have written out the real and imaginary parts of the deviation of ϕ from the ground state value as η_1 and η_2. (The $1/\sqrt{2}$ is a normalization factor which simplifies things but is not important for the physics we want to talk about.) Substituting (17.12) into the action (17.5) and simplifying,

$$S = \int d^4x \left[\frac{1}{2}(\partial_\mu \eta_1 \, \partial^\mu \eta_1) + \frac{1}{2}(\partial_\mu \eta_2 \, \partial^\mu \eta_2) - \frac{1}{2}(4\lambda a)\,\eta_1^2 \right.$$

$$\left. -\sqrt{2a}\,\lambda\,\eta_1(\eta_1^2 + \eta_2^2) - \frac{\lambda}{4}\,(\eta_1^2 + \eta_2^2)^2 \right]$$

$$= \int d^4x \left[\frac{1}{2}(\partial_\mu \eta_1 \, \partial^\mu \eta_1) + \frac{1}{2}(\partial_\mu \eta_2 \, \partial^\mu \eta_2) - \frac{1}{2}(4\lambda a)\,\eta_1^2 \right.$$

$$\left. + \text{interaction terms} \right] \tag{17.13}$$

The nature of excitations can be read off from the terms quadratic in the fields. We see that we have a spin zero particle η_1 of mass $m = \sqrt{4\lambda a}$ and a spin zero *massless* particle represented by η_2. These are all mutually interacting due to the interaction terms which are cubic and quartic in the fields.

We are now ready for a number of clarifications and examples.

(1) Even though the analysis was classical, one can use this to build up the quantum theory, taking η_1, η_2 as the quantum fields representing the excitations, which are interpreted as particles. One can also find the propagators for these from the inverse of the differential operator in the quadratic term and construct Feynman diagrams and amplitudes for processes using the interaction terms.

(2) The appearance of a massless particle in the case of spontaneous breaking of a symmetry which is characterized by a continuous parameter (such as the angle θ in $\phi \to e^{i\theta}\phi$ in the present case) is a generic feature. It can be proved generally, both classically and quantum mechanically, and is known as Goldstone's theorem. We may state this as follows.

Prop 17.1 (Goldstone's Theorem). For every continuous global symmetry (labeled by a continuous parameter) which is *spontaneously* broken, there exists a particle whose energy goes to zero as the momentum goes to zero.

Such a particle is known as a Goldstone boson. It is a massless particle in relativistic physics, it can be viewed as a gapless excitation for the case of nonrelativistic physics.

(3) How can we have $a < 0$ or $a > 0$? Generally speaking this is possible for different values of some externally controlled parameter. For example, a typical situation is when a is a function of temperature T, with the sign of a depending on whether we are above some critical value, say $T > T_c$, or below the same critical value, $T < T_c$. One can model this approximately as

$$a = -c\,(T - T_c), \qquad c > 0, \tag{17.14}$$

so that $a > 0$ for $T < T_c$ and $a < 0$ for $T > T_c$. The fact that ϕ passes from a nonzero value for the lowest energy state at $T < T_c$ to a value equal to zero for the lowest energy state at $T > T_c$ may be interpreted as a phase transition. In the case of $T < T_c$, we may think of the constant term in $\mathcal{E}$ in (17.6) as the energy released by the system or the energy advantage in making a transition to the new phase characterized by the nonzero value of ϕ.

(4) As an example of spontaneous symmetry breaking, consider the ferromagnet. We may view the magnet as made of little atomic magnets, each of magnetic moment $\vec{\mu}$, at sites corresponding to some lattice of atoms. Generally, these atomic magnets have a Hamiltonian of the form

$$H = -J \sum_{\alpha} \vec{\mu}_\alpha \cdot \vec{\mu}_{\alpha+1} \tag{17.15}$$

where α labels the lattice sites and J is a constant, related to the so-called exchange integral. (This is the Heisenberg Hamiltonian for the ferromagnet.) Because we have a scalar product of the vectors $\vec{\mu}_\alpha$ and $\vec{\mu}_{\alpha+1}$, the Hamiltonian is symmetric under rotations. At high temperatures, the orientations of the atomic magnets are completely random due to thermal agitation and the net magnetization of the material is zero. This is the symmetric phase. When the material is cooled below the Curie temperature T_c, it develops a net magnetization, $\langle \sum_\alpha \vec{\mu}_\alpha \rangle \neq 0$. The question is: In which direction will this magnetization be? Since the Hamiltonian has complete rotational symmetry, the direction of the net magnetization is arbitrary. But once there is a net magnetization, we do not have the rotational symmetry any more. There is spontaneous symmetry breaking.

The gapless excitations which must exist according to Goldstone's theorem are the spin waves or magnons. For a ferromagnet, we expect an energy $E_k \sim k^2$, showing the gapless nature of the magnon spectrum.

(5) As another example, we can consider a gas of atoms condensing to form a lattice. In the gas phase, the atoms can move around arbitrarily and the local environment around any point in the gas looks the same as anywhere else. Thus there is symmetry under translations by an arbitrary amount. In other words, $\vec{x} \to \vec{x} + \vec{\epsilon}$, for any amount $\vec{\epsilon}$, is a symmetry. When the gas condenses and forms a lattice we do not have symmetry under translations by an arbitrary amount. Instead, we only have symmetry under translations by a lattice vector, $\vec{x} \to \vec{x} + n_i \vec{G}_i$. ($n_i$ are integers and $\vec{G}_i$ are the unit lattice vectors.) Thus the continuous symmetry of arbitrary translations is spontaneously broken. Since there are three directions of arbitrary translations possible initially, we expect three gapless excitations according to Goldstone's theorem. These are the three acoustic phonons or acoustic modes of lattice vibrations.

The Higgs mechanism

A special case of spontaneous symmetry breaking which is very important for us is when the symmetry is local rather than global. This means that we consider symmetries like $\phi \to e^{-iq\theta}\phi$ where θ can be a function of spacetime coordinates. (q is the analogue of the electric charge for this $U(1)$ symmetry.) Thus the value of θ can change from point to point. We know that this will require a gauge potential, and covariant derivatives which are constructed using it. In the case of the $U(1)$ symmetry for a field ϕ, it is like electromagnetism and we can write the action as

$$S = \int d^4x \; [(D_\mu \phi)^* (D^\mu \phi) - \lambda(\phi^*\phi - a)^2] - \frac{1}{4}\int d^4x \; F_{\mu\nu}F^{\mu\nu} \quad (17.16)$$

where $D_\mu \phi = \partial_\mu \phi + iqA_\mu \phi$. We have also added in the action for A_μ with $F_{\mu\nu} = \partial_\mu A_\nu - \partial_\nu A_\mu$. (We will use the language of electromagnetism to illustrate many points, but it should be kept in mind that A_μ does not have to be the vector potential of the electromagnetic field and the $U(1)$ symmetry we are considering does not have to be the gauge symmetry of electromagnetism.) The Hamiltonian for the action can be written down in analogy to what we did before. It is given by

$$\mathcal{E} = \int d^3x \; \left[|D_0\phi|^2 + |D_i\phi|^2 + \lambda(\phi^*\phi - a)^2 + \frac{1}{2}(F_{0i})^2 + \frac{1}{2}(B_iB_i) - \lambda a^2 \right] \quad (17.17)$$

where $F_{ij} = \epsilon_{ijk}B^k$. Again, as before, we have added a constant term to the energy density. The analysis of the ground state proceeds as before. The expression for the energy has an integrand with positive terms (except for the last term which is irrelevant for the minimization). Thus the minimum of the energy function is obtained as follows.

Case when a < 0

For the ground state we need

$$D_0\phi = 0, \quad D_i\phi = 0, \quad \phi = 0, \quad F_{0i} = 0, \quad F_{ij} = 0 \qquad (17.18)$$

In this case, the choice of values $A_i = 0$, $A_0 = 0$ (up to a gauge transformation) and $\phi = 0$ gives the ground state. The excitations can be analyzed as before. The only difference is that we consider both ϕ and A_μ as fields which can be excited. The action is

$$S = \int d^4x \; [(\partial_\mu\phi)^* \, (\partial^\mu\phi) - 2\lambda\,|a|\phi^*\phi] - \frac{1}{4}\int d^4x \; F_{\mu\nu}F^{\mu\nu}$$

$$+ \int d^4x \; \left[-iqA^\mu(\phi^*\partial_\mu\phi - \partial_\mu\phi^* \, \phi) + q^2 A^\mu A_\mu\phi^*\phi - \lambda(\phi^*\phi)^2\right]$$

$$(17.19)$$

This shows that we have massive spin zero particles (two independent ones corresponding to the real and imaginary parts of ϕ, or, equivalently, a charged spin zero particle and its antiparticle) of mass $m = \sqrt{2\lambda\,|a|}$ and a massless vector particle like the photon corresponding to A_μ (which will have two polarization states, just like the photon). These interact with one another via the interaction vertices in the second line of (17.19).

Case when a > 0

In this case, the ground state must have

$$D_0\phi = 0, \quad D_i\phi = 0, \quad \phi^*\phi = a, \quad F_{0i} = 0, \quad F_{ij} = 0 \qquad (17.20)$$

This can be realized by taking the value of ϕ in the ground state to be independent of spacetime coordinates, but nonzero and equal to $\phi = \sqrt{a}$; for the vector field, as before, we can take $A_\mu = 0$. The choice $\phi \neq 0$ breaks the symmetry.

The excitations can be found by using the parametrization of the field as in (17.12). The covariant derivative can be simplified as

$$D_\mu\phi = \frac{1}{\sqrt{2}}\partial_\mu\eta_1 + iq\sqrt{a}\left(A_\mu + \frac{1}{q\sqrt{2a}}\partial_\mu\eta_2\right) + i\frac{q}{\sqrt{2}}A_\mu(\eta_1 + i\eta_2)$$

$$= \frac{1}{\sqrt{2}}\partial_\mu\eta_1 + iq\sqrt{a}\,(A_\mu + \partial_\mu f) + i\frac{q}{\sqrt{2}}A_\mu(\eta_1 + i\eta_2) \qquad (17.21)$$

where $f = \eta_2/q\sqrt{2a}$. Using this in the action, we now find

$$S = \int d^4x \left[\frac{1}{2}(\partial_\mu \eta_1 \, \partial^\mu \eta_1) - \frac{1}{2}(4\lambda a) \, \eta_1^2 + q^2 a \, (A_\mu + \partial_\mu f)^2 \right.$$
$$\left. + \frac{1}{2}(F_{0i})^2 - \frac{1}{2}B^2 \right] + S_{int} \tag{17.22}$$

where S_{int} contains terms which are at least cubic in the fields and hence are to be interpreted as interaction terms. Now, since $F_{\mu\nu}$ is invariant under $A_\mu \to A_\mu + \partial_\mu \theta$ for any function θ, we can redefine $A_\mu + \partial_\mu f$ as our new A_μ. (In principle, accordingly, we must use the new A_μ minus $\partial_\mu f$ in place of A_μ in $F_{\mu\nu}$ but this does not change anything.) Thus, we may replace (17.22) by

$$S = \int d^4x \left[\frac{1}{2}(\partial_\mu \eta_1 \, \partial^\mu \eta_1) - \frac{1}{2}(4\lambda a) \, \eta_1^2 + q^2 a \, A_\mu A^\mu \right.$$
$$\left. + \frac{1}{2}(F_{0i})^2 - \frac{1}{2}\vec{B}^2 \right] + S_{int} \tag{17.23}$$

Once again, from this action, we can read off the nature of the excitations. We have a massive spin zero particle η_1 of mass $\sqrt{4\lambda a}$; but what is significantly different compared to the case of a global symmetry is that there is no massless particle. Instead the gauge potential A_μ has acquired a mass, as indicated by the $(q^2 a)A^2$ term. This mass is given by $m_A = \sqrt{2q^2 a}$.

Notice that in the case of $a < 0$, we had two particles of equal mass $m_\eta = \sqrt{2\lambda|a|}$ and two polarization states for the vector particle, giving 4 types of particles in all (or 4 particle degrees of freedom). In the present case of $a > 0$, we have one massive spin zero particle (η_1) and a massive vector A_μ. Now a massive vector has 3 polarization states rather than two. Thus we still have exactly the same number, namely 4, of particle degrees of freedom. (A massive vector is a spin-1 particle since a vector has spin $s = 1$. The number of polarization states is $2s+1 = 3$. This argument does not apply to a massless vector because we cannot bring it to a frame where it is at rest to use ordinary angular momentum theory. A more careful analysis is needed and shows that a massless vector has only 2 polarization states.)

What is important to us is that we have a way to generate a mass for a vector particle, namely, by spontaneously breaking the symmetry for which the vector particle is the gauge potential. This method of generating a mass is known as the Higgs mechanism. The reason why this is important is the following theorem.

Prop 17.2 (Theorem on the Higgs mechanism). In quantum field theory, the only way to have a massive vector particle consistent with unitarity (or the conservation of probability) being valid to arbitrarily high energies is by generating a mass via the Higgs mechanism, namely, by spontaneous breaking of the local symmetry for which the vector particle is the gauge potential.

We should emphasize that the only mathematical formalism which can incorporate the principles of many particle quantum mechanics and the possibility of creation and decay of particles via interactions is quantum field theory. Given this situation and the theorem given above, we have to use the Higgs mechanism if we want to have massive vector particles. And, from the phenomenology of weak interactions, we know that we do need a massive $W_\mu^\pm$ vector particle to mediate the weak interactions, so that the $V - A$ theory can be obtained in the limit of low momentum transfer, as we have seen in Lecture 10.

However, notice that the spontaneous symmetry breaking gives us more than the massive vector particle. If we use it for getting massive vector particles, we need to have the η_1 excitation as well. Therefore the price of getting a mass for the vector particle in a way consistent with all the desirable principles of quantum mechanics is that the theory should also include a massive spin zero particle. This latter particle is known as the Higgs boson.

Thus, quite strikingly, without any further discussion of weak interactions, we already have one prediction:

Prop 17.3. There should exist a massive spin zero particle which participates in the weak interactions of quarks and leptons.

This is the famous Higgs boson for which evidence was found in the summer of 2012 and confirmed in March, 2013.

Remark 17.1.
A better parametrization for fields

The parametrization of the field ϕ in the symmetry broken phase in terms of small deviations from $\sqrt{a}$, as in (17.12), illustrates the basic physics, but it is useful to consider another parametrization which highlights the symmetry structure. This is given by

$$\phi = \left(\sqrt{a} + \frac{\eta_1}{\sqrt{2}} \right) \exp\left(i\frac{\chi}{\sqrt{2a}} \right) \tag{17.24}$$

The action (17.4) then simplifies as

$$S = \int d^4x \left[\frac{1}{2}(\partial_\mu \eta_1)^2 + \frac{1}{2}(\partial_\mu \chi)^2 \left(1 + \frac{\eta_1}{\sqrt{2a}}\right)^2 - \frac{1}{2}(4\lambda a)\eta_1^2 \right.$$
$$\left. - \lambda\sqrt{2a}\, \eta_1^3 - \frac{\lambda}{4}\eta_1^4 \right] \tag{17.25}$$

The field χ represents the Goldstone particle. Notice that there are no terms which do not involve derivatives of this field; even the interaction terms have derivatives of the Goldstone field. This is a reflection of the symmetry of the action which allows a constant shift $\chi \to \chi + \text{constant}$.

We can use the same parametrization for the case of the Higgs mechanism. We then find

$$D_\mu \phi = \left[\frac{1}{\sqrt{2}}\partial_\mu \eta_1 + iq\left(\sqrt{a} + \frac{\eta_1}{\sqrt{2}}\right)\left(A_\mu + \frac{\partial_\mu \chi}{q\sqrt{2a}}\right) \right] e^{i\chi/\sqrt{2a}} \tag{17.26}$$

Upon using this in the action (17.16) and redefining $A_\mu + \frac{\partial_\mu \chi}{q\sqrt{2a}}$ as the new A_μ, we get

$$S = \int d^4x \left[\frac{1}{2}(\partial_\mu \eta_1)^2 - \frac{1}{2}(4\lambda a)\eta_1^2 - \frac{1}{4}F_{\mu\nu}F^{\mu\nu} + \frac{1}{2}(2q^2 a)\left(1 + \frac{\eta_1}{\sqrt{2a}}\right)^2 A_\mu^2 \right.$$
$$\left. - \lambda\sqrt{2a}\, \eta_1^3 - \frac{\lambda}{4}\eta_1^4 \right] \tag{17.27}$$

Notice that χ has disappeared from all terms in the action, it is absorbed into the gauge field A_μ. Again this is a reflection of the gauge invariance of the action. Masses and interaction terms can be easily read off from (17.25) and (17.27).

In the context of spontaneous symmetry breaking when we have a gauge symmetry, an observation worth remarking upon is the following. When we defined color confinement in Lecture 15, we made a distinction between gauge transformations which tend to the identity (i.e., with parameters $\theta(\vec{x})$ which tend to zero) and those which go to a constant (not necessarily equal to $\mathbb{1}$) at spatial infinity. A similar distinction is important here. The symmetry under the transformations which go to the identity at spatial infinity is not broken when we say we have spontaneous symmetry breaking. This is important for the consistency of the theory; it is needed to redefine $A_\mu + \partial_\mu f$ as the new potential A_μ in going from (17.22) to (17.23) or from (17.26) to (17.27). The symmetry under the transformations which are $\neq \mathbb{1}$ at spatial infinity is what is lost.

For the $U(1)$ symmetry here, if $\theta(\vec{x}) \to \theta(\infty) \neq 0$ as we approach spatial infinity, we may write it as a global transformation (with a constant parameter $\theta(\infty)$) composed with a transformation which becomes the identity at spatial infinity, i.e., $e^{i\theta(\vec{x})} = e^{i\theta(\infty)} e^{i\tilde{\theta}(\vec{x})}$, where $\tilde{\theta}(\vec{x}) = \theta(\vec{x}) - \theta(\infty)$. What we are saying is that it is the global part of the symmetry which is lost.

Remark 17.2.
A bit on the history of the Higgs mechanism and the theory of weak interactions

The idea of gauge transformations and gauge invariance emerged from the coordinate invariance which is the cornerstone of Einstein's general theory of relativity (1915), as we have already discussed. The first use of gauge invariance was in fact shortly after Einstein's theory, due to Herman Weyl in 1919; he used the idea of the length scale of physical phenomena being an invariance of the physics. (This is where the name "gauge" comes from, the gauge or length unit used in measurements.) This idea did not work out in unifying electromagnetism and gravity Herman Weyl had hoped. Shortly afterwards, T. Kaluza in 1921 tried to use a 5-dimensional version of gravity, taking the fifth dimension to be a circle. This leads to gauge invariance as we know it, but it too did not lead to a satisfactory theory of electromagnetism unified with gravity. Later, in the 1930s Oscar Klein revived the Kaluza idea using a higher dimensional version, with the extra dimensions forming a sphere. This effectively gave the Yang-Mills theory, and Klein tried to apply it to a unified theory of nuclear and electromagnetic forces. Needless to say, it did not work out, although this is remarkably prescient work. (Nowadays, we call this way of obtaining gauge symmetry from higher dimensional gravity as Kaluza-Klein theories.)

The importance of gauge symmetry slowly gained acceptance in the 1930s. Dirac's work (1931) on magnetic monopoles put gauge symmetry at the root of the analysis. Also, Fritz and Heinz London's work on superconductivity (1935) showed the importance of the symmetry.

The generalization of gauge symmetry to matrices (bigger than 1×1), and without any reference to the Kaluza-Klein approach using higher dimensions, is due to C.N. Yang and Robert Mills in 1954 and also due to Shaw (who had it in his thesis at Cambridge). They were trying to use it for vector mesons in particle physics, again leading to a theory which was not really correct, despite some nice features. (The vector mesons, in the context they were thinking of, were the ρ-mesons, although historically the latter were predicted by J. Sakurai based on the Yang-Mills work and were experimentally found only by 1961.) The first attempt to use the newly understood gauge symmetry for weak interactions, with the unification of electromagnetism and weak interactions, was due to Schwinger in 1957. The discovery of more and more particles and the complicated nature of weak interactions showed that this theory was far from adequate. In 1961, Sheldon Glashow extended this work of his thesis advisor Schwinger and constructed a theory of weak interactions based on the $SU(2) \times U(1)$ gauge symmetry, essentially the right group from what we know today. The problem of how to give a mass to the vector bosons remained a troublesome point.

The work of Abdus Salam and J.C. Ward in 1964 on a unified theory of weak interactions is also important in the development of the subject. They obtained, independently, essentially the same symmetry structure as Glashow did. Salam was convinced of the importance of gauge symmetry from the point of renormalizability (one of the consistency requirements, at least as understood at that time) of the theory. The idea of spontaneous symmetry breaking evolved with the work of Jeffrey Goldstone and Yoichiro Nambu in the 1950s. In many ways, the newly established Bardeen-Cooper-Schrieffer (BCS) theory of superconductivity (1957) was the inspiration. The possibility of giving a mass to the vector particle was contained, phrased in a different language, in the work of P.W. Anderson in 1958 (and in 1963), although the full appreciation in relativistic quantum field theory took a little more time.

Schwinger had demonstrated the possibility of obtaining massive vector bosons via symmetry breaking (which was done in a dynamical nonperturbative way in his work) in 1962, in two spacetime dimensions. The generalization to four dimensions came in 1964, due to three groups: Peter Higgs presented the theory essentially as we have done, noting the need for the extra spin zero particle. F. Englert and R. Brout had the same mechanism but in a more technical way, so did the group of F. Guralnik, C.R. Hagen and T.W.B. Kibble. All three papers were published in the same issue of the Physical Review Letters. These groups had presented the idea in the context of a $U(1)$ theory; it was not immediately applicable to weak interactions. The person who used this idea and presented the theory of weak interactions in the form we know it today, including the Higgs mechanism for giving masses to the vector bosons of weak forces was Steven Weinberg in 1967. So in some way, the particle discovered at CERN is something Weinberg predicted. Essentially the same result was obtained by Salam shortly afterwards (1968); Salam emphasized again the possibility of this mechanism giving a renormalizable theory.

The extension of Weinberg's and Salam's work to quarks took many steps as well. (Weinberg's 1967 paper only considered the theory of leptons.) The quark model had been around for some time by this point in history, but had remained a "mathematical model", viewed by many physicists as a clever and useful device but it was unclear if one should attribute any reality to the quark as a particle. The work of J.D. Bjorken who predicted scaling of strong nuclear forces (which in retrospect is the essence of asymptotic freedom) and its subsequent discovery at SLAC provided strong evidence that quarks are really particles, not just a useful concept. The inclusion of quarks (of which only the up, down and strange were known at that time) seemed to lead to many problems. There were two possibilities: one was to abandon the $SU(2) \times U(1)$ theory and make a new theory of weak forces. This was attempted by H. Georgi and S. Glashow using the group $SO(3)$, it was entertained for some time, but later experiments which discovered the weak neutral current processes (1973) disproved it. The second alternative was to postulate a fourth quark. Glashow and Bjorken had suggested such a quark in 1964, but even the theoretical evidence was not compelling at that time. The importance of anomalies was appreciated by 1969, due to the work of S. Adler and J. Bell and R. Jackiw. By 1972, the understanding of the anomaly was precise and comprehensive enough to show that we need a fourth quark. Independently, in 1970, S. Glashow, J. Iliopoulos and L. Maiani had argued that the very low value of the rate of the so-called flavor changing neutral current processes could be explained naturally within the $SU(2) \times U(1)$ theory if one postulated an additional quark. Mary Gaillard and Ben Lee calculated the mass of this putative fourth quark in 1974. The fourth quark, now called charm, was discovered in 1974, with the discovery of the J/ψ particle which is a $c\bar{c}$ bound state, although it took some time to clarify that the J/ψ is indeed made of the charm quark and antiquark.

The renormalizability of the theory, which is tantamount to proving the theorem on Higgs mechanism which we have quoted, is generally attributed to G. 't Hooft and M. Veltman. Following up on the work of L. Faddeev and V. Popov, who showed how to set up the quantum field theory of Yang-Mills fields, at least in a form suitable for perturbative calculations, they were able to come up with a procedure for proving the renormalizability (1971). The full proof and the development of a systematic calculational scheme still took a few years.

There are always many parallel developments which come together to make a successful theory. We have talked about ideas from Einstein's theory, from the theory of superconductivity, etc. So it may also be interesting to note that the idea of connections, which is the mathematician's version of gauge symmetry, had its origins in the work of Eli Cartan in the 1920s, his work on the theory of frames, which is itself a close relative of the idea of coordinate invariance in Einstein's theory. This led to the elegant mathematical idea of fiber bundles which were developed in the 1930s and '40s by the mathematics community. The notion of connection, which was used in the mathematical work, was defined in terms of differential forms and hence is very much what physicists call a gauge field. The general definition of a connection without the use of differential forms was given in the context of fiber bundles by Ehresmann in 1950. None of this was known to physicists, and the possibility of applying any of this to physics was simply not appreciated. It was only years later (1970s onwards), much after the work of Yang and Mills, that related ideas from physics and mathematics were traded back and forth and led to significant new developments in both.

Remark 17.3.
Nuancing QCD: PCAC and the $U(1)_A$ problem

Spontaneous symmetry breaking, as we have already mentioned, is very important for constructing the theory of weak interactions. But even for the strong nuclear forces, namely, for QCD, it plays a significant role. To see how this arises, let us consider again the Lagrangian for the light quarks, as given in (15.9),

$$\mathcal{L}_1 + \mathcal{L}_2 = \bar{Q}^\alpha (i\gamma^\mu D_\mu) Q_\alpha - \bar{Q}^\alpha M_\alpha{}^\beta Q_\beta$$

$$M = \begin{bmatrix} m_u & 0 & 0 \\ 0 & m_d & 0 \\ 0 & 0 & m_s \end{bmatrix} \tag{17.28}$$

Here Qs are 4-component spinors representing the quarks, which also have a color index and a flavor index α. We also know that a spinor can be split into the chiral components, as

$$\Psi_L = \frac{1-\gamma^5}{2}\,\Psi, \qquad \Psi_R = \frac{1+\gamma^5}{2}\,\Psi \tag{17.29}$$

(These are the U and V components in the notation we used when discussing the Dirac equation.) From this definition, $\bar{\Psi}_L = \bar{\Psi}(1+\gamma^5)/2$ and $\bar{\Psi}_R = \bar{\Psi}(1-\gamma^5)/2$. As a result, since γ^μ anticommutes with γ^5, the first term of (17.28) can be written in terms of these components as

$$\mathcal{L}_1 = \bar{Q}^\alpha_L (i\gamma^\mu D_\mu) Q_{L\alpha} + \bar{Q}^\alpha_R (i\gamma^\mu D_\mu) Q_{R\alpha} \tag{17.30}$$

The mass term in (17.28) will mix the left and right chiral components.

If we neglect the masses for a first pass at considering the symmetries which determine the bound state spectrum of the light quarks, which is what we did in Lecture 15, the Lagrangian (17.30) tells us that the symmetry is larger than the flavor $SU(3)_f$ we discussed. In fact, we can do independent $U(3)$ transformations on the left and right components as

$$Q_{L\alpha} \to \mathbf{U}_\alpha^{(L)\,\beta} Q_{L\beta}, \qquad Q_{R\alpha} \to \mathbf{U}_\alpha^{(R)\,\beta} Q_{R\beta} \qquad (17.31)$$

where $\mathbf{U}^{(L)}$ and $\mathbf{U}^{(R)}$ can be two different (independently chosen) 3×3 unitary matrices. They must still be spacetime independent matrices, so the full flavor symmetry of (17.30) is $U(3) \times U(3)$, often referred to as the chiral symmetry of QCD. If we split off the $U(1)$ parts corresponding to the determinants of these matrices, then we have $SU(3)_L \times SU(3)_R$ and two $U(1)$s acting on the Qs as

$$Q_L \to e^{i\theta_L} Q_L, \qquad Q_R \to e^{i\theta_R} Q_R \qquad (17.32)$$

Let us focus first on the $SU(3)_L \times SU(3)_R$; here we have emphasized that there are two independent $SU(3)$s by the subscripts L, R. We also know that under a parity transformation, the left and right chiral components get exchanged, as worked out in (9.15). The flavor symmetry $SU(3)_f$ which we discussed in Lecture 15 corresponds to choosing the same matrix for the left and the right, i.e., the subset of transformations in $SU(3)_L \times SU(3)_R$ with $\mathbf{U}^{(L)} = \mathbf{U}^{(R)}$. For this reason, $SU(3)_f$ is sometimes referred to as the diagonal subgroup of $SU(3)_L \times SU(3)_R$. The charge corresponding to the diagonal $U(1)$ acting on the quarks as in (17.32) with $\theta_L = \theta_R$ can be identified with the baryon number of the quarks.

Now, if we follow Wigner's theorem on symmetries in quantum mechanics, we would expect that the spectrum of mesons and baryons would be grouped into multiplets corresponding to $SU(3)_L \times SU(3)_R$; they would also carry definite $U(1)_L$ and $U(1)_R$ charges. Thus if we have an octet of mesons for $SU(3)_L$, then there should be another octet corresponding to $SU(3)_R$. Further, since QCD preserves parity, the two sets of mesons should have equal masses (or nearly equal even after the effects of the parity-breaking weak interactions are included). A similar argument should hold for the baryons as well. But the observed spectrum does not show this at all. While we have light mesons like the pion, the only partner we may expect for it, the purely scalar meson, has a very high mass. How can we explain this? The suggestion, going back to Nambu, is that the full symmetry $U(3)_L \times U(3)_R$ is not realized *à la* Wigner, that a part of the symmetry is *spontaneously broken* by the strong QCD interactions. More specifically, the symmetry $U(3)_L \times U(3)_R$ is spontaneously broken such that the subset of transformations in $U(3)_f$ are still preserved.

If we have spontaneous symmetry breaking, we must have Goldstone bosons. In particular, since the unbroken transformations have $\mathbf{U}^{(L)} = \mathbf{U}^{(R)}$, the broken transformations must be odd under parity. We see this from the general parametrization of the transformations as

$$\mathbf{U}^{(L)} = e^{it_a \theta_L^a} = e^{i\frac{1}{2}t_a(\theta_L^a + \theta_R^a) + i\frac{1}{2}t_a(\theta_L^a - \theta_R^a)}$$

$$\mathbf{U}^{(R)} = e^{it_a \theta_R^a} = e^{i\frac{1}{2}t_a(\theta_L^a + \theta_R^a) - i\frac{1}{2}t_a(\theta_L^a - \theta_R^a)} \tag{17.33}$$

The unbroken part corresponds to the parameters $\frac{1}{2}(\theta_L^a + \theta_R^a)$ and the broken part $(\frac{1}{2}(\theta_L^a - \theta_R^a))$ is evidently odd under parity. Thus we expect pseudoscalar particles as Goldstone bosons. Since 8 symmetries are broken in going from $SU(3)_L \times SU(3)_R$ to $SU(3)_f$, we should expect an octet of Goldstone bosons. These would have been massless if the starting symmetry were perfect; but we know that the mass term in (17.28) makes the symmetry less than perfect, breaking the $U(3)_L \times U(3)_R$ even if the quark masses have the same nonzero value, so we expect very low mass bosons. This is indeed the case. The octet of mesons made of the pion, the kaon and eta are pseudoscalar and have masses significantly below the masses for the vector mesons, the scalar mesons, etc.

Since the breaking is spontaneous (on top of the smaller explicit breaking due to the mass term and other weak interactions), we can say something more. For this, consider the action for the spontaneous breaking of a $U(1)$ symmetry,

$$S = \int d^4x \; \left[(\partial_\mu \phi)^* (\partial^\mu \phi) - \lambda(\phi^* \phi - a)^2 \right] \tag{17.34}$$

The current corresponding to the symmetry can be obtained as

$$J_\mu = i \left(\phi^* \, \partial_\mu \phi - \partial_\mu \phi^* \, \phi \right) \tag{17.35}$$

(The simplest way to obtain this is to take the gauged version (17.16), find the current for the Maxwell field (via its equation of motion) and then set $A_\mu = 0$.) In accordance with spontaneous symmetry breaking, for small deviations from the ground state, we write $\phi \approx \sqrt{a} + (\eta_1 + i\,\eta_2)/\sqrt{2}$. Using this,

$$J_\mu \approx -\sqrt{2a} \; \partial_\mu \eta_2 + \cdots \tag{17.36}$$

This is interesting, the current is linear in the Goldstone field. So the idea of spontaneously breaking the $U(3)_L \times U(3)_R$ symmetry solves another problem as well. The current should be linear in the pion field and so it naturally explains the weak decay of the pion using the $V - A$ theory with its current-current interaction, as we already mentioned in Lecture 9. Once we put in all the right factors for the $SU(3)_L \times SU(3)_R$ symmetry, rather than the simple $U(1)$ case in (17.36), the current can be written as

$$J_\mu^{(\pi^+)} \approx i f_\pi \partial_\mu \pi^+ + \cdots \tag{17.37}$$

with similar expressions for the other pseudoscalar mesons, the π^0, π^-, $K^\pm$, K^0, $\bar{K}^0$ and η.

Further, if the current is conserved, as it should be for spontaneous breaking, we find from (17.36),

$$\Box \eta_2 + (\text{terms quadratic and higher order in fields}) = 0 \tag{17.38}$$

The term linear in η_2 is consistent with the fact that the Goldstone boson is massless. In fact the conservation law $\partial_\mu J^\mu = 0$ may be viewed as the equation of motion for the Goldstone boson. For the case of the pion, we must have a mass term as well in its equation of motion. Since the symmetry is not perfect, we also do not have a strict conservation law, so there is no inconsistency. From (17.37), we expect

$$\partial_\mu J^{(\pi^+) \mu} = i f_\pi \Box \pi^+ + \cdots = i f_\pi \left(-m_\pi^2 \pi^+\right) + \cdots \approx -i f_\pi m_\pi^2 \pi^+ \tag{17.39}$$

We see that the current is not conserved, but the breaking due to the mass is expected to be small (since we argued that the mass terms can be neglected as a first approximation), so the result (17.39) is referred to as the partial conservation of axial vector current (PCAC). The current is axial since we are considering the parity-odd transformations.

This idea of the spontaneous breaking of the chiral $SU(3)_L \times SU(3)_R$ symmetry explains the absence of additional states in the spectrum and also gives the coupling of the pseudoscalar mesons to the weak interaction part of the theory, as in (9.24). But what about the $U(1)$s? As mentioned before, of the two $U(1)$s, the combination with $\theta_L = \theta_R$ can be considered as baryon number (or quark number). It has its own interesting physics, but for now, we will still leave it alone. The other $U(1)$ with $\theta_L = -\theta_R$ is the axial $U(1)$ (or parity-odd transformation) and it should also be spontaneously broken. But the pseudoscalar meson corresponding to it is the η' meson, which has a very high mass (around 958 MeV) compared to the pion and the kaon. This raises doubts about whether it is really a Goldstone particle (with a small mass generated from weak interactions). This difficulty is known as the $U(1)_A$ problem. The solution, it turns out, is that $U(1)_A$ is not a symmetry, even if we neglect the masses. It is possible that not all classical symmetries (or symmetries visible at the Lagrangian level) can be realized in the quantum theory, since, in addition to the action, we need prescriptions for making the quantum theory well defined without potential infinities. A regularization procedure is needed. A careful calculation of the conservation law for the axial vector current $J_A^\mu = \bar{Q}^\alpha \gamma^\mu \gamma^5 Q_\alpha$ (for the $U(1)_A$ symmetry) gives

$$\partial_\mu J_A^\mu = 2\,i\,\bar{Q}^\alpha\, M_\alpha^\beta \gamma^5 Q_\beta - N_{\rm f}\left(\frac{1}{32\pi^2}\,\epsilon^{\mu\nu\lambda\sigma}\,F_{\mu\nu}^a\,F_{\lambda\sigma}^a\right) \qquad (17.40)$$

Here $\epsilon^{\mu\nu\lambda\sigma}$ is the Levi-Civita symbol in four dimensions and $N_{\rm f}$ is the number of quark flavors, equal to 3 for the present discussion. The first term on the right hand side of (17.40) is the breaking effect due to the mass term. This is as expected and gives a term $-if_{\eta'}m_{\eta'}^2\eta'$ for the η' meson, as in (17.39). But the second term involves the gluon fields $F_{\mu\nu}^a$ and is not small on the scale of the symmetry-breaking effects; its scale is controlled by QCD, which also sets the spontaneous breaking scale for the chiral $U(3)_L \times U(3)_R$ symmetry. So for the $U(1)_A$, the symmetry is already rather badly broken in an explicit fashion that it does not make sense to consider η' as a Goldstone particle, even if we can ignore the mass effects.

The breaking of a classical symmetry due to quantum effects is known as an anomaly. Thus we can say that the $U(1)_A$ transformations are anomalous and do not constitute a true symmetry even when the masses are neglected.

With this understanding of the spontaneous breaking of the chiral $SU(3)_L \times SU(3)_R$ symmetry, we have one more task in the "to be proved" list for QCD. In addition to proving color confinement, we must also prove the spontaneous breaking of the chiral symmetry.

Chapter 18

Superconductivity and Electroweak Interactions

We have talked about spontaneous symmetry breaking and the Higgs mechanism. We also mentioned that much of the inspiration for this came from the theory of superconductivity. We will talk about this in some more detail here, since it provides a very concrete realization of the ideas we want to explore.

Superconductivity, in its basic definition, is the phenomenon that the electrical resistance of certain materials abruptly drops to zero below a certain critical temperature. This was originally found in the case of mercury by Kamerlingh Onnes in 1911. Since then a large number of other examples have been found. The development of a theoretical explanation took a very long time, because the phenomenon is a quantum many-body problem and the ideas and techniques of quantum theory had to come to a mature stage before an explanation could be found. The crucial breakthrough came in 1957 with the Bardeen-Cooper-Schrieffer (BCS) theory, although earlier ideas due to the London brothers, Landau, Ginzburg, Fröhlich and others were significant advances.

We will talk about the theory in terms of an effective field representing the so-called Cooper pair. This is not the BCS theory which is based on more fundamental physics and provides the justification for the effective theory we consider. The key ingredient in superconductivity (at least for the earlier generation of BCS-type superconductors) is the electron-phonon interaction, or the interaction of electrons in a material with the lattice vibrations. We know that electrons repel each other via the electrostatic Coulomb interaction, but it is possible to generate an attractive force between them mediated by the lattice of positive ions in a solid. Qualitatively, we can see this as follows. Consider the lattice of ions as shown in Fig. 18.1. Let us focus on an electron which is near a pair of ions. The attraction

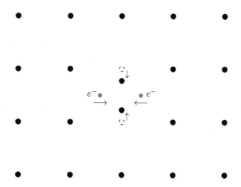

Fig. 18.1: Showing how the movement of lattice ions can lead to an attractive force between electrons in a material

between the electron and the ions can lead to a small deformation of the movement of the ions, making them come a little closer (from the dashed positions which are their normal equilibrium positions). Now considering another electron which is nearby, we see that the increased positive charge between the two electrons can attract them both towards the central charge density. If we view this as something just between the electrons, mentally erasing the ions for the moment, we see that it is an attractive force between the two electrons. This is essentially the point. The ability of the ions to move around their equilibrium position is important; in other words, lattice vibrations come into play. The ions as they come together will impart a mutually attractive impulse to the two electrons, which goes back to being the Coulomb repulsion as the ions move away from each other, so effectively we have a periodic force generated between the electrons. The net result therefore will be not just a static force, but something that depends on the momenta of the electrons involved.

This attractive force can become large enough to overcome the Coulomb repulsion for electrons of energy very close to the Fermi level, which is the highest occupied state for the system of electrons if they are at zero temperature. The effect is thus pronounced at low temperatures. The result of this attraction is that a bound state of two electrons can form. This bound state is called a Cooper pair. Being a state formed of two fermions, this is a bosonic state and hence can, in principle, undergo Bose-Einstein condensation at low temperatures. This condensation is the transition that leads to superconductivity.

The phenomenon can be described in an approximate way by introducing a field Φ which represents the Cooper pair. This is a field of electric charge $-2e$. We can then construct an effective action which will approximately describe the dynamics, including the Bose-Einstein condensation. The needed covariant derivative is $D_\mu \Phi = \partial_\mu \Phi + iqA_\mu \Phi = \partial_\mu \Phi - i(2e)A_\mu \Phi$. We take the action as

$$S = \int d^4x \; [(D_\mu\Phi)^*(D^\mu\Phi) - \lambda(\Phi^*\Phi - a)^2] - \frac{1}{4}\int d^4x \; F_{\mu\nu}F^{\mu\nu} \quad (18.1)$$

This is exactly the action we have already analyzed. The physical effects are thus clear, they are what we already found in the last lecture. But before we go on to talk about them, we have a few more remarks about this action.

First of all, the Cooper pair is formed of two electrons but it is not a compact localized bound state. Rather, the pairing is in terms of momenta, with an electron of momentum $\vec{k}$ pairing up with one of approximately $-\vec{k}$. As a result, a local wave function or field $\Phi(x)$ which depends on a single point x is not quite what we need. Nevertheless, in considering the theory near the transition temperature, this can be shown to be a reasonable approximation.

Secondly, we have used the relativistically invariant combination $(D_\mu\Phi)^*(D^\mu\Phi)$; this is done with an eye towards the Higgs mechanism where we need the relativistic case. For the superconductor, a nonrelativistic approximation is adequate and, for the first set of terms in (18.1), usually one uses

$$S = \int d^4x \; \left[i\,\Phi^* \left(\frac{\partial\Phi}{\partial t} + iqA_0\Phi \right) - |\nabla + iq\vec{A}\Phi|^2 - \lambda(\Phi^*\Phi - a)^2 \right] \quad (18.2)$$

This is known as the Ginzburg-Landau model, since they obtained this, based on phenomenological grounds, a few years before the BCS theory. This model can be derived from the BCS theory in a suitable approximation; this was done by Gor'kov in 1959.

As we discussed before, the theory displays two phases, a normal phase for $T > T_c$ or $a < 0$ and a superconducting phase for $T < T_c$ or $a > 0$. The superconducting phase corresponds to the ground state having a nonzero value for Φ, thereby breaking the $U(1)$ symmetry. The fact that the expectation value of Φ is nonzero in the ground state is equivalent to the statement of (or better still, the definition of) the Bose-Einstein condensation of the Cooper pairs. Notice that in writing $\langle\Phi\rangle = \sqrt{a}$ for the ground state, we have the same x-independent phase (we have chosen it as zero) for this field everywhere. Thus there is phase-coherence, which is one of the hallmarks of Bose-Einstein condensation.

As for the physics of the two phases, in the normal phase, we expect no symmetry breaking and the excitations are the two components of Φ and the photon. In the superconducting phase, with $\langle \Phi \rangle \neq 0$, we have symmetry breaking and the photon behaves as a massive particle. In addition, we have the particle η_1 which is also massive. The statement that the photon has a mass within the superconductor is essentially the London ansatz, a result postulated by the Londons to explain some of the features of superconductivity. If we include the photon mass term $q^2 a\, A^\mu A_\mu$ and work out the equations of motion for A_μ, we find

$$\partial_\mu F^{\mu\nu} + m_A^2\, A^\nu = 0 \tag{18.3}$$

where $m_A^2 = 2q^2 a = 2(2e)^2 a$. Comparing with the Maxwell equations in the usual form, namely,

$$\partial_\mu F^{\mu\nu} = J^\nu \tag{18.4}$$

we see that we may interpret (18.3) as saying that there is a current $J^\nu = -m_A^2\, A^\nu$ inside a superconductor. This is the London ansatz which may be viewed as what replaces Ohm's law ($\vec{J} = \sigma \vec{E}$) in a superconductor. This ansatz has an immediate consequence. First of all, if we write out the spatial component of (18.3), for zero electric field, we get

$$\nabla \times \vec{B} + m_A^2\, \vec{A} = 0 \tag{18.5}$$

Taking the curl of this equation and using $\nabla \cdot \vec{B} = 0$, we find

$$-\nabla^2 \vec{B} + m_A^2\, \vec{B} = 0 \tag{18.6}$$

The solution of this equation, starting from a nonzero value of $\vec{B} = \vec{B}_0$ at the edge of a superconductor, is of the form $\vec{B}_0 \exp(-m_A|x|)$, showing that the magnetic field is exponentially falling off into the interior of the superconductor. Thus magnetic fields are excluded from the bulk of a superconductor; this is known as the Meissner-Ochenfeld effect. The small skin depth $\sim 1/m_A$ to which the field can penetrate into a superconductor is called the London penetration depth.

The physical meaning of η_1 is also interesting. Since $\Phi = \sqrt{a} + (\eta_1 + i\eta_2)/\sqrt{2}$, we see that exciting a large enough negative value for η_1 can, at least locally, overcome $\sqrt{a}$. Thus η_1 excitations can correspond to local restoration of the normal phase, which can locally destroy the coherent value of $\Phi = \sqrt{a}$. If we have a bubble of normal phase inside a superconductor, η_1 can be nonzero inside and on the boundary of the bubble, but it will go to zero exponentially as we move into the superconducting region where Φ has coherence. This fall-off will be controlled by its mass

$m_{\eta_1} = \sqrt{4\lambda a}$ via its equations of motion. For this reason $1/m_{\eta_1}$ is called the coherence length.

Finally, let us talk about the temperature dependence of a. This can be calculated from the statistical mechanics of the theory. The form which we postulated, namely, $a = -c\,(T - T_c)$, is obtained as a first approximation; the power of $T - T_c$ can change with a more accurate calculation. Also, more realistically, the effective action can have terms which are cubic of the form $|\Phi|^3$ as well as higher powers of $|\Phi|$. Such terms can convert the transition from a second order one to a first order one and the whole story of how the transition occurs can get quite complicated. But the basic result that the ground state value of Φ goes from zero to a nonzero value as we decrease the temperature from above T_c to below T_c, or from a nonzero value to zero as we increase the temperature above a critical value, is still obtained. This statement, that symmetry is restored and a normal phase is obtained at high temperatures, is a general result of the Higgs mechanism, applicable to other contexts in which we use this mechanism as well.

Electroweak interactions

We can now apply what we have learnt to weak interactions. Of course, there is no superconductivity or lattice of ions or anything like that, when we consider the weak interactions of particles such as the quarks and leptons. And the "ground state" is really the true vacuum state and not the ground state of some material system. Thus we will not talk of Cooper pairs and phonon interactions. Instead, we only take the mathematical structure of the Higgs mechanism as discussed earlier. This means that we will simply postulate a fundamental field or particle described by a suitable spin zero field. It will just be called the Higgs field.

We know from our discussion of the $V - A$ theory in Lecture 11 that we need vector particles to mediate the weak interactions. We must have vertices like

$$S_{int} \sim \int d^4x \; \bar{e}\,\gamma^\mu(1 - \gamma^5)\,\nu_e\,W_\mu^- \sim 2\int d^4x \; \bar{e}_L\,\gamma^\mu \nu_{eL}\,W_\mu^- \qquad (18.7)$$

so that we can avoid cross sections rising with energy for arbitrarily high energies. Further, as we indicated in Lecture 17, putting a mass into the propagator for the W's is not good enough. The only way forward is to use the Higgs mechanism. So how do we put all this together to construct a theory? It is easiest to just look at the leptons to begin with.

First of all, we know that only the left-chiral components of the electron and the neutrino participate in the usual β-decay type processes. Further, whatever gauge fields we postulate must transform the electron into a neutrino and vice versa. Since the coupling which arises from a covariant derivative involves the matrix form $-ig\, b^r_\mu t_r$, we see that, in the action, we should have something like

$$(\bar\nu_{eL} \; \bar e_L) \begin{bmatrix} 0 & W^+_\mu \\ W^-_\mu & 0 \end{bmatrix} \begin{pmatrix} \nu_{eL} \\ e_L \end{pmatrix} \tag{18.8}$$

However, transformations generated by off-diagonal matrices of the form

$$\begin{bmatrix} 0 & c_1 \\ c_2 & 0 \end{bmatrix} \tag{18.9}$$

do not close, since the product of two such matrices will produce diagonal elements. Thus we have to start with at least a set of transformations which are 2×2 and close under multiplication. The minimal such set would be $SU(2)$, the set of special unitary 2×2 matrices. Since this will involve minimally three matrices, say, $\tau_1/2$, $\tau_2/2$ and $\tau_3/2$ multiplying the corresponding A's in the covariant derivative, we have an immediate prediction:

> There must exist at least one other vector particle in addition to the W's.

Again, the minimal strategy would be to try and interpret this as the only other vector particle we know, namely, the photon. (Gluons are out of the picture, since the leptons do not have strong nuclear interactions.) But the third vector particle, with a coupling of the form $b^3_\mu \tau_3/2$ would have equal and opposite coupling for the neutrino and the electron. Since the neutrino has zero electrical charge, there must not be a direct coupling to the photon. This tells us that the third vector cannot be the photon. Further, the photon has equal coupling to the right-chiral component e_R of the electron, so this is another reason why b^3_μ cannot be the photon. The $U(1)$ transformation corresponding to electromagnetism must act on the fields as

$$\begin{pmatrix} \nu_{eL} \\ e_L \end{pmatrix} \rightarrow \begin{bmatrix} 1 & 0 \\ 0 & e^{i e\theta} \end{bmatrix} \begin{pmatrix} \nu_{eL} \\ e_L \end{pmatrix} = e^{-ie\theta(\tau_3-1)/2} \begin{pmatrix} \nu_{eL} \\ e_L \end{pmatrix}$$

$$e_R \rightarrow e^{i e\theta}\, e_R \tag{18.10}$$

This shows that the electromagnetic $U(1)$ is some combination of the diagonal part of $SU(2)$ and an extra $U(1)$. Therefore we will have to postulate one more vector field and make a suitable combination to be interpreted as the photon. Thus the minimal symmetry we need is $SU(2) \times U(1)$, namely, $SU(2)$ transformations and a separate $U(1)$ transformation. And the theory has to combine weak and electromagnetic interactions into a single theory, to be referred to as the electroweak theory.

We will thus make a doublet of the neutrino and the left-chiral component of the electron, and keep e_R as a singlet under $SU(2)$, i.e., uncharged under the $SU(2)$. This $SU(2)$ gauge symmetry is usually called the weak isospin. The $U(1)$ charge will be referred to as the hypercharge (designated by Y) and taken to be $Y = -1$ for the neutrino-electron doublet and $Y = -2$ for e_R. The fields of relevance to us are thus ℓ_L which will be used for the doublet of ν_{eL} and e_L taken together and e_R which will be used for the right-chiral component of the electron. In other words, the lepton fields are

$$\ell_L = \begin{pmatrix} \nu_{eL} \\ e_L \end{pmatrix}, \qquad e_R \tag{18.11}$$

The transformation laws are

$$\begin{aligned}
\ell_L \to \ell'_L &= e^{i\theta Y/2}\, \mathbf{U}\, \ell_L = e^{-i\theta/2}\, e^{i\theta_a T_a/2}\, \ell_L \\
e_R \to e'_R &= e^{i\theta Y/2} e_R = e^{-i\theta} e_R
\end{aligned} \tag{18.12}$$

Here $\mathbf{U}$ is the $SU(2)$ matrix and $e^{i\theta Y/2}$ is the $U(1)$ transformation. (We use a factor of $\frac{1}{2}$ for the $U(1)$ as well; this is a choice of normalization and turns out to be convenient.) We can now construct the covariant derivatives as

$$D_\mu \ell_L = \partial_\mu \ell_L + i\left(g\, b_\mu^r \frac{T_r}{2} - \frac{g'}{2} c_\mu \right) \ell_L, \qquad D_\mu e_R = \partial_\mu e_R - ig' c_\mu e_R \tag{18.13}$$

We have introduced a gauge field b_μ^r, $r = 1, 2, 3$, for the $SU(2)$ part (corresponding to the three τ's) and a field c_μ for the $U(1)$ part. Further g, g' are coupling constants, the analogues of the charge of the electron (or the unit of electric charge) which we used for the photon coupling.[1]

---

[1] Earlier we defined the covariant derivatives in the form $\partial_\mu - it_a A_\mu^a$, which is natural and convenient for QCD. Here we have changed the sign of the gauge field. This is done so that, upon restriction to the electromagnetic interactions, we can reproduce the QED action with the same sign conventions as in Lecture 8. This will also mean that, for b_μ^r, we should use the field strength tensor $F_{\mu\nu}^r = \partial_\mu b_\nu^r - \partial_\nu b_\mu^r - g\epsilon^{rst} b_\mu^s b_\nu^t$. For QCD, we considered matrices t_a, with a taking values 1 to 8; to avoid confusion, we use letters towards the end of the alphabet such as r, s, etc.. for the $SU(2)$ fields.

Given these covariant derivatives, the part of the action for the neutrino-electron system can be written as

$$
S_{\nu e} = \int d^4x \left[\bar{\ell}_L i\gamma^\mu \left(\partial_\mu + i \left(g\, b_\mu^r \frac{\tau_r}{2} - \frac{g'}{2} c_\mu \right) \right) \ell_L \right.
$$

$$
\left. + \bar{e}_R\, i\gamma^\mu \left(\partial_\mu - ig' c_\mu \right) e_R \right]
\tag{18.14}
$$

We need to simplify the matrix involving the τ-matrices to interpret the various terms. For this, define the combination $g\, b_\mu^3 - g' c_\mu$ which is the top-left entry and which couples to the neutrino as proportional to some field/particle Z_μ. The motivation is that this must not involve the photon, since the neutrino has no charge. The other orthogonal combination of b_μ^3 and c_μ will be taken as the photon field A_μ. To carry out the reduction systematically, we define an angle θ_W by

$$
\frac{g'}{\sqrt{g^2 + g'^2}} = \sin\theta_W, \qquad \frac{g}{\sqrt{g^2 + g'^2}} = \cos\theta_W
\tag{18.15}
$$

We then define the two fields, Z_μ and A_μ, which are normalized linear combinations of b_μ^3 and c_μ, as

$$
\begin{pmatrix} Z_\mu \\ A_\mu \end{pmatrix} = \begin{pmatrix} \cos\theta_W & -\sin\theta_W \\ \sin\theta_W & \cos\theta_W \end{pmatrix} \begin{pmatrix} b_\mu^3 \\ c_\mu \end{pmatrix}
$$

$$
\begin{pmatrix} b_\mu^3 \\ c_\mu \end{pmatrix} = \begin{pmatrix} \cos\theta_W & \sin\theta_W \\ -\sin\theta_W & \cos\theta_W \end{pmatrix} \begin{pmatrix} Z_\mu \\ A_\mu \end{pmatrix}
\tag{18.16}
$$

We will also define

$$
W_\mu^\pm = \frac{1}{\sqrt{2}} (b_\mu^1 \mp i b_\mu^2)
\tag{18.17}
$$

Using these definitions, we find

$$
g\, b_\mu^r \frac{\tau_r}{2} - \frac{g'}{2} c_\mu = \frac{1}{2} \begin{bmatrix} g b_\mu^3 - g' c_\mu & g(b_\mu^1 - i b_\mu^2) \\ g(b_\mu^1 + i b_\mu^2) & -(g b_\mu^3 + g' c_\mu) \end{bmatrix}
$$

$$
= \begin{bmatrix} \frac{g}{\cos\theta_W} Z_\mu \frac{1}{2} & \frac{g}{\sqrt{2}} W_\mu^+ \\ \frac{g}{\sqrt{2}} W_\mu^- & \frac{g}{\cos\theta_W} Z_\mu \left(-\frac{1}{2} + \sin^2\theta_W\right) - e A_\mu \end{bmatrix}
\tag{18.18}
$$

where we identify the unit of electric charge as $e = g\sin\theta_W$. (The theory has two coupling constants g and g'; we can equivalently use e and $\sin\theta_W$. So we may regard the equation $e = g\sin\theta_W$ as the definition of e or as the identification of g in terms of the physically measured constant e.) Similarly,

$$
g' c_\mu = e A_\mu - \frac{g}{\cos\theta_W} \sin^2\theta_W\, Z_\mu
\tag{18.19}
$$

Using these results (18.18) and (18.19) in the action, we get

$$S_{\nu e} = \int d^4x \left[\bar{\nu}_{eL}(i\gamma^\mu \partial_\mu)\nu_{eL} + \bar{e}(i\gamma^\mu \partial_\mu)e + e\,A_\mu\,\bar{e}\gamma^\mu e \right.$$

$$- \frac{g}{\cos\theta_W} Z_\mu \left(\frac{1}{2}\left(\bar{\nu}_{eL}\gamma^\mu \nu_{eL} - \bar{e}_L\gamma^\mu e_L\right) + \sin^2\theta_W\,\bar{e}\gamma^\mu e \right)$$

$$\left. - \frac{g}{\sqrt{2}}W_\mu^- \bar{e}_L\gamma^\mu \nu_{eL} - \frac{g}{\sqrt{2}}W_\mu^+ \bar{\nu}_{eL}\gamma^\mu e_L \right] \tag{18.20}$$

We see that we have the correct electromagnetic coupling and also the required terms with $W_\mu^\pm$. There is also an additional coupling involving the Z_μ.

The action for the gauge fields b_μ^r and c_μ must be of the Yang-Mills form. We will not analyze this part of the action in detail at this point, it will be taken up after we introduce the Higgs mechanism for the masses of the W_μs and Z_μ. The simplification of the Yang-Mills term will make it clear that Z_μ is electrically neutral. (The derivative on Z will end up as an ordinary derivative, but for $W^\pm$ we will find covariant derivatives with A_μ as the potential.) Thus Z_μ is often written as Z_μ^0 and the current in (18.20) which is the coefficient of the Z_μ coupling term, is called the weak neutral current. The discovery of processes involving the neutral current in 1973 was a big step towards confirming this theory.

In the beginning, the choice of $Y = -1$ for ℓ_L and $Y = -2$ for e_R may have seemed a little mysterious. We now see that it is the correct choice to ensure that the neutrino has no direct coupling to the photon and also that we get identical coupling of e_L and e_R to the photon. This is the justification for the assignment of hypercharge values.

The story of the muon and the mu-neutrino is similar, almost an exact copy, and the same for the τ and the tau-neutrino. We may therefore combine the results into the action

$$S = \int d^4x \left[\bar{\nu}_{eL}(i\gamma^\mu \partial_\mu)\nu_{eL} + \bar{\nu}_{\mu L}(i\gamma^\mu \partial_\mu)\nu_{\mu L} + \bar{\nu}_{\tau L}(i\gamma^\mu \partial_\mu)\nu_{\tau L} \right.$$

$$+ \bar{e}(i\gamma^\mu \partial_\mu)e + \bar{\mu}(i\gamma^\mu \partial_\mu)\mu + \bar{\tau}(i\gamma^\mu \partial_\mu)\tau$$

$$\left. - e\,A_\mu J^\mu - \frac{g}{\cos\theta_W} Z_\mu J^{0\,\mu} - \frac{g}{\sqrt{2}}W_\mu^- J^{+\mu} - \frac{g}{\sqrt{2}}W_\mu^+ J^{-\mu} \right] \tag{18.21}$$

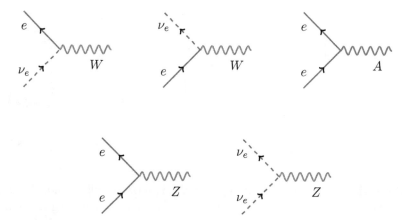

Fig. 18.2: The basic vertices for weak interactions of leptons. Only the electron-ν_e vertices are shown; there are similar ones for the μ-ν_μ and τ-ν_τ pairs.

The currents in this expression are

$$J^\mu = -\bar{e}\gamma^\mu e - \bar{\mu}\gamma^\mu\mu - \bar{\tau}\gamma^\mu\tau$$

$$J^{0\,\mu} = \frac{1}{2}\left(\bar{\nu}_{eL}\gamma^\mu\nu_{eL} - \bar{e}_L\gamma^\mu e_L + \bar{\nu}_{\mu L}\gamma^\mu\nu_{\mu L} - \bar{\mu}_L\gamma^\mu\mu_L + \bar{\nu}_{\tau L}\gamma^\mu\nu_{\tau L}\right.$$
$$\left. - \bar{\tau}_L\gamma^\mu\tau_L\right) + \sin^2\theta_W\left(\bar{e}\gamma^\mu e + \bar{\mu}\gamma^\mu\mu + \bar{\tau}\gamma^\mu\tau\right) \qquad (18.22)$$

$$J^{+\mu} = \bar{e}_L\gamma^\mu\nu_{eL} + \bar{\mu}_L\gamma^\mu\nu_{\mu L} + \bar{\tau}_L\gamma^\mu\nu_{\tau L}$$

$$J^{-\mu} = \bar{\nu}_{eL}\gamma^\mu e_L + \bar{\nu}_{\mu L}\gamma^\mu\mu_L + \bar{\nu}_{\tau L}\gamma^\mu\tau_L$$

We use J^μ for the electromagnetic current, $J^{0\,\mu}$ for the neutral current and $J^{\pm\,\mu}$ are the charged $V - A$ currents we have discussed before. The neutral current can also be written as $J^{0\,\mu} = J^{3\,\mu} - \sin^2\theta_W J^\mu$, where $J^{3\,\mu}$ is the $SU(2)$ current for the $\tau_3/2$ direction,

$$J^{3\,\mu} = \frac{1}{2}\left(\bar{\nu}_{eL}\gamma^\mu\nu_{eL} - \bar{e}_L\gamma^\mu e_L + \bar{\nu}_{\mu L}\gamma^\mu\nu_{\mu L} - \bar{\mu}_L\gamma^\mu\mu_L + \bar{\nu}_{\tau L}\gamma^\mu\nu_{\tau L} - \bar{\tau}_L\gamma^\mu\tau_L\right)$$
$$(18.23)$$

The interaction vertices from the action (18.21) may be represented by the diagrams shown in Fig. 18.2. If we consider a diagram which corresponds to the exchange of $W^\pm$, we find an amplitude of the form

$$\mathcal{A} = -\frac{g^2}{2}\int d^4x\, d^4y\; J^{+\mu}(x)\, D_{\mu\nu}(x,y)\, J^{-\nu}(y)$$

$$\approx -i\int d^4x\; \frac{g^2}{2M_W^2}\, J^{+\mu}\, J^-_\mu \qquad (18.24)$$

where in the second line we have used a massive propagator for the W's and approximated it by the value for small momentum transfer compared to M_W,

$$D_{\mu\nu}(x,y) = -\int \frac{d^4p}{(2\pi)^4} e^{-ip(x-y)} \frac{i}{p^2 - M_W^2 + i\epsilon} \left(\eta_{\mu\nu} - \frac{p_\mu p_\nu}{M_W^2}\right)$$

$$\approx \frac{i}{M_W^2} \delta^{(4)}(x-y)\, \eta_{\mu\nu} \tag{18.25}$$

We see that we do indeed recover the $V - A$ theory, with

$$G_F = \sqrt{2}\, \frac{g^2}{8\, M_W^2} \tag{18.26}$$

In addition to such an interaction of the $V - A$ theory, we also have the neutral current interactions of the form

$$\mathcal{A} = -\frac{1}{2} \left(\frac{g}{\cos\theta_W}\right)^2 \int d^4x\, d^4y\; J^{0\,\mu}(x)\, D^{(Z)}_{\mu\nu}(x,y)\, J^{0\,\nu}(y)$$

$$\approx -i \int d^4x\; \frac{g^2}{2\cos^2\theta_W\, M_Z^2}\, J^{0\,\mu}\, J^0_\mu \tag{18.27}$$

In these low energy simplifications, we have put in a massive propagator for the W's and the Z. But we have not yet addressed the question of how the W's and the Z get their masses. This has to be done via the Higgs mechanism, so we need a suitable Higgs field. This will be taken up in the next lecture.

It is also useful to have the numerical values of the parameters, the masses and the angle θ_W. They have to be experimentally determined and, at the energies of interest, are as follows.

$$M_W \simeq 80.4\,\text{GeV}, \qquad M_Z \simeq 91.2\,\text{GeV}$$

$$\sin^2\theta_W \simeq 0.223, \qquad G_F \simeq 1.166 \times 10^{-5}\,(\text{GeV})^{-2}$$

We will also discuss the situation with the quarks briefly. The left-chiral components of the up and down quarks form an $SU(2)$ doublet similar to the ν_e, e_L, with hypercharge $Y = 1/3$,

$$\begin{pmatrix} u_L \\ d_L \end{pmatrix}, \qquad Y = \frac{1}{3}$$

The right-chiral components u_R and d_R do not transform under $SU(2)$ and have $Y = 4/3$ for u_R and $Y = -2/3$ for d_R. These assignments will correctly yield the electric charges of 2/3 for u and $-1/3$ for d. The covariant derivatives with the electroweak gauge fields are thus

$$D_\mu \begin{pmatrix} u_L \\ d_L \end{pmatrix} = \left(\partial_\mu + i\, g\, b_\mu^r \frac{\tau_r}{2} + i\frac{g'}{6} c_\mu \right) \begin{pmatrix} u_L \\ d_L \end{pmatrix}$$

$$D_\mu u_R = \left(\partial_\mu + i\frac{2\,g'}{3} c_\mu \right) u_R \qquad (18.28)$$

$$D_\mu d_R = \left(\partial_\mu - i\frac{g'}{3} c_\mu \right) d_R$$

The assignments for the second and third generations are similar, so that we can write the full quark part of the action as

$$L_f = \sum_i \bar{Q}_L^i i\gamma^\mu \left(\partial_\mu - ig_s t_a A_\mu^a + ig\frac{\tau_r}{2} b_\mu^r + i\frac{g'}{6} c_\mu \right) Q_L^i$$

$$+ \bar{U}_R^i i\gamma^\mu \left(\partial_\mu - ig_s t_a A_\mu^a + i\frac{2g'}{3} c_\mu \right) U_R^i \qquad (18.29)$$

$$+ \bar{D}_R^i i\gamma^\mu \left(\partial_\mu - ig_s t_a A_\mu^a - i\frac{g'}{3} c_\mu \right) D_R^i$$

Here A_μ^a denote the gluon fields and

$$Q_L^1 = \begin{pmatrix} u_L \\ d_L \end{pmatrix}, \qquad Q_L^2 = \begin{pmatrix} c_L \\ s_L \end{pmatrix}, \qquad Q_L^3 = \begin{pmatrix} t_L \\ b_L \end{pmatrix} \qquad (18.30)$$

$(U_R^1, U_R^2, U_R^3) = (u_R, c_R, t_R)$, $(D_R^1, D_R^2, D_R^3) = (d_R, s_R, b_R)$. We will not go through the simplification of this part of the action, but it can be checked to yield couplings similar to what was obtained for the leptons. There are also some couplings of the quarks to the Higgs field, needed to obtain masses for the quarks after the spontaneous breaking of the electroweak symmetry. We will briefly touch upon these when we discuss CP-violation.

Chapter 19

Electroweak Interactions and the
Story of Mass

We have talked about the fermions and how they couple to the gauge fields which are responsible for the electroweak interactions. We also showed that one can recover the older $V - A$ results in the low energy limit, if we use massive propagators for the W's and the Z's. However, this was done in something of an *ad hoc* fashion, because we did not really discuss how the mass arises. Let us talk about this question now. As mentioned earlier, the masses have to come from a Higgs mechanism. In the case of superconductivity, we had a field corresponding to the Cooper pairs, which are themselves bound states of two electrons. However, for the weak interactions, since we are talking about the real vacuum state of the world, we do not consider such a paired bound state, instead we simply postulate a fundamental field with the required properties.[1] Such a field must give a mass to the W's, so it must break the $SU(2)$ symmetry. This means that it should transform under the $SU(2)$ transformations, so that assigning a nonzero value to this field in the vacuum leads to spontaneous breaking of the symmetry. Further, we do not want the photon to be massive, so we must ensure that whichever field has a nonzero value in the vacuum does not break the electromagnetic symmetry of phase transformations. Since the phases for the latter are of the form $e^{iq\theta}$ where q is the electric charge, this can be done by making sure that the postulated Higgs field has a component with zero charge, and that it is this component which gets a nonzero expectation value in the vacuum. (The Higgs field obviously has

---

[1] We could consider bound states of some kind of fermions forming the Higgs field, but then we would have to postulate additional interactions to provide the binding as well. (There has been such a proposal using new interactions called technicolor.) Ultimately, this is a case of Occam's razor: The simplest scenario without too many additional features (which are experimentally unsupported as well) is to use a fundamental scalar field as the Higgs field.

to have more than one component since it transforms nontrivially under the $SU(2)$ transformations.) The simplest choice consistent with these requirements is a doublet of the form

$$\Phi = \begin{pmatrix} \phi^+ \\ \phi^0 \end{pmatrix} \tag{19.1}$$

The superscripts indicate the electric charges of the two components. This field transforms under $SU(2)$ as expected,

$$\Phi \to \Phi' = \mathbf{U}\,\Phi \tag{19.2}$$

where $\mathbf{U}$ is the 2×2 $SU(2)$ matrix. Further, we take this to have hypercharge (or $U(1)_Y$ charge) equal to 1. (This will ensure that the lower component in Φ has zero electric charge. Notice that for all fields, including the leptons, the quarks and the Higgs, the electric charge is given by the eigenvalue of $\frac{1}{2}\tau_3 + \frac{1}{2}Y$.) Once we have assigned these transformation properties, the covariant derivative of Φ is trivial to construct. We get

$$
\begin{aligned}
D_\mu \Phi &= \partial_\mu \Phi + ig\,b^r_\mu \frac{\tau_r}{2}\,\Phi + i\frac{g'}{2}c_\mu\,\Phi \\
&= \partial_\mu \Phi + \frac{i}{2}\begin{bmatrix} gb^3_\mu + g'c_\mu & g(b^1 - ib^2)_\mu \\ g(b^1 + ib^2)_\mu & -gb^3_\mu + g'c_\mu \end{bmatrix}\begin{pmatrix} \phi^+ \\ \phi^0 \end{pmatrix} \\
&= \partial_\mu \Phi + i\begin{bmatrix} eA_\mu + \frac{g}{\cos\theta_W}Z_\mu(\frac{1}{2} - \sin^2\theta_W) & \frac{g}{\sqrt{2}}W^+_\mu \\ \frac{g}{\sqrt{2}}W^-_\mu & -\frac{1}{2}\frac{g}{\cos\theta_W}Z_\mu \end{bmatrix}\begin{pmatrix} \phi^+ \\ \phi^0 \end{pmatrix}
\end{aligned}
\tag{19.3}
$$

where we have simplified exactly as we did after (18.18). The action for the Higgs field can be taken as

$$S = \int d^4x\,\left[(D_\mu\Phi)^\dagger(D^\mu\Phi) - \lambda\left(\Phi^\dagger\Phi - \frac{v^2}{2}\right)^2\right] \tag{19.4}$$

Notice that this is a straightforward natural extension of the action we used for the Cooper pair field. Here v is a constant real number; the structure of the potential term shows that the ground state (which is the true vacuum in this context) should have $\Phi^\dagger\Phi = v^2/2$. Since $\Phi^\dagger\Phi = |\phi^+|^2 + \phi^{0*}\phi^0$, we can satisfy this condition taking $\langle\phi^0\rangle = v/\sqrt{2}$. The field Φ can then be parametrized as

$$\Phi = \mathbf{U}\begin{pmatrix} 0 \\ \frac{v+\eta}{\sqrt{2}} \end{pmatrix} \tag{19.5}$$

where $\mathbf{U}$ is an $SU(2)$ matrix of fields. It can be absorbed into the gauge fields by a suitable gauge transformation as we did with the field χ for the Higgs mechanism in the $U(1)$ theory in Lecture 17. This is equivalent to choosing a particular gauge condition; the gauge in which **U** has been absorbed into the gauge fields is usually referred to as the unitary gauge. With **U** eliminated in this way, the action (19.4) simplifies as

$$S = \int d^4x \left[\frac{g^2 v^2}{4} W^+_\mu W^{-\mu} + \frac{1}{2} \left(\frac{g^2 v^2}{4 \cos^2 \theta_W} \right) Z_\mu Z^\mu \right.$$
$$+ \frac{g^2 v}{2} \eta \, W^+_\mu W^{-\mu} + \frac{g^2 v}{4 \cos^2 \theta_W} \eta \, Z_\mu Z^\mu$$
$$+ \frac{g^2}{4} \eta^2 \, W^+_\mu W^{-\mu} + \frac{g^2}{8 \cos^2 \theta_W} \eta^2 \, Z_\mu Z^\mu$$
$$\left. - \frac{1}{2} (2\lambda v^2) \eta^2 - \lambda v \, \eta^3 - \frac{\lambda}{4} \eta^4 \right] \tag{19.6}$$

Keeping in mind that this is to be added to the action for the gauge fields b^a_μ and c_μ, we see that this gives masses to the W's and the Z; specifically,

$$M_W = \frac{gv}{2}, \qquad M_Z = \frac{gv}{2} \frac{1}{\cos\theta_W} = \frac{M_W}{\cos\theta_W} \tag{19.7}$$

The action also shows that we have a left-over Higgs boson corresponding to the field η with a mass $\sqrt{2\lambda}\, v$. Also, since we are reading these masses off the action, these results are to the lowest order. Higher order corrections to these formulae are possible. Fortunately, corrections in the electroweak theory are small, so these formulae are still reliable for numerical estimates. In the last lecture, we found that $G_F = \sqrt{2}(g^2/8M^2_W)$. Using (19.7) for M_W, $G_F = (\sqrt{2}\, v^2)^{-1}$, and using the experimental value of G_F, we find

$$v \approx 246\,\text{GeV} \tag{19.8}$$

This sets the scale of the spontaneous symmetry breaking for the weak interactions.

An important feature of the Higgs field is that it is needed and is responsible for giving masses to the quarks and leptons as well. Consider a mass term for the electron, for example. In terms of the left and right components, this is of the form $\bar{e}_L e_R + \bar{e}_R e_L$. This is clearly problematic because we want e_L to be part of the neutrino-electron doublet and transform under $SU(2)$, while e_R does not. In particular, e_L can be transformed to ν_{eL}, but there is no term like $\bar{\nu}_{eL} e_R$ or $\bar{e}_R \nu_{eL}$ in the mass term. So we cannot have a mass term which respects the $SU(2)$ symmetry. The solution is to consider a term involving the Higgs field, of the form

$$S_{mass} = \int d^4x \; \lambda \, \bar{e}_R \, \Phi^\dagger \ell_L \; + \; \text{h.c.}$$

$$= \int d^4x \, \lambda \bar{e}_R \left(\phi^{+\dagger}\nu_{eL} + \phi^{0*}e_L\right) \; + \; \text{h.c.} \tag{19.9}$$

The combination $\Phi^\dagger \ell_L$ is invariant under the $SU(2)$ transformations, since $\mathbf{U}^\dagger$ and $\mathbf{U}$ cancel out in the middle. Further, $\Phi^\dagger$ has $U(1)_Y$ charge -1, so does ℓ_L. Thus the combination $\Phi^\dagger \ell_L$ has $Y = -2$. e_R has $Y = -2$ as well, so that $\bar{e}_R \, \Phi^\dagger \ell_L$ is invariant under the $U(1)_Y$ transformations. Therefore (19.9) is completely acceptable as a term invariant under both $SU(2)$ and $U(1)_Y$. It does not look like a mass term, being naively cubic in the fields, but if we expand ϕ^0 around its ground state value, the lowest order term is

$$S_{mass} = \int d^4x \, \frac{\lambda v}{\sqrt{2}} \, \bar{e}_R e_L \; + \; \text{h.c.} \tag{19.10}$$

which is indeed a mass term for the electron, with $m_e = \lambda v/\sqrt{2}$. (Notice that, gratifyingly, the neutrino does not get a mass. Neutrinos do have a very small mass, but the origin of this is more involved because there is no ν_{eR} with the same mass. So masses for the neutrinos involve the so-called Majorana mass terms; we will briefly touch upon this later.) A term similar to (19.9) works for the quarks and the muon and the tau-lepton as well. With several fields, a matrix of coupling constants, rather than a single λ, is possible and leads to quark-mixing effects, including the possibility of a theory which does not have symmetry under time-reversal. This will also be briefly discussed later. So, in short, a key feature of the Standard Model is that the same Higgs field which is responsible for the masses of the W's and the Z also gives a mass to the fermions.

Does this mean all masses come from the Higgs field? At the level of the quarks and leptons, this is the case, except that neutrinos may need another Higgs field, related to the issue of Majorana masses mentioned earlier. However, this is not saying that all the observed mass in the universe can be traced to the Higgs field. For example, for ordinary matter, the bulk of the mass is in the baryons, primarily the protons and the neutrons which make up the atomic nuclei. These are made of the up and down quarks, which have a mass of only about a few MeV, say, 3 to 4 MeV. However, protons and neutrons have a mass around 938 MeV, so that the bulk of their mass comes from the effects of the strong nuclear force such as the spontaneous breaking of chiral symmetry and the kinetic energy of the motion of the quarks inside the bound states (which are the protons and neutrons) and which is perceived as mass (via the $m = E/c^2$ relation). Thus the bulk of the mass of ordinary matter comes from the dynamics of strong interactions. In addition, ordinary matter makes up only about 4 to

5 percent of the energy/mass budget of the universe. We have dark matter which accounts for about 25% and dark energy which accounts for the rest. The nature of these being unknown, we cannot really say anything about where all the mass comes from. The only safe thing we can say is that, if we consider quarks (rather than their bound states such as the nucleons) and leptons, their mass is due to the Higgs field.

It is worth considering the counting of the degrees of freedom one more time. In any theory with spontaneous symmetry breaking and the Higgs mechanism, we have a phase where symmetry is not broken (usually at high temperatures) and a phase where the symmetry is broken. We have massive vector particles in the latter. In the phase of unbroken symmetry, we have 2 polarizations for the massless vector particle (just like the photon) and the real and imaginary parts of the Higgs field as two additional particle degrees of freedom. In the broken phase we have 3 polarizations for the massive vector and we have one left-over real part (or modulus) of the Higgs field, which is the Higgs particle. Thus the number of degrees of freedom is the same in both phases. For the case of the electroweak theory, in the unbroken phase, we have massless c_μ, b_μ^a, giving 4 vector particles or 8 polarizations in all. In addition we have the complex ϕ^+ and ϕ^0 which give 4 more degrees of freedom. In the symmetry-broken phase, we have A_μ (2 polarizations) and $W_\mu^\pm$ (3 polarizations each, giving 6 polarizations) and Z_μ (3 polarizations) and one Higgs particle (η), so that the total number of particle degrees of freedom is the same.

So, what constitutes the extra polarization for the massive vector particle? A vector field A_i has 3 components, two of which are transverse polarizations. Therefore, the extra polarization is the longitudinal part of the field. Going back to the superconductor case, recall that the mass term started out as $(A_\mu + \partial_\mu \eta_2/q\sqrt{2a})^2$. It is because of the mass that we have 3 polarizations and the third one should be longitudinal, proportional to k_i, or the gradient of a function in x-space. Thus we can identify it essentially as proportional to $\partial_\mu \eta_2$. So what is happening is that one of the components of the Higgs field is transmuted in the symmetry-broken phase to the longitudinal component of the vector field. For the electroweak case, ϕ^+ and the imaginary part (or phase in a phase-modulus decomposition) of ϕ^0, or equivalently the matrix of fields $\mathbf{U}$ in (19.5), become the longitudinal parts of $W^\pm$ and Z.

This has implications for the high energy behavior of the theory. The reason for the use of the Higgs mechanism for obtaining massive vector particles, we have already stated, is that we can obtain good high energy behavior consistent with all the requirements of quantum mechanics. Recall that the propagator for a massive vector was earlier written down as

$$D_{\mu\nu}(x,y) = -\int \frac{d^4p}{(2\pi)^4} e^{-ip(x-y)} \frac{i}{p^2 - M^2 + i\epsilon} \left(\eta_{\mu\nu} - \frac{p_\mu p_\nu}{M^2}\right) \quad (19.11)$$

This formula applies when we put in a mass term in the action by hand, so to speak. And this shows the high momentum behavior $p_\mu p_\nu / p^2 \sim 1$, which is the root of the problem. However, if the mass arises from spontaneous symmetry breaking, the story is a bit different. Equation (19.11) still applies at low energies. But for high energies, we must think of the theory as made of massless vector particles, with the longitudinal component reverting to its behavior as the imaginary part of the Higgs scalar field. Such a theory has the same behavior as the unbroken theory, so the high energy behavior remains good. This is the essence of why the Higgs mechanism helps.

As we have alluded to a couple of times, generally, a theory which admits the possibility of spontaneous symmetry breaking can exist in at least two phases, one where the symmetry is not broken and one where it is broken. This is easy to accept for the case of superconductivity where we know that we get the normal state with no superconductivity, i.e., the unbroken phase, at a high enough temperature. Clearly something similar can happen with the electroweak theory as well. Since $v \approx 246\,\text{GeV}$, the temperatures to which we must heat up a system to see the unbroken phase is very high, of the order of $246 \times 10^{13}\,\text{K}$. While this may seem impractical, such temperatures were indeed obtained in the very early universe. So in terms of cosmology we can consider such a phase and look for any left-over signatures we may find in the present universe. We will touch upon these matters later.

Remark 19.1.
Electroweak theory: The action for the gauge bosons and the Higgs

We have simplified the action for the Higgs field which gave the formulae for the masses of the W- and Z-bosons. We have also indicated how the masses for the fermions arise from the Higgs field. But strictly speaking, to draw conclusions from the action, we have to simplify it as a whole and not piece by piece. For example, the fact that the fields b_μ^3 and c_μ are mixed to get the A_μ and Z_μ was important for the mass terms. Taking this into account, how does the action for the gauge fields simplify? The action for the gauge fields is the Yang-Mills action for $SU(2)$ and $U(1)$ and is given in our case as

$$S = -\frac{1}{4} \int d^4x \left[F^r_{\mu\nu} F^{r\,\mu\nu} + (\partial_\mu c_\nu - \partial_\nu c_\mu)(\partial^\mu c^\nu - \partial^\nu c^\mu) \right] \qquad (19.12)$$

where $F^r_{\mu\nu} = \partial_\mu b^r_\nu - \partial_\nu b^r_\mu - g\,\epsilon^{rst} b^s_\mu b^t_\nu$. Using the definition of Z_μ and A_μ in terms of b^3_μ and c_μ, the components of the field strength tensor become

$$\partial_\mu c_\nu - \partial_\nu c_\mu = \cos\theta_W (\partial_\mu A_\nu - \partial_\nu A_\mu) - \sin\theta_W (\partial_\mu Z_\nu - \partial_\nu Z_\mu)$$

$$F^1_{\mu\nu} = \frac{1}{\sqrt{2}} \left[D_\mu W^+_\nu - D_\nu W^+_\mu + D_\mu W^-_\nu - D_\nu W^-_\mu \right]$$

$$F^2_{\mu\nu} = \frac{i}{\sqrt{2}} \left[D_\mu W^+_\nu - D_\nu W^+_\mu - D_\mu W^-_\nu + D_\nu W^-_\mu \right]$$

$$F^3_{\mu\nu} = \sin\theta_W (\partial_\mu A_\nu - \partial_\nu A_\mu) + \cos\theta_W (\partial_\mu Z_\nu - \partial_\nu Z_\mu)$$
$$+ig(W^+_\mu W^-_\nu - W^-_\mu W^+_\nu) \qquad (19.13)$$

We have also used the notation

$$D_\mu W^+_\nu = (\partial_\mu + ieA_\mu + ig\cos\theta_W Z_\mu) W^+_\nu$$
$$D_\mu W^-_\nu = (\partial_\mu - ieA_\mu - ig\cos\theta_W Z_\mu) W^-_\nu \qquad (19.14)$$

These are the covariant derivatives of the W's with respect to the electromagnetic and Z_μ fields. Notice that we have the correct gauging with respect to A_μ for the charged fields $W^\pm_\mu$. These covariant derivatives naturally emerge from the simplification of the nonlinear terms in the expression for $F^a_{\mu\nu}$ for the b^a_μ fields.

The action (19.12) can now be simplified and combined with the Higgs action (19.6) to get

$$S = \int d^4x \left[-\frac{1}{4}(\partial_\mu A_\nu - \partial_\nu A_\mu)^2 - \frac{1}{4}(\partial_\mu Z_\nu - \partial_\nu Z_\mu)^2 - \frac{1}{2}|\partial_\mu W_\nu - \partial_\nu W_\mu|^2 \right.$$

$$\left. + M^2_W\, W^+_\mu W^{-\mu} + \frac{1}{2}M^2_Z\, Z_\mu Z^\mu + \frac{1}{2}(\partial\eta)^2 - \frac{1}{2}M^2_H\, \eta^2 \right]$$

$$+\; S^{(1)}_{int} + S^{(2)}_{int} + S^{(3)}_{int} + S^{(4)}_{int} \qquad (19.15)$$

$$S^{(1)}_{int} = \int d^4x \left[ieA^\mu \left[W^{-\nu}(\partial_\mu W^+_\nu - \partial_\nu W^+_\mu) - W^{+\nu}(\partial_\mu W^-_\nu - \partial_\nu W^-_\mu) \right] \right.$$

$$\left. - \frac{e^2}{2}|A_\mu W_\nu - A_\nu W_\mu|^2 - i\,e\, W^{+\mu} W^{-\nu}(\partial_\mu A_\nu - \partial_\nu A_\mu) \right]$$

$$\qquad (19.16)$$

$$S_{int}^{(2)} = \int d^4x \left[ig\cos\theta_W Z^\mu \left[W^{-\nu}(\partial_\mu W_\nu^+ - \partial_\nu W_\mu^+) \right. \right.$$

$$\left. -W^{+\nu}(\partial_\mu W_\nu^- - \partial_\nu W_\mu^-) \right] - \frac{g^2}{2}\cos^2\theta_W |Z_\mu W_\nu - Z_\nu W_\mu|^2$$

$$\left. - ig\cos\theta_W W^{+\mu}W^{-\nu}(\partial_\mu Z_\nu - \partial_\nu Z_\mu) \right] \tag{19.17}$$

$$S_{int}^{(3)} = \int d^4x \left[-eg\cos\theta_W Z^\mu \left[(A_\mu W_\nu^- - A_\nu W_\mu^-)W^{+\nu} \right. \right.$$

$$\left. +(A_\mu W_\nu^+ - A_\nu W_\mu^+)W^{-\nu} \right] + \frac{g^2}{4}(W_\mu^+ W_\nu^- - W_\nu^+ W_\mu^-)^2 \right] \tag{19.18}$$

$$S_{int}^{(4)} = \int d^4x \left[2\frac{M_W^2}{v}W^{+\mu}W_\mu^-\eta + \frac{M_W^2}{v^2}W^{+\mu}W_\mu^-\eta^2 \right.$$

$$\left. + \frac{M_Z^2}{v}Z^\mu Z_\mu\eta + \frac{M_Z^2}{2v^2}Z^\mu Z_\mu\eta^2 - \frac{M_H^2}{2v}\eta^3 - \frac{M_H^2}{8v^2}\eta^4 \right] \tag{19.19}$$

In these expressions, $e = g\sin\theta_W$, $M_W = gv/2$, $M_Z = M_W/\cos\theta_W$ as before and $M_H = \sqrt{2\lambda}\, v$. The field η represents the physical Higgs boson, which has a mass equal to M_H. We have separated out the terms quadratic in the fields which tell us what the propagators should look like. There are several interaction terms, so clearly we need to consider many interaction vertices. The interaction terms can be combined with the kinetic terms to write the Yang-Mills part of the action (19.12) as

$$S_{gauge} = \int d^4x \left[-\frac{1}{2}(D_\mu W_\nu^+ - D_\nu W_\mu^+)(D_\mu W_\nu^- - D_\nu W_\mu^-) \right.$$

$$-\frac{1}{4}(\partial_\mu A_\nu - \partial_\nu A_\mu)^2 - \frac{1}{4}(\partial_\mu Z_\nu - \partial_\nu Z_\mu)^2$$

$$+ie(\partial^\mu A^\nu - \partial^\nu A^\mu)W_\mu^- W_\nu^+$$

$$+ig\cos\theta_W(\partial^\mu Z^\nu - \partial^\nu Z^\mu)W_\mu^- W_\nu^+$$

$$\left. +\frac{g^2}{4}(W_\mu^- W_\nu^+ - W_\mu^+ W_\nu^-)^2 \right] \tag{19.20}$$

In addition to the covariant derivatives which take care of the coupling to the electromagnetic field, there is another term quadratic in the W's, namely,

$$ie(\partial^\mu A^\nu - \partial^\nu A^\mu)W_\mu^- W_\nu^+ = ieF^{\mu\nu}W_\alpha^-(I_{\mu\nu})^{\alpha\beta}W_\beta^+ = ieF^{\mu\nu}(W^- I_{\mu\nu}W^+) \tag{19.21}$$

where $(I_{\mu\nu})^{\alpha\beta} = \frac{1}{2}(\delta^\alpha_\mu \delta^\beta_\nu - \delta^\alpha_\nu \delta^\beta_\mu)$. This term (19.21) is of a form similar to the term $\bar{\Psi}[\gamma_\mu, \gamma_\nu]\Psi F^{\mu\nu}$ in (11.41) except for $W^\mp$ replacing $\bar{\Psi}$ and Ψ; it can thus be interpreted as being due to the magnetic moment of the W-bosons, with $I_{\mu\nu}$ playing the role of the spin matrix. We see that the Z-boson has similar couplings to the Ws, with a coupling constant $g\cos\theta_W$. In addition to the cubic vertices, there are also vertices involving all four vector particles as in $S^{(3)}_{int}$; $S^{(4)}_{int}$ gives vertices involving the gauge bosons and the Higgs boson.

Chapter 20

CP-Violation and Matter vs Antimatter

We have gone over some of the key features of the Standard Model. This is by no means a comprehensive study of the Standard Model, but we are now in a position to talk about some of the not-so-well-understood features. This also borders on the many puzzles which are still there.

We want to start by discussing some discrete symmetries in physics. So far, we have talked mostly about continuous symmetries which means that they are characterized by continuous parameters. For example, spatial rotations fall into this category since the parameters of rotations are angles which can take on values from a continuous set. Likewise, Lorentz boosts are continuous transformations, the velocities of the transformations being the continuous parameters. Among the continuous symmetries of interest in physics, there are some which seem to hold perfectly, to the best of our present day experimental accuracies. Lorentz symmetry (including spatial rotations) and the gauge symmetry of the strong nuclear forces are two of these. The symmetry of the electroweak forces is not perfect, being spontaneously broken. The residual symmetry of this breaking, namely, the $U(1)$ symmetry of electromagnetism, seems to hold perfectly as well. There are three discrete symmetries which are related to spacetime symmetries. These are parity, time-reversal and charge conjugation.

(1) **Parity (P)**

Parity (P) refers to the transformation $\vec{x} \to -\vec{x}$. We can classify the properties of the wave functions or fields corresponding to particles according to how they behave under parity. A quantity which is a scalar under rotations, Lorentz transformations, etc., can change sign or not under parity. If it changes sign, we call it a pseudoscalar, to emphasize this; otherwise, it is just a scalar. Clearly ∇

will change sign, since it involves derivatives with respect to x, y, or z. Therefore, usual vectors are odd under parity. However, a vector like the magnetic field $\vec{B} = \nabla \times \vec{A}$ is even under parity since it has two vectors in its definition. It is an "axial vector".

Regarding spinors which describe spin-$\frac{1}{2}$ particles, the left and right chiral components transform into each other, $\psi_L \leftrightarrow \psi_R$, under parity. Thus $\bar{\psi}\psi = \bar{\psi}_R\psi_L + \bar{\psi}_L\psi_R$ is even under parity, $\bar{\psi}\gamma^5\psi = \bar{\psi}_L\psi_R - \bar{\psi}_R\psi_L$ is odd under parity.

Concerning various particle interactions, strong nuclear forces and electromagnetic interactions preserve parity. Weak interactions mediated by $W^\pm$ involve only the left-chiral components of the quarks and leptons, so they do not preserve parity. Likewise, the Z-mediated interactions couple to an asymmetric combination of left and right and do not preserve parity. (Just in case you wonder about this, gravity preserves parity.)

(2) **Time-reversal (T)**

Time-reversal (T) refers to $t \to -t$. This is a bit of a peculiar symmetry, because we cannot simply say whether the Hamiltonian (or Lagrangian) is invariant under this transformation as a statement of symmetry for the theory. This is because of the time-evolution condition

$$i\frac{\partial \Psi_\alpha}{\partial t} = H\,\Psi_\alpha, \qquad \text{or} \qquad i\frac{\partial}{\partial t}\,|\alpha\rangle = H\,|\alpha\rangle. \tag{20.1}$$

We see that saying that H is unchanged does not make sense since the time-derivative term has to change sign. But we notice that if we do $t \to -t$ and consider $\Psi \to \Psi^*$, then we can have T-invariance. Or, in terms of the abstract states $|\alpha\rangle$ we must map to the dual states, $|\alpha\rangle \to \langle\alpha|$. This means that the transformation is not linear, since $\langle\alpha|$ cannot be written as linear combinations of states of the type $|\alpha\rangle$; it is referred to as an antilinear transformation.

We will not discuss how various fields and interaction terms are to be transformed; but we will come back to the question of T-invariance of various interactions shortly.

(3) **Charge conjugation (C)**

This corresponds to the exchange of a particle with its antiparticle. The exchange of electrons with positrons or protons with antiprotons would be examples. For any spin-$\frac{1}{2}$ particle, there is a certain transformation we can identify as charge conjugation, namely, $\psi \to \psi^C = C\gamma^0\psi^*$, where C is a specific 4×4 matrix (acting on the spinor components), which can transform the γ-matrices to their transpose via $C^{-1}\gamma^\mu C = -\gamma^{\mu\,T}$. (With the choice of the γ-matrices as in Lecture 8, we can take $C = -i\gamma^0\gamma^2$.) For the electromagnetic field, we must define charge conjugation as $A_\mu \to -A_\mu$; this is easy to see from the Maxwell equation $\partial_\mu F^{\mu\nu} = J^\nu$, which shows that changing the sign of charge is equivalent to changing the sign of A_μ. For other gauge fields, such as the $SU(2)$ and $SU(3)$ fields, the transformation is more involved, we need $A_\mu^a t_a \to A_\mu^a(-t_a)^T$.

Among the interactions of interest, both strong nuclear forces and electromagnetic interactions preserve invariance under charge conjugation. Weak interactions break this symmetry as well.

In some situations, we can have spinor fields which are self-conjugate under the operation of charge conjugation, obeying a condition $\psi = C\gamma^0\psi^*$. Such fields are called Majorana fermions. We will not need to discuss them in detail at this point.

There is a very important theorem which can be proved very generally in quantum field theory, called the CPT-theorem, which is as follows.

Prop 20.1 (CPT theorem). In a Lorentz invariant local quantum field theory (i.e., one involving fields defined pointwise, with interactions at a point), the product of the three operations C, P and T is a symmetry.

This theorem is important in that, within a field-theoretic framework, the discussion of T-violation, for example, reduces to CP-violation.

We have already mentioned that weak interactions do not preserve parity. However, the bulk of weak interactions do preserve the combination CP. There is a very tiny, but significant, violation of the combination CP. This is what we want to focus on for now.

The first example of this CP-violation was observed in the $K^0\bar{K}^0$-system in 1964. Recall that, in terms of the quark content, $K^0 \sim d\bar{s}$ and $\bar{K}^0 \sim s\bar{d}$. They are also pseudoscalar mesons, so that, strictly speaking, in terms of the spinors for d, s, etc., we must use $K^0 \sim i\,\bar{s}\gamma^5 d$, $\bar{K}^0 \sim i\,\bar{d}\gamma^5 s$. The operation C will involve replacing particles by antiparticles, so clearly, these cannot be eigenstates of C or CP. In fact, with a little bit of work on transformation properties of spinors, one can show that

$$CP\,|K^0\rangle = |\bar{K}^0\rangle, \qquad CP\,|\bar{K}^0\rangle = |K^0\rangle \qquad (20.2)$$

Out of these, we can construct CP eigenstates, which are given by

$$|K_S\rangle = \frac{1}{\sqrt{2}} \left(|K^0\rangle + |\bar{K}^0\rangle \right), \qquad CP\,|K_S\rangle = (+1)\,|K_S\rangle$$

$$|K_L\rangle = \frac{1}{\sqrt{2}} \left(|K^0\rangle - |\bar{K}^0\rangle \right), \qquad CP\,|K_L\rangle = (-1)\,|K_L\rangle \qquad (20.3)$$

Most of the weak interactions conserve CP. This leads to restrictions on how the K-mesons can decay. For example, the two-pion state is CP symmetric, so K_S can decay into two pions, as in $K_S \to \pi^0 \pi^0$ or $K_S \to \pi^+ \pi^-$. But K_L cannot decay into two pions, preserving CP; it can decay into three pions, as in $K_L \to \pi^0 \pi^0 \pi^0$ or $K_L \to \pi^+ \pi^- \pi^0$. Since this decay involves three pions, the energy available, after masses are accounted for, is only about 85 MeV ($\sim M_K - 3\,M_\pi$) Therefore the integration over final states has a smaller contribution, and the three-pion decay rate is smaller. As a result, K_L has a longer lifetime compared to K_S. (The subscripts S and L stand for "short" and "long", referring to the lifetimes.) In fact, the lifetimes are

$$\tau_S = 8.958 \times 10^{-11}\ \text{s}, \qquad \tau_L = 5.18 \times 10^{-8}\ \text{s} \qquad (20.4)$$

The difference in lifetimes plays out in an interesting way in experiments. The K-mesons can be produced by strong nuclear interactions. This will produce the eigenstates of the strong interactions, i.e., either K^0 or $\bar{K}^0$ (not K_S or K_L directly). (Since strong forces respect flavor, they cannot mix states with an s-quark with a state with an $\bar{s}$-quark.) Imagine they are produced in some collision in an accelerator. As the particles propagate, the K_S component of K^0 (or $\bar{K}^0$) will decay rapidly ($\sim$ a thousand times faster than K_L), so that at some distance down the trajectory, we find, almost exclusively, K_L. Thus we should expect, at later points on the trajectory, only three-pion decays. And this is, by and large, what is observed. However, if CP is not a perfect symmetry, then there is a small chance for the CP odd state to decay into two pions. Thus the observation of a two-pion final state, down the trajectory, can be translated into a measurement of CP-violation. This was how it was originally found.

The amount of CP-violation can be characterized by the parameters

$$|\eta_{+-}| = \frac{|\langle \pi^+ \pi^- |K_L\rangle|}{|\langle \pi^+ \pi^- |K_S\rangle|} \approx 2.253 \times 10^{-3}$$

$$|\eta_{00}| = \frac{|\langle \pi^0 \pi^0 |K_L\rangle|}{|\langle \pi^0 \pi^0 |K_S\rangle|} \approx 2.268 \times 10^{-3} \qquad (20.5)$$

(There are other parameters as well, but we will not go over all the possibilities.) We see that the effect is tiny, but, because it is a violation of a quantity conserved in all other interactions, it is significant. The first case of CP violation was in the $K^0 \bar{K}^0$ system, but by now it has been observed in other cases, such as in the decays of $B^\pm$, in the $B^0 \bar{B}^0$-system, etc.

Let us now turn to the theoretical understanding of this. The key point is that, within the Standard Model, there is some freedom in the choice of the term which leads to quark masses. Recall that the electron mass is due to the term

$$S_{mass} = \int d^4x \, \lambda \, \bar{e}_R \, \Phi^\dagger \ell_L \; + \; \text{h.c.} \tag{20.6}$$

Similarly, quark masses can arise from

$$S_{mass} = - \int d^4x \, \left[f^u_{ij} \, \bar{Q}^i_L \tilde{\Phi} U^j_R + f^d_{ij} \, \bar{Q}^i_L \Phi D^j_R \; + \; \text{h.c.} \right] \tag{20.7}$$

where

$$\Phi = \begin{pmatrix} \phi^+ \\ \phi^0 \end{pmatrix}, \qquad \tilde{\Phi} = \begin{pmatrix} \phi^{0*} \\ -\phi^- \end{pmatrix}, \qquad Q^i = \begin{pmatrix} U^i \\ D^i \end{pmatrix}$$

$$U^1 = u, \; U^2 = c, \; U^3 = t, \qquad D^1 = d, \; D^2 = s, \; D^3 = b \tag{20.8}$$

The freedom we mentioned is that we can have a matrix of couplings f^u_{ij} and f^d_{ij}; this does not violate the gauge symmetry in any way, because the coefficients mix fields which transform the same way under gauge transformations. When the symmetry-breaking ground state value $\phi^0 = v/\sqrt{2}$ is used, this will give a "mass matrix", something which is not diagonal in terms of the quarks. In order to identify the true mass eigenstates, we have to do a diagonalization. This is fine, and as expected; but this will "undiagonalize" the interaction term with the W's, since they are originally chosen to be defined in terms of each Q separately. (They do not mix Q^1 with Q^2 or Q^3 to begin with.) The result is that, in the basis in which the mass matrix has been diagonalized, the quark-W interaction terms become

$$S_{int} = -\frac{g}{\sqrt{2}} \int d^4x \, \left[W^+_\mu J^{-\mu} + W^-_\mu J^{+\mu} \right]$$
$$J^{-\mu} = V_{ij} \, \bar{U}^i_L \gamma^\mu D^j_L$$
$$J^{+\mu} = V^*_{ji} \, \bar{D}^i_L \gamma^\mu U^j_L \tag{20.9}$$

where V_{ij} is a unitary 3×3 matrix, related to the matrices used for diagonalizing f^u and f^d. The mass term for the quarks, after diagonalization, has the form $m_i^{(U)} \bar{U}^i U^i + m_i^{(D)} \bar{D}^i D^i$. So we can make additional phase transformations for each flavor of the form $U^i \to e^{i\theta_i} U^i$, $D^i \to e^{i\tilde{\theta}_i} D^i$, without affecting the mass term. This gives $2n$ phases for n generations, which can be used to eliminate some parameters from V_{ij}. Actually one common phase can cancel out between the Us and Ds in (20.9), so we can only remove $2n - 1$ parameters. The number of independent parameters in V is thus $n^2 - (2n - 1) = (n - 1)^2$. If the world had only two generations with the (u, d) and (c, s) quarks, there would only be one parameter in V; it can be chosen to be real. With 3 generations, V_{ij} has 4 independent parameters. A real unitary matrix is real orthogonal and has only 3 parameters. So, with 3 generations, V cannot be entirely real, there will be an extra parameter, which can be taken as an extra phase. In fact, V can be written in the form

$$V_{11} = \cos\theta_{12} \cos\theta_{13}, \quad V_{12} = \sin\theta_{12} \cos\theta_{13}, \quad V_{13} = \sin\theta_{13}\, e^{-i\delta}$$
$$V_{21} = -\sin\theta_{12} \cos\theta_{23} - \cos\theta_{12} \sin\theta_{23} \sin\theta_{13}\, e^{i\delta}$$
$$V_{22} = \cos\theta_{12} \cos\theta_{23} - \sin\theta_{12} \sin\theta_{23} \sin\theta_{13}\, e^{i\delta}$$
$$V_{23} = \sin\theta_{23} \cos\theta_{13} \qquad\qquad (20.10)$$
$$V_{31} = \sin\theta_{12} \sin\theta_{23} - \cos\theta_{12} \cos\theta_{23} \sin\theta_{13}\, e^{i\delta}$$
$$V_{32} = -\cos\theta_{12} \sin\theta_{23} - \sin\theta_{12} \cos\theta_{23} \sin\theta_{13}\, e^{i\delta}$$
$$V_{33} = \cos\theta_{23} \cos\theta_{13}$$

which explicitly displays the 3 real angular parameters θ_{12}, θ_{13}, θ_{23} and the phase δ. (This is one way to parametrize the elements of the matrix V; there are other useful parametrizations as well.) The fact that V is not real, as seen from the $e^{i\delta}$-factors in (20.10), leads to CP-violation in the interactions in (20.9). The parameters η_{+-} and η_{00} are calculable in terms of δ.

The matrix V is known as the Cabibbo-Kobayashi-Maskawa (CKM) matrix. The version for two generations was obtained by Cabibbo in 1963 (although not quite in this language), and the generalization was done by M. Kobayashi and T. Maskawa in the 1973. This was done before the discovery of the third generation of quarks and leptons. The work of Kobayashi and Maskawa made clear that a third generation would give a simple way to incorporate CP-violation in the Standard Model. (It is not the only way; there are other ways to include CP-violation. However, experiments to date indicate that the CKM method works and there is no need for other ways.)

One may ask if something similar can happen with the leptons. The answer is that, if the neutrinos have no mass, the corresponding V-matrix can be taken as the identity. However, we know that neutrinos do have a mass as well as mixing of different generations. This leads to the so-called neutrino oscillations. Thus a similar story can be played out for the leptons as well, but not quite the same way. This is because the left-chiral and right-chiral neutrinos must have different masses. We know this because all low energy physics sees only neutrinos which are primarily of the left chirality; therefore right-chiral ones must have a much higher mass. So the details of how neutrino-mixing happens differs a bit from the CKM scenario. Also, the experiments to date have not managed to sort out all the mixings and masses accurately enough to pin down everything about neutrino-mixing. We will comment on neutrino masses later.

Let us now turn to another question: Why is this small effect of *CP*-violation of so much importance, why should we pay so much attention to this tiny little feature of the Standard Model? The answer has to do with the puzzle of why the world has matter, but so little of antimatter. Since strong interactions and the electromagnetic interactions have complete symmetry between particles and antiparticles, it is possible to make anti-atoms and anti-molecules and so on, so that a world of antimatter seems entirely feasible. Further, in the early universe, when the temperature was very high, all particles were in thermal equilibrium. The thermal production of particles and antiparticles was possible since the temperature was high enough; equilibrium would involve detailed balance of various reactions, so that, if the forward and backward reaction rates are identical, there would be essentially equal numbers of particles and antiparticles. When the universe cooled, we could then have annihilation of matter with antimatter, resulting in a universe of photons or, if we are lucky, with separated islands of matter and antimatter. In reality, this is not so. The world is almost entirely made of matter. We know this from the lack of direct evidence for antimatter in cosmic rays, the lack of evidence for high energy photons from matter-antimatter annihilation and other observations. This is primarily a baryon-over-antibaryon asymmetry, since baryons are what we can most easily observe. A quantitative way to characterize the asymmetry, relevant for attempts at calculating it, is by the ratio of the average number density of baryons (n_B) to the number density of photons (n_γ) in the universe, i.e., n_B/n_γ. Or, since the antibaryons are negligible, we may view this as $(n_B - n_{\bar{B}})/n_\gamma$. Quantitatively, from astrophysical observations,

$$\frac{(n_B - n_{\bar{B}})}{n_\gamma} \approx 5 \times 10^{-10} \qquad (20.11)$$

How do we understand this? Many years ago, in 1967, Andrei Sakharov argued that one could expect a preponderance of particles of one kind, say, matter rather than antimatter, if three conditions were obtained in the early universe. These are:

(1) Fundamental reactions which do not preserve baryon number
(2) Fundamental reactions which do not preserve C and CP (or T)
(3) Nonequilibrium evolution of the universe

We know that the last condition is in fact obtained, since the universe is not in equilibrium because it is expanding, although it does have local and temporary equilibrium. The presence of C and CP-violation in weak interactions shows that the second condition could also be satisfied. (The importance of CP-violation is thus in its potential to explain the observed preponderance of matter over antimatter.) What about the first condition of baryon number violating reactions? The Standard Model does have such reactions via a very nonperturbative process whose rate is very small, exponentially small, of the order 10^{-137} times typical rates.[1] However, there may be enhancement due to temperature-dependent effects. So, in principle, we have all the ingredients. Unfortunately, calculations show that we do not have quantitative agreement; the strength of baryon number violation in the Standard Model is not adequate.

What if we have other baryon-number violating interactions? In the Standard Model, the weak and electromagnetic interactions are unified (into the $SU(2) \times U(1)$ theory), but the strong nuclear forces (with the $SU(3)$ color gauge symmetry) stand separate, not unified with the electroweak ones. Suppose we have a single unified theory, with a single group for gauge symmetry so that all gauge fields belong to a single Yang-Mills action. Such a theory is called a grand unified theory; it would unify all interactions except for gravity. The hallmark of such a theory would be interactions which directly connect quarks and leptons, and, hence, would lead to baryon number violating transitions. This idea has been entertained and studied starting from the early 1970s. There are the so-called $SU(5)$ and $SO(10)$, and the even more exotic E_6, theories. The telltale signature would be proton decay, since the proton does not decay with all the known interactions. Of course, the rate must be very small, since protons are known to be quite stable. The initial expectation, when grand unified theories were first introduced, was that the proton lifetime would be of the order of 10^{32} years. This means that if we take 10^{32} protons (approximately 10^5 kilograms of matter) and watch it for a year, we might see one proton

---

[1] This is due to the so-called instantons of the electroweak theory.

decay. Clearly, it is not an easy thing to detect. Nevertheless, on the experimental side, a lot of effort has been made to look for proton decay, the most famous one being the nucleon decay experiment (nde) at Kamioka in Japan, hence "kamiokande". To minimize contamination or the chance of false positives, the mass of material under study must be shielded from cosmic rays, so it is basically a large tank of pure water, about 3000 tons, buried deep underground (for shielding), surrounded by 1000 photomultiplier tubes to detect the Čerenkov radiation given off by possible decay products.[2] The experiment ran for many years starting around 1982, but has not seen proton decay. The result of the experiment is best expressed in terms of a limit on the proton lifetime, $\tau_{proton} \gtrsim 10^{34}$ years.

So where do we stand? There is a circle of ideas which could explain the matter versus antimatter asymmetry. *CP*-violation is real and well-tested. Baryon number violation is more problematic. So, as of now, we do not have a quantitatively satisfactory explanation of why there is more matter than antimatter in the universe.

---

[2]Čerenkov radiation refers to radiation given off by a charged particle when it travels in a medium with a speed greater than the speed of light in that medium.

Chapter 21

Many Big Questions Remain

We have talked about particle physics and the Standard Model. This theory achieves the unification of the weak and electromagnetic interactions and also provides the proper description of the strong nuclear forces. Further, the Standard Model, when combined with classical gravity, explains phenomena over a wide range of scales, from 10^{-18} m to 10^{25} m or so, about 43 orders of magnitude in length scale. This is a truly amazing achievement. Remember that at the time of Newton, a little over three hundred years ago, we were still at the level of terrestrial phenomena occurring on a scale of a few meters, a typical human scale. In some ways, Newton's achievement was to realize that the phenomena on Earth and in the heavens should have the same set of physical laws and hence what was observed on Earth, such as gravity, could be used to understand planetary motion. So it was an enhancement of scale from the human dimensions to the scale of the solar system. Simultaneously, we started a journey to the smaller scales as well, with the work of Leeuwenhoek and Hooke. In about 300 years, we can now cover roughly 43 orders of magnitude. This does not mean we understand all physics and can give an explanation for all experimental results. No, many details are yet to be worked out, many collective phenomena may require new concepts. But there is good reason to believe that while there are so many details at so many levels to be worked out and understood, no new physical principles will be needed for the majority, with significant exceptions, of the phenomena we have observed in the range of length scales indicated. And yet, many big questions remain, the exceptions mentioned above, some of which may require new laws of physics. Let us talk about some of these remaining big questions, as we know of them, or understand them, at this point in history. We should keep in mind that our perspective on this may change over time as well.

There are three, partially overlapping, broad categories of these questions. One of them refers to refinements of the Standard Model, without dramatically altering the framework. These include neutrino oscillations, deeper understanding of flavor, etc. These are what we might call the "known unknowns". The second set would be problems we think we might be able to answer without new laws of physics, by simply extending existing paradigms for incorporating new particles. Some new ingredients might be needed, but again, no dramatic changes. The third category consists of problems which may require a real extension of the presently known laws of physics.[1] Let us talk about these in turn.

Refinements of the Standard Model

Neutrino masses and mixing angles

There is convincing evidence by now that neutrinos have nonzero masses and that different flavors of neutrinos get mixed in the weak interaction processes in much the same way (with details differing somewhat) as the Cabibbo-Kobayashi-Maskawa matrix describes the mixing of different generations of quarks in weak interactions. The history of this discovery is an interesting saga of precision experiments and the interplay of particle physics and astrophysics. Let us start by recalling that the neutrino, postulated by Pauli and Fermi in 1932, was finally detected by Reines and Cowan in 1956. (Strictly speaking it was the antineutrino, detected via the reaction $\bar{\nu}_e + p \to n + e^+$.) Shortly afterwards, in 1962, the work of Lederman, Schwartz and Steinberger revealed that there are at least two distinct flavors of neutrinos. A few years later, Raymond Davis started a series of experiments which turned out to be crucial in neutrino physics. (It is important to mention John Bahcall here. He collaborated with Davis at the earlier stages and also was important in refining the solar model, which we will talk about in a moment.) Electron-neutrinos are produced by nuclear reactions in the interior of stars, including our star the Sun, mostly by the process[2]

$$4p \to {}^4\text{He} + 2\,e^+ + 2\nu_e$$

---

[1]And, of course, there is always the possibility of the "unknown unknowns", completely beyond our imagination or our ability of conceptualization at present.

[2]There are several chains of nuclear processes; this is the net effect of some of the pathways.

Davis was trying to measure the flux of these electron-neutrinos produced by the Sun, using effectively the inverse β-decay process

$$\nu_e + {}^{37}\text{Cl} \rightarrow {}^{37}\text{Ar} + e^-$$

The amount of argon produced could be chemically estimated and then used to work back to obtain an estimate of the neutrino flux. The result of the Davis experiment was that the measured flux was significantly less than (less than half of) what was expected from the rather widely accepted model of the Sun. There were three explanations possible. One was that the experiment was not right, maybe the nuclear physics of the detector was not understood precisely enough or that more statistics would be needed to rule out statistical flukes. The experiment was refined over the years and led to an enormous accumulation of data. Many other experiments, using other methods such as Gallium for detection, enlarging the accessible kinematic regimes, etc. gave independent confirmation of the solar neutrino deficit as well. So the possibility that the experiment was wrong could be ruled out.

The second possibility was that the parameters of the solar model were not quite right. In particular, the flux of neutrinos is sensitive to the temperature in the interior of the Sun (which can be estimated from other processes), but if this was incorrect by a small amount, Davis' result could be explained without any new physics. Over the years, the parameters of the solar model were pinned down accurately, so that by the 1990s, this possibility could also be ruled out.

The third possibility was neutrino oscillations. If the neutrinos created by the nuclear processes are not mass eigenstates, then the mass eigenstates contained in the initial neutrino propagate independently on their way to Earth from the Sun, and what is detected by inverse β-decay can be only a fraction of the flux produced. (This idea was originally due to Pontecorvo.) In more detail, suppose $|\nu_e\rangle$ is the state produced in the reaction, and suppose that it is a linear combination of mass eigenstates $|1\rangle$ and $|2\rangle$. (We just consider ν_e to be made of two flavors to illustrate the scenario). We can then write

$$|\nu_e\rangle = \cos\theta\,|1\rangle + \sin\theta\,|2\rangle \tag{21.1}$$

for some angle θ. After time t, say the time it takes for the particles to reach Earth, the state becomes

$$|\nu_e, t\rangle = e^{-iHt}\,|\nu_e\rangle = \cos\theta\,e^{-i\omega_1 t}\,|1\rangle + \sin\theta\,e^{-i\omega_2 t}\,|2\rangle \tag{21.2}$$

While the two components have the same momentum, since the left side is produced as an eigenstate of momentum, the masses are different and $\omega_1 = \sqrt{\vec{p}^2 + m_1^2}$ and $\omega_2 = \sqrt{\vec{p}^2 + m_2^2}$. The detector again responds to $|\nu_e\rangle$, so what is observed is the overlap of this state with ν_e. Thus the fraction of the neutrinos seen by the detector is the absolute square of the amplitude $\langle \nu_e | \nu_e, t \rangle$,

$$\mathcal{A} = \langle \nu_e | e^{-iHt} | \nu_e \rangle = \cos^2 \theta \, e^{-i\omega_1 t} + \sin^2 \theta \, e^{-i\omega_2 t}$$
$$|\mathcal{A}|^2 = 1 - \sin^2(2\theta) \sin^2(\Delta\omega \, t/2) \tag{21.3}$$

$\Delta\omega = \omega_2 - \omega_1 \approx (m_2^2 - m_1^2)/2\omega$, since the masses are small compared to the momentum. The fraction given by this formula is generally smaller than 1 and can account for the observation if $(\Delta\omega \, t)$ has just the right value. Notice that for this, we need different masses for the different flavors as well as nonzero mixing angles (θ in (21.1)). In fact, mixing of flavors can be eliminated if the neutrinos are massless. When this idea was suggested, there was (and there still is) no experimental evidence for right-chiral neutrinos, so we must presume that the latter are very massive, beyond the observable limits of today. The only way to give different masses to the right-chiral and left-chiral components is to use a Majorana mass term.

A priori, it may not seem economical to postulate so much, bringing in masses, right-chiral neutrinos and mixing angles, to explain one set of observations, but by the 1990s it was clear that other possible explanations had to be ruled out. A direct observation of neutrino oscillations would be the clearest signal. This was finally achieved by the Super-Kamiokande experiment using atmospheric neutrinos in 1998. Additional experiments with neutrinos produced in nuclear reactors and by particle accelerators have confirmed neutrino oscillations. The data from the Sudbury Neutrino Observatory and the KAMLAND (a liquid scintillator antineutrino detector facility at Kamioka) data have provided convincing evidence.

So now there is a whole new set of parameters, neutrino masses and mixing angles, which we need to measure accurately to pin down the Standard Model.

Axions and the strong CP-problem

In the matter of quantum field theory, we might say that physicists cut their teeth on quantum electrodynamics (QED), which was developed, starting with Dirac's paper in 1927 through the 1930s and 1940s, and even into the 1960s. But in retrospect, QED is a fairly simple theory. It was realized by the 1970s that fields which occur in quantum chromodynamics (QCD) and the electroweak theory have more interesting topologies and that this can affect the quantum theory. In particular, for QCD, in addition to all the terms in the action which we have discussed, there is one more term which can be added, given by

$$S_{top} = \theta \left[\frac{1}{64\pi^2} \int d^4x \; \epsilon^{\mu\nu\alpha\beta} \, F^a_{\mu\nu} F^a_{\alpha\beta} \right]$$

$$F^a_{\mu\nu} = \partial_\mu A^a_\nu - \partial_\nu A^a_\mu + g_s \, f^{abc} A^b_\mu A^c_\nu \tag{21.4}$$

where θ is an arbitrary parameter. It ranges over the real interval from zero to 2π, so it may be regarded as angular parameter. In terms of consequences, it is like a new coupling constant in the theory.

This term is peculiar in many ways. First of all, the integrand is formally a total derivative, so it has no contribution to the equations of motion, and hence, no contribution at the classical level. It is a term which is allowed in the quantum theory. In other words, the classical action does not serve to define the quantum theory, there can be some ambiguities or freedom of extra terms when we go from the classical theory to the quantum theory. In the quantum theory, this term does have an effect. Even though formally a total derivative, the integral can be nonvanishing since the boundary values of the fields need not be zero; they should be zero only up to a gauge transformation.[3] The result is that quantum wave functions see the effect of the term (21.4) as a phase. There is nothing bad about such a situation *per se*. However, the term (21.4) does not preserve parity and time-reversal symmetry. So if this term exists, we should see that strong nuclear forces do not preserve parity or time-reversal symmetry. (This is called the strong CP-problem.) This is not the case experimentally, strong nuclear forces do preserve parity and time-reversal symmetry. In fact, experimental bounds (for example, from the electric dipole moment of the neutron) on θ is $< 10^{-11}$. This extremely small value, unnaturally small compared to most other parameters, suggests that it might actually be zero. So the question is whether there is any mechanism which eliminates this term. This can be achieved naturally if we have an additional axial $U(1)$ symmetry (known as the Peccei-Quinn symmetry) and one additional particle (from spontaneous breaking of the PQ symmetry) which can be very light and whose coupling is very small. Such a particle is called an axion. The corresponding axion field should be odd under parity and should couple in such a way that θ can be eliminated by a shift of this field.

---

[3] Field configurations for which the integral in (21.4) is nonzero and which obey the Yang-Mills equations are called instantons.

Axion searches have been made and are still going on. So far we have not found it. A number of variants of the basic idea have also been explored which are consistent with the lack of evidence for axions so far. (These include the 'invisible axion' which is so weakly coupled that its escape from observation can be easily accounted for.)

From the point of view of the internal consistency of quantum field theory, there is no problem in simply declaring that nature just happens to choose $\theta = 0$, so it may not be a problem, it may only be a matter of discomfort to physicists because we have some prejudices on the aesthetics of physical theories. But it would be nice to have a better explanation.

The flavor problem

A look at the particle data booklet is sufficient to make anyone worry that we are missing something when it comes to the fundamental particles. The masses are spread over a very wide range, from perhaps a few electron volts for neutrinos to 175 GeV or so for the top quark. The mixing angles are a similar story. There is no discernible pattern among these parameters and the whole set hardly looks like what we may call "fundamental". Nature, while choosing well-defined groups of symmetries such as the Lorentz symmetry, or the $SU(3)$, $SU(2)$ and $U(1)$ of the Standard Model, seems to have just thrown in a jumble of parameters for the masses, mixing angles and coupling constants. Could there be a better understanding or deeper explanation?

Again, it could be that this is not a real problem. After all, in the early days of the study of planetary motion, it was thought that there would be a rationale behind the pattern of orbital radii (and other orbital parameters) for the planets in the solar system. (Kepler's *Mysterium Cosmographicum*, his book from before his discovery of the laws of planetary motion, and the Titius-Bode law, which came more than a century after, exemplify this way of thinking.) But later, it seemed to be just a coincidence since the dynamics would allow a very wide range of values for the orbital parameters of any system of planets. And now, with the discovery of thousands of exoplanets, we do see it as just a coincidence. Our solar system just happens to have the set of values we measure, and there are many others with different values for planetary orbital parameters. Could it be that there are thousands of universes with many, many different choices for the masses and mixing angles and so on, and we just happen to be in one with the specific values we have measured? This "anthropic" explanation may be comforting, even acceptable to some physicists, but it is hard not to feel that this is something of a cop-out.

Another possibility is that the particles we know of today are themselves composite. This is in tune with our experience. For example, if we take the energy levels and mixing of electronic states for a complicated atom, like, say, Zn, the values are not very illuminating. Seeking a symmetry-based or group theory based explanation is not what is needed. The realization that the apparent lack of rhyme or reason for such numbers is due to composit-eness is the key. In terms of the more fundamental constituents and our understanding of atomic structure, we have a simpler theory and a better explanation. Like the opening of the Russian *matryoshka* dolls, maybe we need to go one step further, from the periodic table to the atoms and their substructure, to quarks and leptons, to yet another deeper level. But we have, so far, no evidence for the composite nature of quarks or leptons, al-though people have tried to make such models. The postulated elementary constituents of quarks and leptons have even been given a name: "pre-ons". Some of the models utilize ideas of supersymmetry as well, but as mentioned above, we have no evidence so far.

The compositeness idea is in some ways the antithesis of grand unifi-cation. In a grand unified theory where all interactions and particles are obtained from a single group such as $SU(5)$ or $SO(10)$, the quarks and leptons retain their fundamental nature at least up to energy scales of the order of 10^{17} GeV or so; flavor parameters such as masses and mixing an-gles will need some explanation other than compositeness, or the idea of compositeness has to be invoked at a much deeper level, length scales below $10^{-17}(\text{GeV})^{-1}$. Anyway, so far, there is no compelling evidence either for compositeness or grand unification.

Worry about hierarchy

Here is something else we might worry about. If we have grand unifica-tion, we have to put all three symmetries $SU(3)$, $SU(2)$ and $U(1)_Y$ of the Standard Model into a single symmetry. This larger symmetry, call it G (it could be $SU(5)$, $SO(10)$ or E_6 or something else), must somehow be broken, since we do not see it manifest at the energies we have explored so far. So we might ask for spontaneous breaking of this symmetry at some scale V. Since grand unification also gives proton decay, we can put a lower bound on this scale; it should be at least 10^{17} GeV or so. But we also have a smaller scale of about $v \approx 246$ GeV for breaking $SU(2) \times U(1)_Y$ to get massive $W^{\pm}$ and Z (and masses for quarks and leptons). In general, it is hard to keep these scales so widely different, within the usual scheme of using perturbation theory. The reason is that, generally in quantum field theory, higher order effects or corrections to the scales of symmetry breaking are controlled by the highest mass involved. Typically, corrections to the lower scale, say v^2 will go like $\delta v^2 \sim \lambda V^2$, with λ being a coupling constant. Thus if we do the calculation for the scales up to the k-th order, we would find something like

$$v^2 = v_0^2 + c_1 \lambda V_0^2 + \cdots + c_k \lambda^k V_0^2 \tag{21.5}$$

where v_0 is the value we start with and c_i are generally coefficients of order 1, and λ is also typically a number of order 1. To the lowest order in the calculation, we can fix up v to be the desired low value (say, 246 GeV), by choosing v_0 appropriately. But if we consider the first set of quantum corrections, we get a term proportional to λV_0^2, pulling the value of v^2 to something close to the higher scale; we have to adjust v_0 to an accuracy of several decimal places, if the scales are very different, to regain the 246 GeV. For example, with the first correction, we have the combination $v_0^2 + c_1 \lambda V_0^2$. We would have to choose v_0^2 such that it will cancel out the first several decimal places, around 25 or so, of $c_1 \lambda V_0^2$, but the values of v_0^2 and $c_1 \lambda V_0^2$ for the decimal places beyond that should be such that they add up to give the scale of 246 GeV. This requires specifying the starting value of v_0^2 to an accuracy of better than 25 decimal places. Add one more order in perturbation theory, we have to do the same all over again, due to the $\lambda^2 V_0^2$ term. The addition of each order in perturbation theory upsets the whole hierarchical set-up, with the scales getting mixed up. So in perturbation theory we have to redefine our choice of the starting value v_0 every time we calculate to one higher order. This is clearly an unsatisfactory situation as regards the perturbative treatment of the theory.

Physicists have explored ways around it. Maybe we do not have symmetry-breaking using some scalar field for the electroweak theory. Maybe we should have a composite field do the job, just as the Cooper pair in superconductivity is a bound state of something more elementary. Or maybe there is some other symmetry, the candidate being supersymmetry, which can help to avoid generating a series like (21.5). But in all cases, there is a much larger structure, with many more particles and interactions, needed.

But one could also play the devil's advocate and say that we have no evidence for grand unification anyway. So maybe we are tying ourselves in knots for no reason, postulating grand unification and then trying to solve the problems it generates. It would be nice to resolve this with some experimental inputs.

A bit of cosmology

One of the hallmarks of physics today is the convergence of cosmology and particle physics. The small scale and the large scale are coming together in an interesting new way.

We need a bit of cosmology to see how this comes about. We know that we live in an expanding universe, an observation which goes back to Hubble in 1929. The key issue in those days was a method to estimate distances to distant galaxies. For the distances to planets in our solar system, we can use simple triangulation. We observe the planet from two different points on Earth and from the angle between the horizontal and the line of sight to the planet from both observation points and knowing the baseline (the distance between the two observation points) we can calculate the distance to the object, by elementary trigonometry. For stars we need a larger baseline and this is provided by the orbit of Earth around the Sun. We make observations of the same star from two different points on the orbit, at two different times of the year. But when it comes to galaxies, this is inadequate. Hubble's method was to use Cepheid variables, which are variable stars (pulsating in luminosity) that are easily identifiable and have a definite relationship between the pulsation frequency and luminosity. (This standardization could be done by studying such stars in our own galaxy.) By identifying the Cepheid variable stars in a galaxy and then comparing their apparent luminosity with the expected absolute luminosity, one can estimate the distance. This was how Hubble was able to make measurements of the distances to various galaxies. Spectroscopic analysis showed redshift of spectral lines from these galaxies which could then be matched to a recession velocity, to arrive at the conclusion that the universe is expanding.

Over the course of the twentieth century, this has evolved into a standard cosmology as well. There is very good evidence for overall homogeneity and isotropy of the universe and that it is accurately described by a metric of the form

$$ds^2 = dt^2 - a^2(t)\,(dx^2 + dy^2 + dz^2) \qquad (21.6)$$

where $a(t)$ only depends on time t and is a scale factor for distance measurements. This is the so-called Robertson-Walker metric. Hubble's observation is equivalent to the statement that $a(t)$ is an increasing function of time.

It is possible to combine (21.6) with Einstein's equations for gravity (i.e., equations for the metric of spacetime, equations (10.30) given in Lecture 10) to relate $a(t)$ to the pressure and density of the material which constitutes the universe, and which to a reasonable approximation can be taken to be uniformly distributed. These equations reduce to

$$\frac{\dot{a}^2}{a^2} - \frac{8\pi G}{3}(\rho + \Lambda) = 0$$

$$\dot{\rho} + 3\frac{\dot{a}}{a}(p + \rho) = 0 \tag{21.7}$$

where ρ is the energy density, p is the pressure and Λ is a constant known as the cosmological constant. These equations are called the Friedmann-Lemaitre-Robertson-Walker equations. For a solution, they have to be supplemented by an equation of state. If we consider the universe to be dominated by radiation so that $p = \rho/3$ and if we further neglect Λ, then $\rho = \sigma/a^4$ for some constant σ, and $a(t) \sim \sqrt{t}$. Comparing the radiation density ρ with the Stefan-Boltzmann law ($\rho \sim T^4$), we see that we may take the temperature of the gas of radiation to go like a^{-1}. Thus in the early universe with a smaller value for a, we had a higher temperature; as the universe expands, it cools down.

The broad picture of the evolution of the universe is then as follows. The universe started out in a hot dense phase, so hot that we can take it to be a gas of photons, quarks, leptons, gluons, etc. in more or less thermal equilibrium. As the universe cooled down, quarks combined to form protons and neutrons and eventually more complex nuclei like He, Li, etc. This was still a phase with ionized matter in temporary equilibrium with photons. Then came a recombination era when the universe had cooled down enough for electrons to get bound to nuclei, forming neutral atoms. Since the coupling of photons to neutral atoms is very weak, the photon gas effectively decoupled from matter at this point and continued to cool down as a Planck distribution of decreasing temperatures. (After decoupling, we have a matter dominated era, which can be modeled as dust with $p = 0$, which leads to the behavior $a \sim t^{2/3}$.) If this scenario is right, we can expect to calculate the abundance of light nuclei such as He and Li from the nuclear physics of how they are formed. Further, there should be relic radiation left over, namely, the photon gas that was decoupled from matter. The latter is the cosmic microwave background radiation (at a present day temperature of ~ 2.7 K). The observed abundances of He, Li, etc. also match well with calculations.

The expansion rate is given by what is now called Hubble's constant,

$$H = \frac{\dot{a}}{a} \tag{21.8}$$

The distance to a galaxy at time t is given by $D(t) = D(t_0)(a(t)/a(t_0))$, or

$$\dot{D} = \frac{\dot{a}}{a} D(t) = H D(t) \tag{21.9}$$

Thus galaxies farther away seem to recede faster, in a way proportional to their distance from us, with the constant of proportionality being the Hubble constant. Numerically, the observed value of H is around 70 km s^{-1} (Megaparsec)$^{-1}$.

From the metric structure (21.6), we infer that over small intervals of time for which a is approximately constant, the wave equation has the form

$$\frac{\partial^2 \phi}{\partial t^2} - \frac{1}{a^2} \nabla^2 \phi \approx 0 \tag{21.10}$$

with a solution of the form $\phi = \exp(i|\vec{k}|t/a - i\vec{k} \cdot \vec{x})$. Thus if an atom (with energy levels E_2, E_1) emits light of frequency $E_2 - E_1$ at time t_e, then the observed frequency at time t would be

$$\omega = \frac{a(t_e)}{a(t)} (E_2 - E_1) = (E_2 - E_1) \frac{1}{1 + z} \tag{21.11}$$

We see a redshift in the spectrum, quantified as the factor z defined by the second equality. Light from further away, because it was emitted earlier, would have more redshift compared to light from sources closer to us. This is the essence of Hubble's observation as interpreted in terms of the Robertson-Walker metric (21.6).

The successes of calculations involving nuclear and particle physics in the early universe show how distinctions between the domains of cosmology and particle physics fade away as we get to the high temperatures involved. As our understanding of the early universe develops, we can expect that there will be more and more overlap of ideas from particle physics and cosmology.

Dark matter

One of the issues we have already discussed during the last lecture is the observed preponderance of matter over antimatter. Let us now talk of some other questions, starting with the so-called dark matter. This has been an issue since the 1930s but has only recently come into sharper focus as new and more accurate data became available and our understanding of the astrophysics got refined. The problem is the following. Galaxies are made of stars and in some ways they are an upgraded version of the solar system, with the stars orbiting the galactic center. But unlike the solar system, the mass in a galaxy is more distributed; one does not have a single compact central mass. The distribution of mass can be inferred from Kepler's third law. Recall that, since the required centripetal acceleration for circular motion is provided by gravity, we have, for a small mass in a circular orbit around a mass M,

$$\frac{GM}{r^2} = \frac{v^2}{r}, \qquad \text{or} \qquad v^2 = \frac{GM}{r} \tag{21.12}$$

(A slightly more refined version of this holds for elliptical orbits as well.) Thus the speed of the object is a definite function of the distance from the center. Further, we know that the gravitational force on a body inside a hollow spherical shell is zero, so that for a spherical distribution of matter, M should only be the amount of mass inside the orbit of the body under consideration, or $v^2 = GM(r)/r$. The result is slightly modified for non-spherical distributions, but the idea is the same. We see that, if we can measure the speed of orbiting stars (at various values of the radius r), we can obtain $M(r)$ or the distribution of mass in the galaxy. The speed can be measured by Doppler effect on the spectral lines emitted by the orbiting stars and, in fact, the distribution of mass was obtained in this way. Independently, the distribution of luminous matter, namely, mass distributions using all the stars whose light we can see, can be directly obtained by adding up the masses of the stars up to the desired radius. Now one can compare the distribution of mass based on its gravitational effect (via Kepler's law) with the distribution of luminous mass; or one can directly compare the speeds of stars as a function of the distance from the center. What is observed versus what is obtained from the distribution of luminous mass is shown in Fig. 21.1. (We show one typical case; similar results hold for other galaxies as well.) The problem is that these two answers clearly do not agree. From the slow fall-off of the speeds as we move out from the center, we see that the amount of mass enclosed within a given radius should be much larger than what is given by the luminous stars. This "missing mass" is not seen in any of the usual modes of detection such as light, radio waves, etc., except by its gravitational effect. Hence we call it "dark matter". The distribution suggests that the galaxies have a halo of mass around the luminous part which we see.

There is also other evidence supporting this. Similar analyses have been done at the level of galactic clusters, where individual galaxies play the role

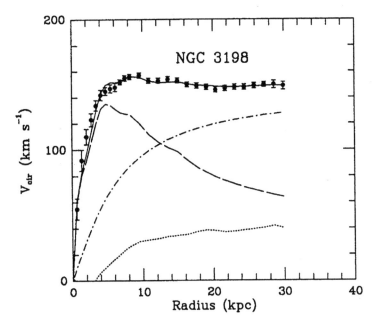

Fig. 21.1: Galactic rotation curves showing the observed speeds of stars as a function of distance (marked points) and the expected curve from the distribution of luminous matter (dashed curve). (The dotted curve is the contribution from gas and the dashed-dotted curve is for the halo; they are not important for our present discussion.) Reprinted with permission from: K.G. Begeman, A.H. Broeils and R.H. Sanders, MNRAS, **249**, 523 (1991)

that stars play at the galactic level. Another piece of evidence comes from fitting the parameters of standard cosmology (of the expanding universe) with observation.

What is this dark matter made of? The short answer is: We do not know, not yet. There are however many candidates for it. For example, one possibility is that the galactic halo is made of dead stars (brown dwarfs, black dwarfs) which have burnt out all fusion generating material and are too cold to radiate anything we can see, or they could be made of small black holes. These are all collectively referred to as MAssive Compact Halo Objects (MACHOs). One may hope to detect them by the fact that they can gravitationally bend light coming towards us from objects even further away, such as other galaxies. There have been attempts to see dark matter via this gravitational lensing effect, so far with no success. In fact, a large class of candidates for MACHOs seems to be ruled out.

Another possibility is that they are made of elementary particles, a matter of interest to particle physicists. Such particles have to be very weakly interacting to have escaped detection so far (in laboratory experiments), so they are referred to as Weakly Interacting Massive Particles, with the cutely contrasting acronym WIMPs. What kind of particles can they be? They could be axions. As we mentioned earlier, these are particles which have been postulated to solve a problem about why strong nuclear forces do not show CP-violation, even though QCD can accommodate it. There are many theoretical variants of the axion, and there have been axion searches going on for a while, but so far none has been detected. Another possibility might be some supersymmetric particle or any of the other particles needed for various extensions of the Standard Model which people have considered with different motivations. They could also be sterile neutrinos which some models do admit. There are searches for such particles, both at accelerators and at detectors placed deep underground for possible occurrences in cosmic rays. But again, so far, we have no definite answers.

Dark energy

The discovery that the rate of expansion of the universe is increasing with time, in other words, the universe is undergoing accelerated expansion, is one of the most dramatic changes in our view of the universe since Hubble's discovery of the expansion itself. Regarding the expansion of the universe, it should be kept in mind that it is not like the expansion of a certain volume of gas with the molecules moving away from each other as they move into a pre-existing ambient space. In the case of the universe, there is no ambient space into which it can expand into. The expansion is really the change of scale for distance measurements. This is evident from the Robertson-Walker metric (21.6). A pictorial analogy for the expanding universe, if one is needed, would be more like the surface of a balloon which is being inflated, but erase from your vision that there is an ambient space and also that there is gas being pumped into the balloon. Instead, imagine that the whole world is just the surface of the balloon. We would then find that the distance between any two points on the surface increases with time.[4]

---

[4]Admittedly, this picture is not the most apt analogy; if and when pictures seem inadequate, it is good to recall what Paul Dirac said in his book *The Principles of Quantum Mechanics*: "..the main object of physical science is not the provision of pictures, but is the formulation of laws governing phenomena and the application of these laws to the

But the universe is not empty, there are big clumps of matter in it, galaxies, galactic clusters, etc. And they tend to attract each other and so we would expect that this can soften the effect of galaxies moving away from each other, slowing down the expansion. And this was, more or less, the general belief until the late 1990s. But how do we measure this expected slowing down? This was a question of great importance to astronomers. For nearby galaxies, as we discussed a little earlier, Hubble was able to use Cepheid variables, but they are too faint to be seen in galaxies further away. The possibility developed in the 1990s was the use of type IA supernovae. These are supernova explosions so powerful that they can outshine an entire galaxy for a few weeks just after the explosion. While there are different types of supernova explosions, type IA supernovae are special because they have a very specific profile for intensity as a function of time. And while the intensity curves do differ from one supernova to another by some amount, there is a simple scaling based on the curve itself which can standardize them completely. Thus the absolute energy output of a type IA supernova can be determined with reasonable accuracy. The apparent luminosity can then be used to estimate the distance to the galaxy in which the supernova occurred. The spectrum of type IA supernovae show a lack of Hydrogen lines, but there are well defined Si, Ca and Fe lines. So they can be identified fairly easily. Further, supernovae occur with a reasonable frequency so that, with billions of galaxies out there, a decent amount of data can be collected over a short time. This understanding of type IA supernovae in the 1990s led to their possible use as standard candles for distance measurements. Once this was available, one could examine the distance-redshift relation or luminosity-redshift relation to say something about the expansion rate.

The actual astrophysics of how type IA supernovae are formed is not entirely clear. The commonly accepted scenario is that they are formed from white dwarfs. These are stars that have come to the end of their Hydrogen fusion cycles. They are mostly formed of Carbon and the temperature is not adequate for Carbon fusion. Further compression and heating up is prevented by the degeneracy of the electron gas and the Pauli exclusion principle, so their fate is usually a slow burning out, to end up as black dwarfs. However, some of them can acquire extra mass, grabbed from a companion star or a passing star and this can raise the temperature enough to ignite Carbon fusion. An extremely rapid thermonuclear process occurs and the result is a type IA supernova, with a notable absence of Hydrogen but characteristic lines of higher elements such as Si, Ca or Fe.

---

discovery of new phenomena. If a picture exists, so much the better; but whether a picture exists or not is a matter of only secondary importance."

The key to understanding the expansion rate is the relation between the observed (or apparent) luminosity and the redshift of distant galaxies, which is

$$I_{obs} = \frac{H_0^2 L}{4\pi} \frac{1}{(1+z)^2 f(z)^2} \tag{21.13}$$

Here $H_0 = \dot{a}/a$ is the Hubble constant as it is today, L is the total energy output per unit time (which is proportional to the absolute magnitude), and $f(z)$ is given by

$$f(z) = \int_0^z \frac{du}{(H(u)/H_0)} \tag{21.14}$$

where $H(u)$ is the Hubble constant at redshift u. If the Hubble constant is independent of time (or equivalently independent of redshift), then

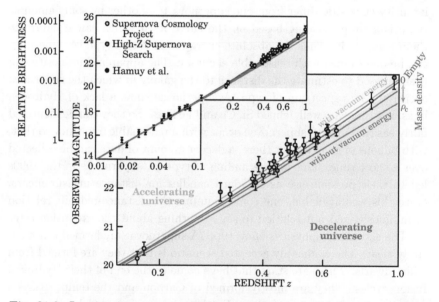

Fig. 21.2: Luminosity versus redshift for distant galaxies based on supernova observations. The observed magnitude is proportional to the negative logarithm of the observed intensity, thus higher magnitudes mean fainter supernovae. The line labeled "without vacuum energy" is what is expected for constant Hubble parameter, with the clustering of observed supernovae above this line indicating an accelerating universe. Reproduced from S. Perlmutter, Physics Today 56.4, 53 (2003), with the permission of the American Institute of Physics.

$f(z) = z$. A graph of $\log I_{obs}$ versus $\log z$, should be a straight line at large z. If the universe is accelerating in its expansion, $H(u) < H_0$ and $f(z) > z$ and I_{obs} falls below what is given by $f(z) = z$. The galaxies far away would appear fainter than what we would expect for constant H at a fixed value of redshift. This was indeed what was observed, as shown in the graph Fig. 21.2. (In reading the graph, it is useful to recall that the magnitude m of an astronomical object is defined in terms of the negative logarithm of the intensity I_{obs}, $m \sim -2.5 \times \log_{10} I_{obs}$ so that larger values of the magnitude correspond to fainter objects.) The graph shows that the universe is accelerating in its expansion, very different from what the expectation was, based on the gravitational attraction of clumps of matter slowing it down.

What is the meaning of this acceleration? Going back to the FLRW equations (21.7), there is one more equation which follows from the Einstein equations for gravity. It is actually related to (21.7), but it is useful to write it separately. This gives $\ddot{a}/a$ as

$$\frac{\ddot{a}}{a} = -\frac{4\pi G}{3}\rho - 4\pi G p + \frac{8\pi G}{3}\Lambda \qquad (21.15)$$

This equation shows a way of relating the acceleration to the matter (or energy density) and the cosmological constant. One can fit the data to the equations (21.7) and (21.15). One way to read the results of such a fit is in terms of the density of matter and the cosmological constant. Rewriting (21.7) at the present time as

$$1 = \frac{8\pi G}{3 H_0^2}\rho + \frac{8\pi G}{3H_0^2}\Lambda \qquad (21.16)$$

we find, from the fit to data, that the two terms on the right hand side are approximately 0.3 and 0.7. Thus the matter density of the world, in units given by G and the Hubble parameter, is only about 30%, with the rest being what could be identified as the cosmological constant. The contribution from the cosmological constant is known as dark energy.

The cosmological constant is, at best, a way to parametrize the observed results. It does not give us a real understanding of where it comes from or of the physics which drives the accelerated expansion. If we also separate out the dark matter, we find that about 25% is dark matter, 5% is luminous known matter and about 70% is dark energy. Phrased this way, we realize that we do not know about 95% of the universe, a rather humbling thought. But this may not convey an accurate sense of proportion; not knowing 95% of the energy budget of the universe does not necessarily mean ignorance of 95% of theoretical framework to describe it, it could be more, it could be less.

The puzzle of dark energy gets worse. The quantity Λ is roughly like the energy of the vacuum and if we try to calculate it from particle physics parameters, the value comes out to be about 10^{120} times the actual value. This depends on how far we can trust our current theories of particle physics, down to what small length scale or up to what high energy scale, or whether we think there is some supersymmetry in the real world. So depending on the assumptions, the calculated value could be as low as 10^{60} times the observed value, still far from anything sensible. So this is a big puzzle. What is dark energy? How do we calculate it? Is it even sensible to consider it as defined by the energy of the vacuum? Λ is one way to parametrize dark energy as a term in the Einstein theory of gravity. Could it be that we need to change the theory of gravity yet again?

Quantum gravity?

There is yet another big puzzle, perhaps the biggest puzzle, remaining. Quantum theory is inconsistent with Einstein's theory of gravity. Recall that in the quantum theory observables are operators on a Hilbert space. Thus all fields like the electric and magnetic fields and the metric of spacetime should become operators. If the metric becomes an operator, with quantum fluctuations in its value, then the very notion of distance becomes problematic. Further, treating the metric as an operator within Einstein's theory leads to problems related to unitarity. A good way to illustrate this is through the notion of a black hole. The metric around a point mass is given in Einstein's theory as

$$ds^2 = \left(1 - \frac{2GM}{r}\right) dt^2 - \frac{1}{(1 - 2GM/r)} dr^2 - r^2 d\theta^2 - r^2 \sin^2\theta\, d\varphi^2 \quad (21.17)$$

This is the Schwarzschild metric, which was also briefly mentioned in Lecture 12. We have written it out in coordinates which reduce to the usual spherical coordinates for the spatial part in the limit of M taken to be zero. One can see that there are two singularities in this expression. The first one, at $r = 0$, is similar to the singularity which occurs in the Newtonian gravitational potential. This is a genuine singularity in the sense that it cannot be removed by a coordinate transformation. The second singularity of (21.17) occurs when r is equal to the so-called Schwarzschild radius $R_S = 2\,GM$. Since it is at a finite radius, we actually have a singular surface corresponding to a two-sphere. One can show that this is a coordinate singularity in the sense that it can be removed by a coordinate transformation. Even so, it has the effect that things falling towards the body can no longer communicate with anything outside R_S, including sending light signals out. Roughly speaking, things can fall in, but do not come out from within R_S. To an observer far away at $r > R_S$, the frequency of light coming from an infalling object will be redshifted by the $(1 - 2GM/r)$-factor, eventually being shifted to zero frequency as the object crosses the Schwarzschild radius. So the sphere at $r = R_S$ is referred to as a horizon. Since there is no communication possible between an object which has fallen inside this horizon and the outside, the region inside constitutes a black hole. Notice that the real singularity at $r = 0$ is also hidden from the outside world by this horizon.

We cannot use (21.17) inside a mass distribution, so we cannot use this metric inside a star (like the Sun) and argue for the existence of a horizon. (There is a different interior metric which is to be used inside the star.) But if the mass is compressed to within its R_S (as defined by its mass), then the horizon is outside of the mass, the metric (21.17) is applicable and we get a black hole, where things can fall in but nothing can come out of the inside region. For the case of the Sun, this can occur (and the Sun turns into a black hole) only if the entire mass of the Sun is compressed to within a radius of ~ 3 km.

Classically, this is the whole story. A black hole, once formed, lives forever, accumulating more and more matter. In the quantum theory, quantum fluctuations can generate black holes. So we have a problem if the black holes cannot disappear; they cannot "unfluctuate" to get back to the starting state and the states of any quantum system can become unstable to black hole formation. The likely scenario is that the quantum theory avoids this by, somehow, making black holes disappear. And this is indeed so; black holes give out radiation, thereby evaporating away. Particle creation by gravitational fields was shown in certain special contexts by Parker, Starobinskii, Unruh and others, but the result that black holes can radiate was most generally and clearly shown by Hawking. The radiation from black holes is therefore referred to as Hawking radiation. But the trouble is that the radiation, at least in the approximations in which we can reliably calculate, is thermal, corresponding to particular temperature T_H, known as the Hawking temperature. In other words, for the photons coming out of a black hole we would have a Planck spectrum corresponding to a temperature T_H. For example, for a black hole of the Schwarzschild type given by the metric (21.17), the temperature is

$$T_H = \frac{1}{8\pi \, GM} \tag{21.18}$$

(Notice that as the black hole evaporates and the mass M decreases, T_H increases, leading to higher rate of radiation. This is very unlike ordinary thermodynamic systems.) The problem with thermal radiation is that it is completely random and does not correspond to a pure quantum state. So the process still leads to loss of unitarity, i.e., a loss of conservation of probability. A pure state in quantum mechanics corresponds to a density matrix ρ which obeys $\rho^2 = \rho$, while a mixed state has $\rho^2 \neq \rho$. The pure state condition is preserved by unitary time evolution, $\rho(t) = U(t)\,\rho(0)\,U^\dagger(t)$, $U(t)$ being a unitary operator. One could consider a black hole formed from the collapse of a pure state, but if it evaporates away completely by thermal radiation, the final state (which is all radiation) is mixed and there is a problem with unitarity.

There are other related issues as well. The temperature T_H and the thermal radiation show that there is entropy associated with the black hole. This may be calculated from T_H, and the fact that the internal energy is just the mass M, via the thermodynamic relation $dM = T\,dS$, and gives

$$S_{\text{BH}} = \frac{A}{4\,G} \tag{21.19}$$

where $A = 4\pi R_S^2$ is the area of the horizon. S_{BH} is known as the Bekenstein-Hawking entropy. For normal thermodynamic systems, one expects to have an explanation of entropy based on statistical mechanics, in terms of the number of microstates which correspond to the same values for conserved macroscopic observables such as mass (or energy), angular momentum, charge, etc. The number of microstates is usually proportional to the phase volume of the system. However, the entropy of a black hole as given by (21.19) has the peculiar feature that it is proportional to the area of the surface of the region accessible to an outside observer, not to anything that looks like a phase volume.

These features illustrate some of the problems of quantum gravity. We will need a quantum version of gravity because classical gravity with a quantum theory for all other fields would not be consistent; yet conservation of probability or unitarity of the quantum theory is in jeopardy because of gravity. As yet we have no complete solution to this situation. There are candidate theories of quantum gravity which people have tried out, such as string theory, loop quantum gravity, noncommutative geometry, emergent spacetime theories and so on. String theory is perhaps the best-developed case among these. Here the notion of particles is replaced by fundamental strings, with each species of particles identified as a particular mode of vibration of the string. Within this theory, in some limited cases with supersymmetry, one can find black hole solutions for which a description in terms of microstates can be developed, and this does lead to the formula (21.19). So the suggestion which emerges is that the thermal radiation may only be a coarse-grained phenomenon and as one gets to smaller and smaller black holes, a different analysis in terms of the microscopic string degrees of freedom has to be done to see how the black hole evaporates. It is expected that this would lead to a consistent unitary time-evolution for the black hole as it evaporates.

Does this mean that we can take string theory as *the* quantum theory of gravity? Since it gives a correct microscopic counting of states for black holes (in the cases where a reliable counting can be done), it certainly passes at least this one test. (There are other aspects of string theory which also support the idea that it is a quantum theory of gravity. For example, string theoretic calculations of perturbative graviton processes also seem to work out in terms of unitarity.) But we could also argue, if we were inclined to play the devil's advocate, that there may be such universality (as with many things in thermodynamics) that any sensible microscopic theory will lead to the formula (21.19). So (21.19) may not be sufficiently discriminating, any theory which encodes certain features of quantum gravity may suffice for it.

If we can consider the entropy as arising from a number of microstates of the black hole, since it goes as the area A of the horizon, the natural question to ask would be whether this can be a more general feature. Can a lower dimensional surface such as the area of the horizon encode enough information about states to reconstruct dynamics in a spacetime of one higher dimension? This would be like thinking about spacetime as a hologram. So we could rephrase this as: Is there a holographic formulation of the laws of physics? This possibility is realized, at least for a restricted class of theories, in the so-called AdS/CFT correspondence (or holographic correspondence). The original conjecture for this is due to J. Maldacena and states that a particular version of string theory, the Type IIB string theory on an anti-de Sitter(AdS) spacetime background in five dimensions (with an additional 5-sphere, making a total of 10 dimensions) is dual to the maximally supersymmetric Yang-Mills gauge theory (which is a conformal field theory (CFT)) on the boundary of the AdS space (which is 4-dimensional Minkowski space). One can, in principle, go back and forth, calculating quantities in one using the other. There has been an enormous amount of research done on developing this idea, and although still a conjecture, it does seem to hold for all cases where calculations have been possible.

So this is certainly an interesting and exciting new direction, but, on the general question of quantum gravity, it is fair to say that we are still far from a complete answer.

A few more words

There is an underlying unity to physics as Feynman has repeatedly remarked. There is a single logical structure which we believe can explain all the disparate physical phenomena we observe, although we are far from sorting out the derivations and details. The existence of such a structure is important in obtaining mutually consistent explanations of different experimentally observed phenomena, ultimately rendering the world comprehensible. The Standard Model represents a major watershed in our attempt to understand and elucidate this structure. It is consistent with the general principles of physics, with quantum mechanics and at least the special theory of relativity, and does explain a host of phenomena. And as the foundational material for much of known physics, it is *the* fundamental theory as of now. But there are already many indicators of the incompleteness of the Standard Model, as we have discussed. So, of course, it will be superseded and absorbed into a larger framework. As Einstein has remarked, "There could be no fairer destiny for any physical theory than that it should point the way to a more comprehensive theory in which it lives on as a limiting case". Building a more complete theory will require painstaking experimentation, itself based on technological progress, and theoretical analyses, and will also demand unprecedented levels of imagination on our part. But that is something wonderful to look forward to.

Remark 21.1.
Neutrino masses and the seesaw mechanism

We have talked about neutrino masses and mixing angles. While the quarks and leptons get masses from their coupling to the Higgs field, as in (19.9) (or (20.7)) and (20.8), one cannot directly use a similar idea for the neutrino masses. This is because the neutrinos we observe at low energies have only the left chiral components which show up in the weak interactions, but no right chiral component. Recall that the mass term for a spinor has the form $\bar{\Psi}_L \Psi_R + \bar{\Psi}_R \Psi_L$, and we cannot form such a term in the absence of the right chirality. The left chiral components of a spinor can be viewed as the upper two components (denoted by U in the notation we used in Lecture 8), and under a Lorentz transformation, one can show that it changes as

$$U_r \to g_{rs} U_s \qquad (21.20)$$

where g is a *complex* 2×2 matrix satisfying $\det g = 1$. (Since g is complex and has unit determinant, it is like an $SU(2)$ matrix, but with complex angles, so there are 6 real parameters, three corresponding to spatial rotations and three to the Lorentz boosts.) This tells us that the combination $U_1 U_2 - U_2 U_1 = U^T(i\sigma_2) U$ is invariant under Lorentz transformations. This term is not zero, because U's are operators with anticommuting properties (as is appropriate for fermions in the quantum field theory), so naively commuting the fields is not proper. This result means that we could write a mass term[5]

$$S_{mass} = m \int d^4x \; \left(U^T(i\sigma_2) U + \text{h.c.} \right) \qquad (21.21)$$

Nice as this is, we cannot use it for neutrinos because they are part of the doublet ℓ_L in the electroweak theory and a term like (21.21) will not preserve the gauge symmetry. One solution is to introduce a right chiral component for the neutrino as well, but use the mass term of the type (21.21) just for the right part to give it a much larger mass. More specifically, this means that we consider a mass term

$$S_{mass} = \int d^4x \; \left[\lambda \left(\bar{e}_R \, \Phi^\dagger \ell_L + \bar{\ell}_L \tilde{\Phi} \, \nu_R \right) + M \, \nu_R^T(i\sigma_2)\nu_R \right] \; + \; \text{h.c.}$$

$$\ell_L = \begin{pmatrix} \nu_e \\ e_L \end{pmatrix}, \qquad \Phi = \begin{pmatrix} \phi^+ \\ \phi^0 \end{pmatrix}, \qquad \tilde{\Phi} = \begin{pmatrix} \phi^{0*} \\ -\phi^- \end{pmatrix} \qquad (21.22)$$

Here M has the dimensions of mass. The right chiral component ν_R does not respond to the $SU(2)$ or $U(1)$ gauge transformations of the electroweak symmetry. So the extra mass term for it is consistent with the gauge symmetry. Expanding (21.22) around the vacuum value of ϕ^0, we get

$$S = \int d^4x \Big[m(\bar{e}_R e_L + \bar{e}_L e_R + \bar{\nu}_R \nu_L + \bar{\nu}_L \nu_R)$$

$$+ M \left(\nu_R^T(i\sigma_2)\nu_R - \nu_R^{*T}(i\sigma_2)\nu_R^* \right) + \cdots \Big] \qquad (21.23)$$

where $m = \lambda v/\sqrt{2}$. The mass term for the electron field is as before. To simplify the mass term for the neutrino, we introduce a 4-component notation, writing

$$\psi = \begin{pmatrix} U \\ i\sigma_2 U^* \end{pmatrix}, \qquad \chi = \begin{pmatrix} -i\sigma_2 V^* \\ V \end{pmatrix} \qquad (21.24)$$

---

[5]A mass term of this type is known as a Majorana mass term.

(Here, in effect, U is ν_L and V is ν_R.) These spinors obey the Majorana condition $C\gamma^0\Psi^* = \Psi$ mentioned in Lecture 20. In terms of these spinors, the mass term for the neutrinos becomes

$$S = \int d^4x \, (\bar\psi \ \bar\chi) \begin{pmatrix} 0 & m \\ m & M \end{pmatrix} \begin{pmatrix} \psi \\ \chi \end{pmatrix} \tag{21.25}$$

We now take M to be significantly larger than m. Diagonalizing the mass term, we find the eigenvalues $\frac{1}{2}M\left(1 \pm \sqrt{1 + 4m^2/M^2}\right) \approx M, -m^2/M$. Thus the mass of the familiar neutrino becomes m^2/M which is very small compared to the electron mass since $M \gg m$. (The minus sign is immaterial for this.) The other eigenstate has a large mass M. The eigenstates themselves have small admixtures of the neutrino of the other type, being approximately $\psi - (m/M)\chi$ and $\chi + (m/M)\psi$. For small m/M we retain all the observed properties of the left chiral neutrino as we know it, yet we can get a small mass for it after spontaneous symmetry breaking. The right chiral neutrino has a large mass, consistent with the lack of evidence for it at present day energies. Typically, we expect M to be significantly larger than the masses of the W and Z bosons.

Since, compared to the starting mass parameters, one eigenvalue gets pushed down and one gets pushed up (albeit slightly), this way of getting neutrino masses is known as the seesaw mechanism. We have used just one flavor of neutrinos to illustrate the basic idea. In the realistic case, one has to introduce all three flavors and a matrix of coupling constants so that we get masses and mixing angles. Another interesting point is that in some of the grand unified theories, notably the one based on the group $SO(10)$, there is a right chiral neutrino which does not respond to the gauge transformations of the electroweak theory, making it a good candidate for this mechanism. M is then naturally very large, of the scale of the grand unified theory.

Remark 21.2.
Supersymmetry

Supersymmetry refers to transformations which connect fermionic fields to bosonic fields or the corresponding states. Because fermionic and bosonic fields have different spin angular momenta and transform differently under Lorentz transformations, supersymmetry should be viewed as part of the spacetime symmetry of a theory rather than some internal symmetry.

The symmetry transformations utilize Grassmann numbers or Grassmann variables, so we start with a brief explanation of what they are. A Grassmann algebra consists of a set of basis elements, say θ_i, $i = 1, 2, \cdots, n$ such that

$$\theta_i\,\theta_j + \theta_j\,\theta_i = 0 \qquad (21.26)$$

This property says that the θ's anticommute. In particular $(\theta_1)^2 = (\theta_2)^2 = \cdots = (\theta_n)^2 = 0$. The algebra is defined over either real or complex numbers so that one can make combinations like $a\,\theta_1 + b\,\theta_2$, $c\,\theta_k + d\,\theta_l$, etc., where a, b, c, d are real or complex numbers. A Grassmann variable is an element of the Grassmann algebra. Notice that any element of the algebra squares to zero, for, with the anticommutation property, we have

$$(a\,\theta_1 + b\,\theta_2)^2 = 0, \qquad \text{etc.} \qquad (21.27)$$

An explicit basis may be constructed as follows. We have seen the algebra of γ-matrices in Lecture 8. For a metric with Euclidean signature, it is given by

$$\Gamma_\mu\Gamma_\nu + \Gamma_\nu\Gamma_\mu = 2\,\delta_{\mu\nu} \qquad (21.28)$$

(We use Γ's here so as not to confuse them with the Dirac γ-matrices which are defined with the metric of Minkowksi space.) Consider a $2n$-dimensional case of the algebra (21.28) and define

$$\theta_k = \frac{(\Gamma_k + i\,\Gamma_{n+k})}{\sqrt{2}}, \qquad k = 1, 2, \cdots, n. \qquad (21.29)$$

(The $\sqrt{2}$ in the denominator is just for normalization purposes unrelated to the present discussion.) It is easy to see that $\theta_k^2 = 0$ and that dissimilar θ's anticommute. Since the Γ-matrices, and hence the θ_k, are not zero, (21.29) gives a nontrivial representation of the algebra (21.26). For actual calculations involving Grassmann variables, it is cumbersome to use explicit matrix representations, most calculations can be done using just the properties following from (21.26).

Returning to our main theme of supersymmetry, it is simplest to illustrate by an example. Consider a theory with a complex scalar field (equivalent to two real fields) and a left-handed spinor field Ψ similar to what we used for neutrinos in the discussion about weak interactions. With our choice of γ_5, we can write

$$\Psi = \begin{pmatrix} \psi \\ 0 \end{pmatrix} \qquad (21.30)$$

where ψ is a two-component spinor. The action is taken to be

$$S = \int d^4x \left[\partial_\mu \phi^\dagger \, \partial^\mu \phi + \bar\Psi \, i\gamma^\mu \partial_\mu \Psi \right] \tag{21.31}$$

It is easy to verify that this action is invariant under the transformation

$$\delta\phi = \bar\Lambda \, \Psi, \qquad \delta\phi^\dagger = \bar\Psi \, \Lambda$$

$$\delta\Psi = -i(\gamma^\mu \Lambda) \, \partial_\mu \phi, \qquad \delta\bar\Psi = i\bar\Lambda \, \gamma^\mu \, \partial_\mu \phi^\dagger \tag{21.32}$$

where Λ and $\bar\Lambda$ are two independent Grassmann variables which are also chiral spinors; they are right handed to match with Ψ in forming combinations like $\bar\Lambda\Psi$. Λ may be taken to be of the form

$$\Lambda = \begin{pmatrix} 0 \\ \zeta \end{pmatrix} \tag{21.33}$$

The variables ζ, $\bar\zeta$ are to be viewed as the parameters of the transformation. As mentioned before, the transformation connects the bosonic field ϕ and the fermionic field Ψ. The change in the action takes the form

$$\delta S = \int d^4x \, \partial_\nu \left[\left(\bar\Psi \Lambda \, \partial_\mu \phi + \bar\Lambda \Psi \, \partial_\mu \phi^\dagger \right) \eta^{\mu\nu} - \partial_\mu \phi^\dagger \, \bar\Lambda \gamma^\mu \gamma^\nu \Psi \right] \tag{21.34}$$

This can be taken to be zero, with suitable conditions on the fields on the boundary of the spacetime region of integration, so the action is invariant. It is useful to introduce a different 4-component spinor notation defining

$$\chi = \begin{pmatrix} \psi \\ i\sigma_2 \psi^* \end{pmatrix}, \qquad \xi = \begin{pmatrix} \zeta \\ i\sigma_2 \zeta^* \end{pmatrix} \tag{21.35}$$

The spinors χ, ξ obey the Majorana condition $\chi = C\bar\chi^T$, $\xi = C\bar\xi^T$, with C being the charge conjugation matrix $C = -i\gamma^0\gamma^2$, as in Lecture 20. This notation is more suitable for generalizations. In terms of χ, the action (21.31) is

$$S = \int d^4x \left[\partial_\mu \phi^\dagger \, \partial^\mu \phi + \frac{1}{2} \, \bar\chi \, i\gamma^\mu \partial_\mu \chi \right] \tag{21.36}$$

Another simple example is given by a generalization of the free Maxwell theory with

$$S = \int d^4x \left[-\frac{1}{4} F_{\mu\nu} F^{\mu\nu} + \frac{1}{2} \bar\chi \, i\gamma^\mu \partial_\mu \chi + \frac{1}{2} G^2 \right] \tag{21.37}$$

with the transformations

$$\delta A_\mu = i \, \bar\xi \gamma_\mu \chi$$

$$\delta\chi = \frac{1}{2} F^{\mu\nu} \, \gamma_\mu \gamma_\nu \, \xi + i\gamma_5 \xi \, G \tag{21.38}$$

$$\delta G = \bar\xi \gamma_5 \gamma^\mu \partial_\mu \chi$$

Here G is an auxiliary field since it has no time-derivatives in S; so it may be eliminated by solving its equations of motion (which gives $G = 0$) and substituting back into the action. Thus we can drop the G^2 term in (21.37). It is however convenient to keep it for verifying the supersymmetry of the action and the closure of the algebra under composition of two transformations with two sets of parameters. (The theory defined by (21.37) is not electrodynamics; the fermion χ is uncharged. A supersymmetric extension of electrodynamics is also possible, although we do not discuss it here.)

The actions (21.36) and (21.37) correspond to free theories, but there are generalizations to interacting theories. For example, one generalization of (21.36) which still has invariance under supersymmetry, is given by

$$S = \int d^4x \left[\partial_\mu \phi^\dagger \, \partial^\mu \phi - m^2 \phi^\dagger \phi + \frac{1}{2} \bar{\chi} i \gamma^\mu \, \partial_\mu \chi - \frac{m}{2} \bar{\chi} \chi \right.$$

$$-\frac{\lambda}{2} \bar{\chi} \left[\phi(1 - \gamma_5) + \phi^\dagger(1 + \gamma_5) \right] \chi$$

$$\left. -m\lambda(\phi^\dagger \phi^2 + \phi^{\dagger 2} \phi) - \lambda^2 \left(\phi^\dagger \phi \right)^2 \right] \tag{21.39}$$

(Notice that if we simplify $\bar{\chi}\chi$ using (21.35), we get the expression $\psi^T(i\sigma_2)\psi$ + h.c.; so this is the Majorana mass term we used for neutrinos.) In (21.39), λ is a coupling constant. The same two parameters m, λ control the masses for both types of particles and the vertices for the different interactions. This is needed for the supersymmetric invariance of this action. The theory defined by (21.39) is often referred to as the Wess-Zumino model.

Let us now briefly go over why supersymmetry is interesting to physicists. We start with an observation that the algebra of supersymmetry transformations will involve anticommutation rules. For example, consider two supersymmetry transformations with parameters ξ and η. Designating the generator of the transformation as Q (which must be a spinor because ξ, η are spinors), the unitary transformations in the quantum theory are of the form $\exp(i\bar{\xi}Q)$ and $\exp(i\bar{\eta}Q)$. The composition of such transformations requires commutation rules for $\bar{\xi}Q$ and $\bar{\eta}Q$. But notice that

$$[\bar{\xi}Q, \bar{\eta}Q] = -\bar{\xi}_r \bar{\eta}_s \left(Q_r Q_s + Q_s Q_r \right) \tag{21.40}$$

(Here r, s are spinor indices.) This is because of the Grassmann nature of the parameters ξ and η. (We have also taken them to anticommute with the Q's, but this is not so important for the point we are making.) Thus commutators in terms of the infinitesimal transformations end up as anticommutators for the generators when we seek to remove the parameters by collecting them in a given order. If the parameters are ordinary real or complex numbers, we would get commutation rules as usual.

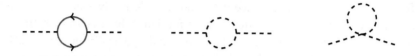

Fig. 21.3: One loop diagrams which contribute to the mass of the ϕ-particle

For theories formulated on flat Minkowski space, which is adequate for most of particle physics, the basic spacetime symmetry of the scattering matrix is the Poincaré symmetry which is the aggregate of Lorentz transformations (spatial rotations and velocity boosts) and spacetime translations. An important no-go theorem in this context is the Coleman-Mandula theorem, which tells us that the largest spacetime symmetry group of the scattering matrix of a relativistic theory with local interactions under certain reasonable assumptions is the Poincaré symmetry. Any other symmetry must be viewed as some internal symmetry which commutes with the spacetime transformations. Here the symmetry is defined in terms of a Lie group with commutation rules for the generators. However, one can evade the theorem if we allow for anticommutation rules for the symmetry generators. The more elaborate version of the Coleman-Mandula theorem is the Haag-Lopuszanski-Sohnius theorem which tells us that the largest spacetime symmetry possible is the extension of Poincaré symmetry with the addition of supersymmetry transformations. This shows why supersymmetry is very special. And as the first hint of a larger spacetime symmetry beyond what is encoded in the theory of relativity, any evidence for supersymmetry would be dramatic.

Supersymmetric theories also have nicer renormalization properties than ordinary field theories. For example, from the vertices in the action (21.39), one can work out corrections due to loops in Feynman diagrams, a simple case being the diagrams shown in Fig. 21.3. These diagrams are potentially divergent, so they have to be evaluated with a cut-off, i.e., a finite upper limit for the momentum integrals. We expect the loops involving the bosonic propagators to give a positive contribution. However, because the fermion loops carry an additional minus sign (see Lecture 8), they can cancel out much of the contribution from the bosons. Indeed this happens and there is no mass correction due to the diagrams shown. (There is a potentially divergent normalization correction for the field ϕ; this is a milder logarithmic divergence.) This lack of renormalization of the mass is also related to the fact that the same mass parameter m should occur for the bosonic and fermionic terms in (21.39) to maintain supersymmetry. This improved behavior under renormalization is also the basis for the expectation that the hierarchy problem can be solved in a supersymmetric grand unified theory.

One can take this cancellation of potential divergences between fermion and boson loops, and the improved renormalization behavior, further by considering extended supersymmetries where we use $\mathcal{N}$ independent Grassmann variables for the transformation and correspondingly there will be $\mathcal{N}$ generators Q_r^i, $i = 1, 2, \cdots, \mathcal{N}$. The renormalization behavior improves to the extent that one can even have fully interacting field theories with no potential divergence in loop diagrams. In four dimensions, this happens for the maximally extended (which is $\mathcal{N} = 4$) theory.[6] It is a Yang-Mills theory with matter fields and is described by the action

$$
S = \int d^4x \left[-\frac{1}{4} F_{\mu\nu}^A F^{A\,\mu\nu} + \frac{1}{2} \bar{\chi}_i^A \gamma^\mu D_\mu \chi_i^A + \frac{1}{2} (D_\mu \phi_a)^A (D^\mu \phi_a)^A \right.
$$
$$
- \frac{g^2}{4} f^{ABC} f^{AMN} \phi_a^B \phi_b^C \phi_a^M \phi_b^N
$$
$$
\left. + \left(\frac{i\,g}{4} f^{ABC} C^{aij} \bar{\chi}_i^A \phi_a^B (1 + \gamma_5) \chi_j^C + \text{h.c.} \right) \right] \qquad (21.41)
$$

The capital roman indices A, B, etc. refer to the component in the Lie algebra of the gauge group with f^{ABC}, f^{AMN} as structure constants of the algebra. The indices i, j take values 1 to 4 while the indices a, b take values 1 to 6. Thus there are four fermion fields (which are Majorana spinors) and six scalar fields in addition to the gauge field. There is an additional symmetry (often referred to as an R-symmetry) of unitary transformations among the four fermion fields which forms $SU(4)$; the scalar fields transform as a 6-dimensional representation of $SU(4)$. The coefficients C^{aij} are needed for an $SU(4)$-invariant coupling of the scalars to the fermions; they are like the Clebsch-Gordan coefficients familiar from angular momentum theory, but for the group $SU(4)$ in the present case. The transformation connecting the gauge field A_μ^A to the fermions is similar to what is given in (21.38), but now we need 4 independent Grassmann-valued parameters $\bar{\xi}^i$ since there are four fermion fields. Correspondingly, there will be four supersymmetry charges, hence $\mathcal{N} = 4$ for this theory.

---

[6]There are many problems in constructing field theories with particles of spin greater than 2. A specific theorem which highlights some of these problems is due to Case and Gasiorowicz and Weinberg and Witten. Without gravity, this limits $\mathcal{N}$ to be ≤ 4, with gravity $\mathcal{N} \leq 8$.

The $\mathcal{N} = 4$ Yang-Mills theory given by (21.41) has no divergences at the upper limit of integration over loop momenta for any Feynman diagram for any physical process; it can also be argued to be finite even nonperturbatively. Although we have no experimental evidence for supersymmetry so far, let alone $\mathcal{N} = 4$ supersymmetry, this theory is an important theoretical laboratory for many ideas currently in vogue in physics. It is also the basis for the AdS/CFT conjecture for the holographic understanding of string theory.

It is possible to consider theories where the parameters ξ are functions of spacetime coordinates, in other words, to have local supersymmetry. Since supersymmetry is a spacetime symmetry, making it local necessarily implies a supersymmetric extension of gravity, i.e., supergravity. A large number of different types of supergravities have been constructed. In four dimensions, the maximal supergravity has $\mathcal{N} = 8$. If we go up into higher dimensions, the maximal case is the $\mathcal{N} = 1$ supergravity in 11 dimensions. This theory is also expected to be a low energy limit of the M-theory.

Remark 21.3.
The propagator in FLRW cosmology

We have talked about the redshift for light reaching us from distant galaxies and how this led to the idea of the expanding universe. We also talked about the observation that the expansion of the universe is accelerating. This was based on measurements of the intensities of Type IA supernovae and the comparison of the observed (or apparent) luminosities and absolute luminosities. But how do we relate the observations to these conclusions? And how does the metric of the universe (21.6) play into this? After all, the bare bones of the process is that an atom in a distant galaxy emits a photon and it propagates to our telescopes and spectrometers; the universe expands while the photon is in transit. Should we not be able to describe this using the photon propagator in an expanding universe? This would be a nice example of the role of the propagator and so here we will attempt to work this out. For simplicity, we will use a scalar field propagator, rather than the real photon propagator. Since the polarization effects are not important, this should be adequate.

The equation of motion for a massless scalar field propagating in a curved space with metric $g_{\mu\nu}$ is given by

$$\frac{1}{\sqrt{-g}} \frac{\partial}{\partial x^\mu} \left(g^{\mu\nu} \sqrt{-g} \frac{\partial \phi}{\partial x^\nu} \right) = 0 \tag{21.42}$$

In our case, this simplifies to

$$\ddot{\phi} + 3\frac{\dot{a}}{a}\dot{\phi} - \frac{\nabla^2\phi}{a^2} = 0 \tag{21.43}$$

We want to define the propagator for the field ϕ; it satisfies the equation

$$\frac{1}{\sqrt{-g}}\frac{\partial}{\partial x^\mu}\left[g^{\mu\nu}\sqrt{-g}\frac{\partial}{\partial x^\nu}G(x,x')\right] = -i\frac{\delta^{(4)}(x-x')}{\sqrt{-g}} \tag{21.44}$$

The right hand side of this equation is $-i$ times the covariant δ-function, which integrates to 1 with the invariant measure $\sqrt{-g}\,d^4x$. To construct G, we first consider separation of variables, since there is no explicit $\vec{x}$-dependence for a, so we can write

$$\phi(x) = \sum_k \phi_k(t)\,\exp(i\vec{k}\cdot\vec{x}) \tag{21.45}$$

Thus (21.43) reduces to

$$\ddot{\phi}_k + 3\frac{\dot{a}}{a}\dot{\phi}_k + \frac{k^2}{a^2}\phi_k = 0 \tag{21.46}$$

This is a second order ordinary differential equation and it has two independent solutions, which we will denote by $u_k(t)$ and $v_k(t)$. These need not be real; reality of ϕ can be obtained by a suitable linear combination. Since $u_k(t)$ and $v_k(t)$ obey the equation (21.46), we also have the relation

$$\begin{aligned}
0 &= u_k\left(\ddot{v}_k + 3\frac{\dot{a}}{a}\dot{v}_k + \frac{k^2}{a^2}v_k\right) - v_k\left(\ddot{u}_k + 3\frac{\dot{a}}{a}\dot{u}_k + \frac{k^2}{a^2}u_k\right) \\
&= \frac{u_k}{a^3}\frac{\partial}{\partial t}(a^3\dot{v}_k) - \frac{v_k}{a^3}\frac{\partial}{\partial t}(a^3\dot{u}_k) \\
&= \frac{1}{a^3}\frac{\partial}{\partial t}\left[(u_k\dot{v}_k - v_k\dot{u}_k)\,a^3\right]
\end{aligned} \tag{21.47}$$

This means that we have the Wronskian condition

$$(u_k\dot{v}_k - v_k\dot{u}_k)\,a^3 = \text{constant in time} \tag{21.48}$$

We can thus set this quantity to a constant, which we choose to be i, so that

$$u_k\dot{v}_k - v_k\dot{u}_k = \frac{i}{a^3} \tag{21.49}$$

For the spatial part, with the plane wave behavior as in (21.45), we choose periodic conditions in a cubic box of volume V, with the idea of taking $V \to \infty$ eventually. The propagator can now be constructed as

$$G(x,x') = \sum_k \left[\theta(t-t')\,u_k(t)\,v_k(t') + \theta(t'-t)\,v_k(t)\,u_k(t')\right]\frac{1}{V}\,e^{i\vec{k}\cdot(\vec{x}-\vec{x}')} \tag{21.50}$$

By differentiating with respect to t, we find

$$\frac{\partial}{\partial t} G(x, x') = \sum_k \Big[\dot{u}_k(t) v_k(t') \theta(t - t') + \delta(t - t') u_k(t) v_k(t')$$
$$+ \dot{v}_k(t) u_k(t') \theta(t' - t) - \delta(t - t') v_k(t) u_k(t') \Big] \frac{1}{V} e^{i\vec{k} \cdot (\vec{x} - \vec{x}')}$$
$$= \sum_k \Big[\dot{u}_k(t) v_k(t') \theta(t - t') + \dot{v}_k(t) u_k(t') \theta(t' - t) \Big] \frac{1}{V} e^{i\vec{k} \cdot (\vec{x} - \vec{x}')}$$

$$(21.51)$$

$$\frac{\partial^2}{\partial t^2} G(x, x') = \sum_k \Big[\dot{u}_k(t) v_k(t') - \dot{v}_k(t) u_k(t') \Big] \delta(t - t') \frac{1}{V} e^{i\vec{k} \cdot (\vec{x} - \vec{x}')}$$
$$+ \sum_k \Big[\ddot{u}_k(t) v_k(t') \theta(t - t') + \ddot{v}_k(t) u_k(t') \theta(t' - t) \Big] \frac{1}{V} e^{i\vec{k} \cdot (\vec{x} - \vec{x}')}$$
$$= -i \frac{\delta^{(4)}(x - x')}{a^3}$$
$$+ \sum_k \Big[\ddot{u}_k(t) v_k(t') \theta(t - t') + \ddot{v}_k(t) u_k(t') \theta(t' - t) \Big] \frac{1}{V} e^{i\vec{k} \cdot (\vec{x} - \vec{x}')}$$

$$(21.52)$$

where we have used (21.49). Using (21.51) and (21.52), we can easily verify that $G(x, x')$ as given by (21.50) does indeed satisfy (21.44). Taking the large volume limit, we get

$$G(x, x') = \int \frac{d^3k}{(2\pi)^3} \left[\theta(t - t') u_k(t) v_k(t') + \theta(t' - t) v_k(t) u_k(t') \right] e^{i\vec{k} \cdot (\vec{x} - \vec{x}')}$$

$$(21.53)$$

We shall now consider an approximate solution for u_k and v_k which we can then use in (21.53). Writing $\phi_k = a^{-\frac{3}{2}} f_k$, we find that (21.46) reduces to

$$\ddot{f}_k - \left(\frac{3}{2} \frac{\ddot{a}}{a} + \frac{3}{4} \frac{\dot{a}^2}{a^2} - \frac{k^2}{a^2} \right) f_k = 0 \qquad (21.54)$$

Typically we want to consider propagating waves of optical or radio frequencies, so that $k \sim 10^9 \, s^{-1}$ or so. On the other hand, $(\dot{a}/a) \approx (13 \times 10^9 \text{years})^{-1} \approx 10^{-17} \, s^{-1}$. So it is a very good approximation to neglect $\dot{a}/a$ and $\ddot{a}/a$ in (21.54). The solutions are thus

$$u_k(t) = C \, a^{-\frac{3}{2}} \, e^{-i(k/a)t}$$
$$v_k(t) = C \, a^{-\frac{3}{2}} \, e^{i(k/a)t}$$

$$(21.55)$$

The normalization condition (21.49) identifies $C = \sqrt{a/2k}$. Using this value of C and the solutions (21.55) we find

$$G(x, x') \approx \int \frac{d^3k}{(2\pi)^3} \frac{1}{2k\, a\, a'} \left[\theta(t - t') \exp\left[-ik \left(\frac{t}{a} - \frac{t'}{a'} \right) + i\vec{k} \cdot (\vec{x} - \vec{x}') \right] \right.$$
$$\left. + \theta(t' - t) \exp\left[ik \left(\frac{t}{a} - \frac{t'}{a'} \right) - i\vec{k} \cdot (\vec{x} - \vec{x}') \right] \right] \quad (21.56)$$

where $a = a(t)$, $a' = a(t')$.

This propagator can be used to calculate the probability amplitude for processes of interest in the expanding universe. As an example, consider the emission of light by an atom in a distant star or galaxy which is then detected at the present time on Earth. We are interested in the flux of particles observed; this can then be compared to the absolute luminosity of the source. For this process, it is useful to simplify (21.56) by carrying out the k-integration. Writing $\tau = t/a$, $\tau' = t'/a'$, we have the identity

$$\int \frac{dk_0}{2\pi} \frac{i}{k_0^2 - k^2 + i\epsilon} e^{-ik_0(\tau - \tau')} = \frac{1}{2k} e^{-ik(\tau - \tau')} \quad (21.57)$$

for $\tau > \tau'$ (which is the ordering of time of interest to us). Using this identity, we may write the propagator as

$$G(x, x') = \frac{1}{a\, a'} \int \frac{dk_0}{2\pi} \frac{d^3k}{(2\pi)^3} \frac{i}{k_0^2 - k^2 + i\epsilon} e^{-ik_0(\tau - \tau')} e^{i\vec{k} \cdot \vec{R}}$$
$$= -\frac{i}{a\, a'} \frac{1}{4\pi R} \int \frac{dk_0}{2\pi} \exp\left(-ik_0(\tau - \tau') + ik_0 R \right) \quad (21.58)$$

where $\vec{R} = \vec{x} - \vec{x}'$ and we have carried out the k-integration.

Now consider a source at t', $\vec{x}'$ which produces a field $\phi(x)$ at $(t, \vec{x})$. This field is given by

$$\phi(x) = \int d^3x' dt' \, (a')^3 \, G(x, x') \, J(x') \quad (21.59)$$

Here $J(x')$ corresponds to the matrix element for some atomic transition $|\alpha\rangle \to |\beta\rangle$, so it has a factor $\exp(-i(E_\alpha - E_\beta)t')$. The transition takes a short time which is much larger than $(E_\alpha - E_\beta)^{-1}$ (so that we have narrow spectral lines), but is negligible compared to the time-scale over which $a(t)$ varies. So in the exponential in (21.58) we may approximate $a(t') \approx a(t_e) \equiv a_e$, where t_e is the time of emission of the particle corresponding to ϕ. Further, we may take the source to be sufficiently localized in space, since a distant source is essentially a point on the length scales over which the observation is carried out. Thus we may approximate

$$J(x') \approx J_s \frac{\delta^{(3)}(x - x_e)}{a'^3} \exp(-i(\Delta E)t') \quad (21.60)$$

where $\Delta E = E_\alpha - E_\beta$. Using this source in (21.59), we find

$$\phi(x) = -\frac{i}{4\pi\, a\, R}\, J_s\, \exp\left[-i\left(\frac{a_e \Delta E}{a}\right) t + i a_e(\Delta E)R\right] \tag{21.61}$$

We can immediately read off the detected frequency at $(t, \vec{x})$ as

$$\omega = \frac{a_e \Delta E}{a} = \frac{\Delta E}{1+z}, \qquad \frac{a_e}{a} = \frac{1}{1+z} \tag{21.62}$$

Here z is the redshift of the emitter or source.

Going back to (21.42), for complex solutions, we have

$$\frac{\partial}{\partial x^\mu}\left[\phi^*\, g^{\mu\nu}\sqrt{-g}\, \partial_\nu \phi - \partial_\nu \phi^*\, g^{\mu\nu}\sqrt{-g}\, \phi\right] = 0 \tag{21.63}$$

Integrating over space-time,

$$\begin{aligned}
0 &= \int d^4x\, \frac{\partial}{\partial x^\mu}\left[\phi^*\, g^{\mu\nu}\sqrt{-g}\, \partial_\nu \phi - \partial_\nu \phi^*\, g^{\mu\nu}\sqrt{-g}\, \phi\right] \\
&= \oint d\sigma^\mu\, \frac{\partial}{\partial x^\mu}\left[\phi^*\, g^{\mu\nu}\sqrt{-g}\, \partial_\nu \phi - \partial_\nu \phi^*\, g^{\mu\nu}\sqrt{-g}\, \phi\right]
\end{aligned} \tag{21.64}$$

This identifies the total flux through a hypersurface as

$$P = -i \int d\sigma^\mu\, \frac{\partial}{\partial x^\mu}\left[\phi^*\, g^{\mu\nu}\sqrt{-g}\, \partial_\nu \phi - \partial_\nu \phi^*\, g^{\mu\nu}\sqrt{-g}\, \phi\right] \tag{21.65}$$

For a sphere at radius $|\vec{x}| = r$, we find

$$P = -i \int dt\, d\Omega\, r^2 a^2\, \left[\frac{1}{a}\left(\phi^*\frac{\partial\phi}{\partial r} - \frac{\partial\phi^*}{\partial r}\phi\right)\right] \tag{21.66}$$

The flux per unit area per unit time should thus be given by

$$F = -\frac{i}{a}\left(\phi^*\frac{\partial\phi}{\partial r} - \frac{\partial\phi^*}{\partial r}\phi\right) \tag{21.67}$$

Using the result (21.61) for $\phi(x)$, we get

$$F = \frac{J_s^2}{8\pi^2(aR)^2}\left(\frac{a_e \Delta E}{a}\right)\hat{n} \tag{21.68}$$

where $\hat{n}$ is the unit vector along the line of sight. This quantity F gives the flux of particles; to get the intensity, we must multiply by the energy of each quantum, namely, by $(a_e\Delta E/a)$. Thus the observed intensity is given by

$$I_{obs} = \frac{J_s^2}{8\pi^2}\left(\frac{a_e}{a}\right)^2 \frac{(\Delta E)^2}{(aR)^2} \tag{21.69}$$

The full energy output (which is proportional to the absolute luminosity), observed close to the source just after ϕ-emission, is given by

$$L = \left[I_{obs} \times 4\pi (a_e R)^2 \right]_{a=a_e, R\to 0}$$

$$= \frac{J_s^2 (\Delta E)^2}{2\pi} \tag{21.70}$$

The observed intensity at Earth, from (21.69), may then be written as

$$I_{obs} = \left(\frac{a_e}{a} \right)^2 \frac{L}{4\pi (aR)^2} \tag{21.71}$$

This result can be expressed in terms of the redshift as follows. Recall that the redshift is defined by

$$\frac{a(t')}{a(t)} = \frac{1}{1+z'} \tag{21.72}$$

so that

$$\dot{a}(t') \, dt' = -\frac{a(t)}{(1+z')^2} \, dz' \tag{21.73}$$

Consider the propagation of light from $\vec{x}_e$ to $\vec{x}$. This is given by a null geodesic, namely, by the condition $ds = 0$, so that $dt = a\,dr$. The distance R is then given by

$$R = \int_{t_e}^{t} \frac{dt'}{a(t')} = \int_{t_e}^{t} dt' \frac{\dot{a}(t')}{\dot{a}(t')\,a(t')} = \frac{1}{a} \int_0^{z_e} \frac{dz'}{H(z')} \tag{21.74}$$

where we have used the definition of the Hubble expansion rate of the universe at time t' as $H(z') = \frac{\dot{a}(t')}{a(t')}$. This leads to the result

$$(aR) = \int_0^{z} \frac{dz'}{H(z')} = \frac{1}{H_0} \int_0^{z} \frac{dz'}{h(z')} \equiv \frac{f(z)}{H_0} \tag{21.75}$$

where H_0 is the Hubble rate as observed at the present time and $h(z) = H(z)/H_0$. Using this formula, we can finally write (21.71) as

$$I_{obs} = L \frac{H_0^2}{4\pi} \frac{1}{(1+z)^2 f(z)^2} \tag{21.76}$$

If the Hubble expansion rate is truly a constant independent of t (or z), $f(z) = z$. In this case

$$I_{obs} = L \frac{H_0^2}{4\pi} \frac{1}{(1+z)^2 z^2} \tag{21.77}$$

so that, for high z, $\log I_{obs} \approx -4 \log z + \text{constant}$. We get a straight line for the graph of the apparent magnitude versus the redshift, in a log-log plot.

If the expansion of the universe is accelerating, $H(z) < H_0$ which means that $f(z) > z$ and we expect

$$I_{obs} < L \frac{H_0^2}{4\pi} \frac{1}{(1+z)^2 \, z^2} \tag{21.78}$$

In this case, galaxies at a given redshift will be fainter than expected from the behavior given by (21.77). Once the absolute luminosities of the Type IA supernovae were standardized, one could check this relation for distant galaxies by observing Type IA supernovae in such galaxies. The observation that the supernovae came out to be fainter than expected was the first piece of evidence that the expansion of the universe is accelerating.

Remark 21.4.
Of strings and alternatives

All our discussion so far has been about particles, point-particles whose propagation and interactions account for various observable phenomena. The action for a point-particle on a general spacetime was given in (10.36) as

$$S = -m \int ds = -m \int \sqrt{G_{\mu\nu} \, dx^\mu \, dx^\nu} \tag{21.79}$$

Here we use $G_{\mu\nu}$ for the metric tensor of spacetime, reserving the lower case for another metric to be introduced shortly. We can also take the path to be parametrized by a real variable τ so that $dx^\mu = \dot{x}^\mu \, d\tau$ where $\dot{x}^\mu = dx^\mu/d\tau$. Thus

$$S = -m \int d\tau \sqrt{G_{\mu\nu} \, \dot{x}^\mu \, \dot{x}^\nu} \tag{21.80}$$

The path of the particle $x^\mu(\tau)$ may be regarded as a map from the one-dimensional world of τ to spacetime. Let us introduce a metric on this one-dimensional world (the world line) by writing

$$ds = g_{ab} \, d\xi^a \, d\xi^b = g \, d\tau \, d\tau \tag{21.81}$$

We have only one coordinate $\xi^1 = \tau$, so the metric simplifies as shown in the second term in (21.81). We now consider the action

$$\begin{aligned} S &= -\frac{1}{2} \int d\tau \sqrt{g} \left[G_{\mu\nu} \, g^{-1} \frac{dx^\mu}{d\tau} \frac{dx^\nu}{d\tau} + m^2 \right] \\ &= -\frac{1}{2} \int d\tau \sqrt{g} \left[G_{\mu\nu} \, g^{ab} \frac{\partial x^\mu}{\partial \xi^a} \frac{\partial x^\nu}{\partial \xi^b} + m^2 \right] \end{aligned} \tag{21.82}$$

The elimination of g via its equation of motion gives $m^2 g = G_{\mu\nu}\, \dot{x}^\mu\, \dot{x}^\nu$ and, upon using this, the expression for S in (21.82) reproduces the action (21.80). The second line of (21.82) is redundant for this, but it points the way to a possible generalization. If we take flat Euclidean spacetime with $G_{\mu\nu} = -\delta_{\mu\nu}$, then the action in (21.82) becomes

$$S = \frac{1}{2}\int dV\, g^{ab}\frac{\partial x^\mu}{\partial \xi^a}\frac{\partial x^\nu}{\partial \xi^b} - \frac{m^2}{2}\int dV \qquad (21.83)$$

where $dV = \sqrt{g}\, d\tau$ is the "world-volume" (actually just the world-length in this case). The first term of this action looks like a one-dimensional field theory on a curved spacetime, where x^μ (as functions of τ) are the fields. Ultimately the world coordinate τ is just one way to parametrize the path of the particle. We can do any other parametrization by choosing the parameter to be $\tilde{\tau}$ which is some function of τ. This change $\tau \to \tilde{\tau} = f(\tau)$ is a coordinate transformation on the world-line. The action (21.83) is written in a form which has manifest coordinate invariance, since we can also transform g_{ab}. Thus the invariance under reparametrizations of τ is built in. On a general curved spacetime, we must include the appropriate metric $G_{\mu\nu}$. The action (21.82), with a general $G_{\mu\nu}$, has invariance under coordinate transformations of the world-line and under coordinate transformations in spacetime. Notice also that it is easy to set $m = 0$ in the version (21.82) or (21.83) to describe massless point-particles.

It is now easy to see how we can generalize from point-particles to strings. A point-particle evolving in spacetime traces out a one-dimensional trajectory, so can use just one variable τ to parametrize it. A string which has a certain spatial extent will trace out a two-dimensional surface in spacetime, a world-sheet rather than a world-line. So we need two world coordinates $\xi^0 = \tau$ and $\xi^1 = \sigma$. The action can be taken as

$$S = -\frac{M^2}{2}\int dV\, G_{\mu\nu}(X)\, g^{ab}\frac{\partial X^\mu}{\partial \xi^a}\frac{\partial X^\nu}{\partial \xi^b} \qquad (21.84)$$

Here a, b take values $0, 1$ and $dV = \sqrt{g}\, d\tau d\sigma$. We also use the capital X for the spacetime coordinates. Since X has the dimensions of inverse mass, the action becomes dimensionless if we have a prefactor with the dimensions of $(\text{mass})^2$; this is indicated by M^2. Varying g^{ab} in the action, we can see that the equation of motion for the world-sheet metric is

$$G_{\mu\nu}\frac{\partial X^\mu}{\partial \xi^a}\frac{\partial X^\mu}{\partial \xi^b} - \frac{1}{2}G_{\mu\nu}\, g^{cd}\frac{\partial X^\mu}{\partial \xi^c}\frac{\partial X^\nu}{\partial \xi^d}\, g_{ab} = 0 \qquad (21.85)$$

If we take, for simplicity, $G_{\mu\nu} = -\delta_{\mu\nu}$, calculate the determinant of g_{ab} from this equation, the action (21.84) can be reduced to

$$S = M^2 \int d\tau d\sigma \, \sqrt{\det(\partial_a X^\mu \, \partial_b X_\mu)} \qquad (21.86)$$

The integrand is the Jacobian of a coordinate transformation from (τ, σ) to two of the spacetime coordinates; thus the action is M^2 times the area traced out by the string as it evolves in spacetime. This is clearly an appropriate generalization of the spacetime path length in (21.79) for the point-particle. (This also shows that we do not need an additive term like m^2 for this case.)

The basic idea of string theory is to replace the concept of point-particles by strings with an action for their dynamics given by (21.84). The area form of the action (21.86) is known as the Nambu-Goto action while the version (21.84) is known as the Polyakov form of the action. The latter form allows us to view string dynamics as a two-dimensional field theory on the world-sheet where $X^\mu(\xi) = X^\mu(\tau, \sigma)$ are the fields. Thus a number of techniques of field theory can be brought to bear on the analysis. We can take $\xi^0 = \tau$ as the "time coordinate" and $\xi^1 = \sigma$ as the "space coordinate" of the two-dimensional world-sheet. Further we can consider σ to lie in a line segment or on a closed curve such as a circle. This means that in general we can have open strings and closed strings.

The string action (21.84) has another very important property: It is invariant under local scale transformations. Notice that

$$S[X, \tilde{g}_{ab} \equiv e^\phi \, g_{ab}] = S[X, g_{ab}] \qquad (21.87)$$

since $\sqrt{\det \tilde{g}} = e^\phi \sqrt{\det g}$ and $\tilde{g}^{ab} = e^{-\phi} g^{ab}$, where ϕ is an arbitrary function of ξ^a. This is special to two dimensions. Since the theory (21.84) may be viewed as a local field theory, the local scale invariance leads to the full conformal invariance.

The equation of motion for g_{ab}, namely (21.85), tells us that the dynamics of the string will be independent of the world-sheet metric. Therefore it is possible to take σ to be in some standard interval; conventionally one takes σ to be in the interval $[0, \pi]$ for an open string and $[0, 2\pi]$ for the closed string with $X^\mu(\tau, 0) = X^\mu(\tau, 2\pi)$. We can then expand $X^\mu(\tau, \sigma)$ in terms of a complete set of modes for the appropriate range of σ. Each mode effectively behaves as a point-particle. A single string may thus be viewed as an infinite collection of point-particles of different masses with the scale for the mass given by M in (21.84). The lowest mass is zero for the supersymmetric string, the higher masses are multiples of M. The parameter

M is usually taken to be the Planck mass $M_{Pl} \sim 10^{19}$ GeV, so that the spin-two massless particle, whose interactions are controlled by M, can be identified as the graviton. The hope is that the other massless modes can be identified as the particles we know, thus recovering the good results of the Standard Model as a low energy approximation to the full string theory. The particles of the Standard Model do have nonzero masses, but the idea is that they can be understood as arising from the spontaneous symmetry breaking . Since these masses are very small compared to $M \sim 10^{19}$ GeV, starting with zero (pre-symmetry-breaking) masses for them is a reasonable situation. Having said that, so far we do not have a phenomenologically satisfactory realization of this scenario. For the complete string theory, one has to consider multi-string configurations and the possibility of incorporating the creation and annihilation of strings. This is similar to how we need to consider fields like $\Phi(x)$, $A_\mu(x)$, etc. and a field theory action leading to propagators and vertices, rather than the world-line action (21.79), to describe multi-particle dynamics. In short, we need a "string field theory". We will not discuss how one can construct such a theory, but will make a few more observations on the physics of string theory.

The two-dimensional conformal invariance we mentioned is very important. With this symmetry, one can show that the full theory of interacting strings in an ambient space is consistent with unitarity which is a crucial requirement for the quantum theory. But generally, scale invariance is difficult to maintain in the quantum theory since we will need to introduce a cut-off on the momentum integrations when we do renormalization, and such a cut-off breaks the conformal invariance. So viewed as a two-dimensional field theory, the action (21.84) does have such a problem, a lack of invariance under conformal transformations in the quantum theory. However, if we do a supersymmetric version of the theory and we choose the dimension of spacetime appropriately, we can still maintain the scale invariance in the quantum theory. This is because of various ingenious cancellations due to supersymmetry. The simplest case where this can be obtained is in 10-dimensional spacetime with a supersymmetric theory. The real 4-dimensional world is interpreted as the dimensions accessible to us, the remaining being a small compact manifold which is accessible only at very high energies or it could be that we are on a 4-dimensional wall embedded in ten dimensions. The pros and cons of such scenarios have been explored quite a bit by now; a completely satisfactory model, needless to say, is not yet possible.

On the good side of things though, among the modes of the string are spin-2 particles like the graviton, so a consistent quantum theory of gravity seems possible. Further, even without a string field theory, one can calculate amplitudes in perturbation theory using the world-sheet action (21.84). The world-sheet is to be taken to be a general 2-dimensional manifold, the sphere leading to tree level diagrams, the torus, which has genus 1, giving the one-loop results, the genus two manifold (a sphere with two handles attached) giving two-loop results, etc. For example, we can view the graviton as a small deformation of the spacetime metric, so we may consider the action (21.84) with $G_{\mu\nu} \approx \eta_{\mu\nu} + h_{\mu\nu}(X)$, so that S becomes the action for flat spacetime plus a correction $-\frac{M^2}{2} \int dV \, h_{\mu\nu}(X) \, g^{ab} \frac{\partial X^\mu}{\partial \xi^a} \frac{\partial X^\nu}{\partial \xi^b}$. If we take the average (in the 2d field theory sense) of a product of such terms on the two-dimensional sphere, we can get the tree level multi-graviton scattering amplitude; a similar average on the torus would give the one-loop amplitude and so on. This approach has been very successful in testing out the consistency of string theory, for example, for checking unitarity.

Nonperturbatively, the situation is more difficult. String theory, it became apparent in the 1990s, must also include other extended objects such as membranes of various dimensions, which are truly nonperturbative configurations. By analyzing such membrane dynamics one can also get a microscopic counting of degrees of freedom which can explain the entropy formula for black holes, at least for a class of supersymmetric ones. There are also strong indications that all consistent string theories are special cases or special compactifications of a single 11-dimensional theory, which has been christened the M-theory, which also includes supersymmetric 11-dimensional gravity as one of the possible low energy limits.

String theory has thus given us a rich variety of results and new way to think about a number of issues. It has also shed new light on some of the old problems of field theory. For example, string theory techniques can be used for the efficient calculation of the sum of large numbers of Feynman diagrams in gauge theories. But notice that in a quantum theory of gravity, where the metric itself can undergo quantum fluctuations, formulating string theory in terms of the spacetime metric as in (21.84) is conceptually unsatisfactory. This action is also geared to perturbative calculations via averages on the 2-sphere, the torus, etc. So one might ask for a different formulation. The Maldacena conjecture identifying Type IIB string theory on five-dimensional AdS ($\times S^5$) with the maximally supersymmetric Yang-Mills theory (the $\mathcal{N} = 4$ Yang-Mills theory which is a conformal field theory) on Minkowski space (which is the boundary of the AdS space) gives one way of doing this, effectively defining string theory (albeit on a special background) by the Yang-Mills theory. This holographic way of considering various physical phenomena has now spread to even condensed matter physics and may give us a completely new paradigm for physical processes.

The subject of string theory is by now very well developed, with many lengthy books written on it, although we are still far from the possibility of any experimental checks. This short set of comments is only a view through a keyhole; the reference books cited can give a more comprehensive understanding.

There have also been many other, non-string, suggestions regarding quantum gravity. Among the extensively studied alternatives are loop quantum gravity and noncommutative geometry. Loop quantum gravity has its genesis in a formulation (due to Ashtekar) of standard Einstein gravity using variables similar to those of nonabelian gauge theories. This formulation in terms of Ashtekar variables, as they are called, naturally led to a view of spacetime as a network of loops, the loops being labeled by elements of the group $SU(2)$. Detailed studies of observables in this theory have been carried out. Radiation from black holes and the Bekenstein-Hawking area law for entropy emerge as general features.

It is possible to reconstruct a manifold and its geometry from the algebra of functions defined on it; this is a result which goes back to von Neumann. Alain Connes showed that one can extend this to cases where the algebra of functions is a noncommutative algebra satisfying certain conditions, thus implicitly defining a noncommutative geometry. The required data include an algebra of observables $\mathcal{A}$, a sequence of Hilbert spaces $\mathcal{H}$ and an abstractly defined Dirac operator $\mathcal{D}$ (which encodes information about the metric). One can formulate gravity in terms of such a spectral triple $(\mathcal{A}, \mathcal{H}, \mathcal{D})$.[7] So this provides another alternative approach to quantum gravity which is also under active investigation. Spaces exhibiting noncommutative geometry also arise in special situations in string theory, so there may be overlap with string-based approaches as well.

A common theme of many of these approaches is that spacetime itself is an emergent concept, a convenience which applies in a certain coarse-grained regime of some underlying dynamics. Gravity itself may thus fade away as one gets to phenomena at very fine scales of spacetime. There have been a number of analyses focusing on this aspect, trying to extract general results on gravity independent of the underlying dynamics.

---

[7]The Hilbert space of a physical system is the quantum version of the phase space of the corresponding classical system, the latter being a smooth manifold. This is the essence of the idea of replacing smooth manifolds in terms of a Hilbert space.

References

General References: Field Theory

(1) Quantum field theory is the basic theoretical structure behind particle physics. The subject is very vast and there are a large number of textbooks which treat the subject from different perspectives. A sample is as follows.

    (a) C. Itzykson and J-B. Zuber, *Quantum Field Theory*, McGraw Hill Inc. (1980).

    (b) F. Mandl and G. Shaw, *Quantum Field Theory*, John Wiley (1984).

    (c) L. H. Ryder, *Quantum Field Theory*, Cambridge University Press (1985 & 1996).

    (d) P. Ramond, *Field Theory: A Modern Primer*, Addison-Wesley Pub. Co. Inc. (1990).

    (e) L. S. Brown, *Quantum Field Theory*, Cambridge University Press (1992).

    (f) M. Kaku, *Quantum Field Theory: A Modern Introduction*, Oxford University Press, Inc. (1993).

    (g) Michael E. Peskin and Daniel V. Schroeder, *An Introduction to Quantum Field Theory*, Westview Press (1995).

    (h) A. Zee, *Quantum Field Theory in a Nutshell*, Princeton University Press (2003).

    (i) V. P. Nair, *Quantum Field Theory: A Modern Perspective*, Springer (2005).

    (j) M. Srednicki, *Quantum Field Theory*, Cambridge University Press (2007).

(2) A monumental treatise on the subject is:

S. Weinberg, *The Quantum Theory of Fields: Volume I Foundations*, Cambridge University Press, (1995);
The Quantum Theory of Fields: Volume II Modern Applications, Cambridge University Press, (1996);
The Quantum Theory of Fields: Volume III Supersymmetry, Cambridge University Press, (2000).

(3) Among older books which still contain a lot of useful material are:
J. M. Jauch and F. Rohrlich, *The Theory of Photons and Electrons*, Springer-Verlag (1955 & 1976);
S. S. Schweber, *An Introduction to Relativistic Quantum Field Theory*, Harper and Row, New York (1961); Dover Publications (2005).

General References: Particle Physics

(4) There are also a number of books on particle physics.

    (a) C. Quigg, *Gauge Theories of the Strong, Weak and Electromagnetic Interactions*, Westview Press (1983).

    (b) H. Georgi, *Weak Interactions and Modern Particle Theory*, Dover Publications (2009).

    (c) F. Halzen and A.D. Martin, *Quarks and Leptons: An Introductory Course in Modern Particle Physics*, John Wiley and Sons, Inc. (1984).

    (d) T-P. Cheng and L-F. Li, *Gauge Theory of Elementary Particle Physics*, Oxford University Press (1984).

    (e) D. Griffiths, *Introduction to Elementary Particles*, Wiley-VCH Verlag GmBH&Co. KGaA, Weinheim (2004).

    (f) P. Langacker, *The Standard Model and Beyond*, Taylor & Francis (2010).

    (g) D. Carlsmith, *Particle Physics*, Pearson Education, Inc. (2013).

    (h) M. Thomson, *Modern Particle Physics*, Cambridge University Press (2013).

    (i) M.D. Schwartz, *Quantum Field Theory and the Standard Model*, Cambridge University Press (2013).

Lectures 1-8

(5) The books cited under General References cover more details of all the material needed for Lectures 1 to 7, and most of Lecture 8.

(6) Lamb shift was originally measured by Lamb and Retherford in the 1940s. Both theory and experiment have improved over time. A review article with a critique of the latest experimental data and theoretical calculations on Lamb shift is M.I. Eides, H. Grotch and V. A. Shelyuto, *Theory of light hydrogenlike atoms*, Physics Reports **342**, 63 (2001).

(7) The experimental values for anomalous magnetic moment of the electron have been measured with increasing accuracy since the original measurements due to P. Kusch. The latest experimental values quoted are from D. Hameke, S. Fogwell and G. Gabrielse, Phys. Rev. Lett. **100**, 120801 (2008); D. Hameke, S. Fogwell Hoogerheide and G. Gabrielse, Phys. Rev. **A83**, 052122 (2011).
The theoretical calculation has also been improving by inclusion of higher orders and other effects; the latest situation is reviewed in T. Aoyama, M. Hayakawa, T. Kinoshita and M. Nio, Phys. Rev. **D84**, 053003 (2011).

(8) On the history of QED, see S. Schweber, *QED and the men who made it*, Princeton University Press (1994).

Lecture 9

(9) The concepts introduced here such as the $V - A$ interaction, parity violation, CVC hypothesis, PCAC, Adler-Weisberger sum rule, etc. are mostly discussed in more detail in the books cited under General References, see for example the book by Cheng and Li in particular.
PCAC is rarely mentioned these days as it can be incorporated into an effective action for the pseudoscalar mesons. The effective action approach started with S. Weinberg, Phys. Rev. Lett. **18**, 188 (1967). For updated versions and expository discussions, see H. Leutwyler, Ann. Phys. **235**, 165 (1994); J.F. Donoghue, E. Golowich and B.R. Holstein, *The Dynamics of the Standard Model*, Cambridge University Press (1992); S. Scherer and M.R. Schindler, *A Primer for Chiral Perturbation Theory*, Lecture Notes in Physics **830**, Springer-Verlag (2012).

(10) For some recent notes on the history of the subject, see
http://quest.ph.utexas.edu/Reviews/VA/VA.pdf.
Another useful article is G. Rajasekharan, arXiv:1403.3309.

Lecture 10

(11) There are many books on the general theory of relativity. A small useful sample is:

S. Weinberg, *Gravitation and Cosmology: Principles and Applications of the General Theory of Relativity*, John Wiley and Sons (1972); R.M. Wald, *General Relativity*, The University of Chicago Press (1984); A. Zee, *Einstein Gravity in a Nutshell*, Princeton University Press (2013).

Lecture 11

(12) Most of the books on field theory mentioned under General References also discuss gauge theories. Original references, if desired, can be traced from there.

(13) Dirac's comment on the Schrödinger equation is from Walter Moore, *A Life of Erwin Schrödinger*, Cambridge University Press (1994), p. 145.

(14) The modifications of the geodesic motion for spinning particles is given in M. Mathisson, Acta Phys. Polon. **6**, 163 (1937); A. Papapetrou, Proc. Roy. Soc. Lond. **A209**, 248 (1951); W.G. Dixon, Proc. Roy. Soc. **A314**, 499 (1970); Gen. Rel. Grav. **4**, 199 (1973).

Lecture 12

(15) Kaluza-Klein theories have a long history. A collection of important papers is in

T. Appelquist, A. Chodos and P.G.O. Freund, *Modern Kaluza-Klein Theories*, Addison-Wesley (1987).

Another useful book is

P.S. Wesson, *Space-Time-Matter: Modern Kaluza-Klein Theory*, World Scientific (1999).

Since string theories involve higher dimensions, they have become the natural habitat for Kaluza-Klein theories. Most books on string theory will contain some discussion of Kaluza-Klein theories; see, for example,

M.B. Green, J.H. Schwarz and E. Witten, *Superstring Theory*, Vols 1 and 2, Cambridge University Press (1987); J. Polchinski, *String Theory*, Vols 1 and 2, Cambridge University Press (2001 and 2005).

(16) The formulation of general relativity in terms of frame fields can be found in the books mentioned in Lecture 10. See also S. Chandrasekhar, *The Mathematical Theory of Black Holes*, Oxford University Press (1983).

(17) For the use of the idea of fiber bundles in physics, see the book by Nair in the General References. See also W. Drechsler and M.E. Mayer, *Fiber Bundle Techniques in Physics*, Lecture Notes in Physics **67**, Springer-Verlag Berlin Heidelberg (1977); A.P. Balachandran, G. Marmo, B-S. Skagerstam and A. Stern, *Gauge Symmetries and Fibre Bundles*, Lecture Notes in Physics **188**, Springer-Verlag Berlin Heidelberg(1982); C. Nash and S. Sen, *Topology and Geometry for Physicists*, Academic Press (1983); M. Nakahara, *Geometry, Topology and Physics*, Taylor & Francis (2003).

Lecture 13

(18) Although the formalism of group theory is not explicitly used, it is the mathematical backbone of much of the discussion on gauge symmetries. Some books which treat group theory from a physicist's point of view are:

   (a) R. Gilmore, *Lie Groups, Lie Algebras and Some of Their Applications*, John Wiley and Sons (1974).
   (b) W.-K. Tung, *Group Theory in Physics*, World Scientific (1985).
   (c) H. Georgi, *Lie Algebras in Particle Physics: From Isospin to Unified Theories*, Westview Press (1999).
   (d) Z.-Q. Ma, *Group Theory for Physicists*, World Scientific (2007).
   (e) P. Ramond, *Group Theory: A Physicist's Survey*, Cambridge University Press (20100.
   (f) A. Zee, *Group Theory in a Nutshell for Physicists*, Princeton University Press (2016).

(19) The Baker-Campbell-Hausdorff formula is central to the construction of Lie groups from Lie algebras; it is discussed in many of the books mentioned above, see the first one by Gilmore in particular.

(20) The fact that gauge theories are the only consistent way to obtain field theories of vector particles is implicit in many of the books on field theory. The proof of unitarity for such theories is tied in with

the proofs of renormalizability due to G. 't Hooft and M. Veltman, Nucl. Phys. **B50**, 318 (1972); B.W. Lee and J. Zinn-Justin, Phys. Rev. **D5**, 3121 (1972); ibid. **D7**, 1049 (1972).

A more streamlined and mathematical proof is in T. Kugo and I. Ojima, Prog. Theor. Phys. **60**, 1869 (1978); Prog. Theor. Phys. Suppl. **66**, 1 (1979).

The inverse way of looking at things where we ask for conservation of probability and deduce the need for gauge invariance is explained in J.M. Cornwall, D.N. Levine and G. Tiktopoulos, Phys. Rev. **D10**, 1145 (1974); Erratum: Phys. Rev. **D11**, 972 (1975).

Lecture 14

(21) QCD and asymptotic freedom are discussed in almost all books on particle physics listed under General References. The original references on asymptotic freedom are

D.J. Gross and F. Wilczek, Phys. Rev. Lett. **30**, 1343 (1973); H.D. Politzer, Phys. Rev. Lett. **30**, 1346 (1973).

(22) The particular kinematic regime of the vertex-type correction of Fig. 14.3 mentioned in text is the so-called pinching limit. The calculation is given in the book by Nair in the General References. The pinch technique is explained in J.M. Cornwall, J. Papavassiliou and D. Binosi, *The Pinch Technique and its Applications to Non-Abelian Gauge Theories*, Cambridge University Press (2011).

(23) The graph on the experimental verification of the formula for the effective coupling, Fig. 14.6 is from the Particle Data Group, C. Patrignani *et al.* (Particle Data Group), Chin. Phys. C, **40**, 100001 (2016), http://pdg.lbl.gov.

(24) The picture for confinement in terms of the string of lines of force from the quark to the antiquark is due to Y. Nambu, in Phys. Rep. **23**, 250 (1976); S. Mandelstam, Phys. Lett. **B53**, 476 (1975). It was further developed by G. 't Hooft, Nucl. Phys. **B138**, 1 (1978); ibid. **B153**, 141 (1979); S. Mandelstam, Phys. Rev. **D19**, 2391 (1979).

Lecture 15

(25) A summary of QCD which gives a good overview of the subject is in W. Marciano and H. Pagels, Physics Reports **36**, 137 (1978).

(26) The use of potential models for heavy quark bound states started with T. Appelquist and H.D. Politzer, Phys. Rev. Lett. **34**, 43(1975). For recent updated review of the status of the field, see N. Brambilla, S. Eidelman, B.K. Heltsley *et al*, Eur. Phys. J. C **71**, 1534 (2011); W. Buchmuller, *Quarkonia*, Vol.9 of *Current Physics Sources and Comments*, Elsevier Science Publishers B.V. (1992).

(27) For the approach based on lattice gauge theories, see
M. Creutz, *Quarks, Gluons and Lattices*, Cambridge University Press (1983); C.B. Lang and C. Gattringer, *Quantum Chromodynamics on the Lattice: An Introductory Presentation*, Lecture Notes in Physics **788**, Springer-Verlag Berlin Heidelberg (2010).
The FLAG (Flavor Lattice Averaging Group) gives updated information on the status of lattice-based calculations, see http://itpwiki.unibe.ch/flag/index.php/.
For a recent FLAG update, see S. Aoki *et al*, arXiv:1310.8555

(28) For a recent summary of the approach based on Schwinger-Dyson equations, see
N. Vandersickel and D. Zwanziger, Physics Reports **520**, 175 (2012); J.M. Cornwall, J. Papavassiliou and D. Binosi, *The Pinch Technique and its Applications to Non-Abelian Gauge Theories*, Cambridge University Press (2011).

(29) The first successful use of supersymmetric theories to work out the vacuum structure of Yang-Mills theories is in N. Seiberg and E. Witten, Nucl. Phys. **B426**, 19 (1994).
A good review is in L. Alvarez-Gaume and S.F. Hassan, Fortsch. Phys. **45**, 159 (1997), arXiv:hep-th/9701069.

(30) The key early references on large N_c approximation, and which are still very much worth reading, are G. 't Hooft, Nucl. Phys. **B72**, 461 (1974); ibid. **B75**, 461 (1974); E. Witten, Nucl. Phys. **B160**, 57 (1979).
A good review article is A.V. Manohar, *Large N QCD*, Les Houches Lectures 1997, in *Probing the Standard Model of Particle Interactions*, F. David and R. Gupta (eds.), Elsevier Science B.V. (2008).

(31) The Runge-Lenz vector is discussed in H. Goldstein, C.P. Poole and J.L. Safko, *Classical Mechanics*, Addison-Wesley (2001).

Lecture 16

(32) Two good references to read more about quarks and the analysis based on symmetry are A.W. Hendry and D.B. Lichtenberg, Rep. Prog. Phys. **41**, 1707 (1978); D.B. Lichtenberg, *Unitary Symmetry and Elementary Particles*, Academic Press (2001).

(33) Recent comparison with data can be obtained from the Particle Data Group, http://www-pdg.lbl.gov

Lecture 17

(34) Spontaneous symmetry breaking and the Higgs mechanism are standard topics by now and are discussed in the books on quantum field theory listed under General References.

(35) The $U(1)_A$ problem was first identified by S. Glashow; the problem was sharpened by S. Weinberg with a bound on the mass of the η'. The solution based on anomalies is due to G. 't Hooft, Phys. Rev. Lett. **37**, 8 (1976). See also E. Witten, Nucl. Phys. **B156**, 269 (1979); G. Veneziano, Nucl. Phys. **B159**, 213 (1979); Phys. Lett. **B95**, 90 (1980).

Lecture 18-19

(36) Superconductivity is standard textbook material in condensed matter physics. A few book suggestions are:
J.F. Annett, *Superconductivity, Superfluids and Condensates*, Oxford University Press (2004); G.D. Mahan, *Condensed Matter in a Nutshell*, Princeton University Press (2011); C. Mudry, *Lecture Notes on Field Theory in Condensed Matter Physics*, World Scientific (2014); P. Coleman, *Introduction to Many-Body Physics*, Cambridge University Press (2015).

(37) The material on electroweak theory is also standard in particle physics. The books listed under General References have more advanced discussions of this topic.

Lecture 20

(38) Discrete symmetries and the CPT theorem are discussed in books on quantum field theory listed under General References.

(39) I. Bigi and A. Sanda, *CP Violation*, Cambridge University Press (1999).

(40) Updated information on CP-violation, including different parametrizations of the CKM matrix and experimentally measured values, can be found from the Particle Data Group. For their recent survey, see K.A. Olive *et al* (PDG), Chin. Phys. **C38**, 090001 (2014) (http://pdg.lbl.gov)

(41) The observation that there is baryon number violation in the Standard Model via weak instantons is due to G. 't Hooft, Phys. Rev. Lett. **37**, 8 (1976); For reviews of attempts to apply this to explain the baryon asymmetry of the universe, see M. Trodden, Rev. Mod. Phys. **71** (5), 1463 (1998) [arXiv:hep-ph/9803479]; M. Dine and A. Kusenko, Rev. Mod. Phys. **76**, 1 (2003) [arXiv:hep-ph/0303065].

(42) The Sakharov criteria for baryogenesis were first enunciated in A.D. Sakharov, Pisma. Zh. Eksp. Theor. Fiz. **5**, 32 (1967)[JETP Lett. **5**, 24 (1967)].

(43) Baryogenesis, including possibilities within a grand unified theory, is reviewed in J.M. Cline, *Baryogenesis*, Lectures at the 2006 Les Houches Summer School in Particle Physics and Cosmology: The Fabric of Spacetime, arXiv:hep-ph/0609145.

Lecture 21

(44) Updates on the experimental front regarding neutrino masses and mixing can be obtained from the Particle Data Group, http://pdg.lbl.gov.

(45) Solar models and the neutrino problem are reviewed in J.N. Bahcall and M.H. Pinsonneault, Rev. Mod. Phys. **64**, 885 (1992).

(46) Theoretical aspects of neutrino masses and mixing, including the see-saw mechanism are reviewed in R.N. Mohapatra *et al*, Rep. Prog. Phys. **70**, 1757 (2007); S.F. King *et al*, New Journal of Physics **16**, 045018 (2014).

(47) The Peccei-Quinn symmetry is introduced in R.D. Peccei and H.R. Quinn, Phys. Rev. **D16**, 1791 (1977). Axions as a consequence of the spontaneous breaking of the PQ symmetry was first pointed out in S. Weinberg, Phys. Rev. Lett. **40**, 223 (1978); F. Wilczek, Phys. Rev. Lett. **40**, 279 (1978). For a review of more general axion scenarios and the experimental searches, see J.E. Kim and G. Carosi, Rev. Mod. Phys. **82**, 557 (2010). The Particle Data Group also has updates on the searches.

(48) For an overview of models of quarks and leptons as composite parti-

cles, see C.S. Kalman and I.A. D'Souza, *Preons: Models of Leptons, Quarks and Gauge Bosons as Composite Objects*, World Scientific (1992).

(49) Grand unification has been an extremely popular idea, although we have not gone into details of this scenario. In addition to proton decay and the circle of ideas related to it, grand unification also brings in issues of mass hierarchy and the question of understanding the pattern of masses and mixing angles. For general discussions of grand unified theories, beyond the particle physics books mentioned under General References, see R.N. Mohapatra, *Unification and Supersymmetry: The Frontiers of Quark-Lepton Physics*, Springer-Verlag New York Inc. (2003); G. Ross, *Grand Unified Theories*, Westview Press (2003).

(50) Much of cosmology has also become standard textbook material, see Weinberg's book listed in Lecture 10 and also S. Weinberg, *Cosmology*, Oxford University Press (2008); S. Dodelson, *Modern Cosmology*, Academic Press (2003).

(51) Dark matter is discussed in most books on cosmology and astrophysics, including the ones listed above. See also the recent reviews: M. Bartelmann, Rev. Mod. Phys. **82**, 331 (2010) [arXiv:0906.5036]; M. Lisanti, *Lectures on Dark Matter Physics*, Lectures at the Theoretical Advanced Study Institute 2015 [arXiv:1603.03797].

(52) For axions as a candidate for dark matter, see the recent review L.D. Duffy and K. van Bibber, New Journal of Physics **11**, 105008 (2009).

(53) For supersymmetric particles as candidates for dark matter, see the review G. Jungman, M. Kamionkowski and K. Griest, Physics Reports **267**, 195 (1996).

(54) In addition to Weinberg's book on cosmology, different aspects of the cosmological constant are reviewed in S. Weinberg, Rev. Mod. Phys. **61**, 1 (1988); S.M. Carroll, Liv. Rev. in Rel. **4**, 1 (2001); P.J.E. Peebles and B. Ratra, Rev. Mod. Phys. **75**(2), 559 (2003).

(55) The original announcements of the discovery of the accelerated expansion are A. Riess *et al*, The Astronomical Jour. **116**, 1009 (1998); S. Perlmutter *et al*, Astrophys. Jour. **517**(2), 565 (1999). For recent analyses of cosmological data, see also M. Tegmark *et al*, Phys. Rev. **D69**, 103501 (2004)[arXiv:astro-ph/0310723]; C. Patrignani *et al* (PDG), Chin. Phys. **C40**, 100001 (2016).

(56) Some of the subtleties in interpreting type IA supernova data in terms of accelerated expansion of the universe should be clear from J.T. Nielsen, A. Guffanti and S. Sarkar, Nature Sci. Rep. **6** :35596 (2016); H.I. Ringermacher and L.R. Mead, arXiv:1611.00999 [astro-ph.CO].

(57) General discussions of black holes and the Hawking evaporation process can be found in most books on gravity, see books in Lecture 10 and R.M. Wald, *Quantum Field Theory in Curved Space-time and Black Hole Thermodynamics*, University of Chicago Press (1994); R.B. Mann, *Black Holes: Thermodynamics, Information, and Firewalls*, Springer International Publishing (2015). A concise review is D.N. Page, New Journ. of Phys. **7**, 203 (2005).

(58) The microscopic counting of states for supersymmetric black hole solutions in string theory and the agreement with the Bekenstein-Hawking formula is due to A. Strominger and C. Vafa, Phys. Lett. **B379**, 99 (1996). There have been a large number of papers elaborating on this as well.

(59) There are many books on supersymmetry as well as a large number of review articles. A small useful list is: S.J. Gates, Jr., M.T. Grisaru, M. Rocek and W. Siegel, *Supersymmetry or one thousand and one lessons in supersymmetry*, Addison-Wesley (1983); available as arXiv:hep-th/0108200; J. Wess and J. Bagger, *Supersymmetry and Supergravity*, Princeton University Press (1992); M. Dine, *Supersymmetry and string theory: Beyond the Standard Model*, Cambridge University Press (2007).

(60) The difficulties of field theories with particles of higher spin are discussed in many papers; the specific theorem which was mentioned is in K.M. Case and S.G. Gasiorowicz, Phys. Rev. **125**, 1055 (1962); S. Weinberg and E. Witten, Phys. Lett. **B96**, 59 (1980).

(61) For string theory, the standard references include the book by Green, Schwarz and Witten and the one by Polchinski, listed under Lecture 12. Other books include the one by Dine listed above and K. Becker, M. Becker and J.H. Schwarz, *String theory and M-theory: A modern introduction*, Cambridge University Press (2007).

(62) The original reference on the AdS/CFT correspondence is J. Maldacena, Adv. Theor. Math. Phys. **2**, 231 (1998), arXiv:hep-th/9711200. The correspondence and its ramifications are elaborated on in a large number of papers. For recent reviews, see J. Mal-

dacena, *TASI 2003 Lectures on AdS/CFT*, arXiv:hep-th/0309246; H. Nastase, *Introduction to the AdS/CFT correspondence*, Cambridge University Press (2015); M. Natsuume, *AdS/CFT Duality User Guide*, Lecture Notes in Physics 9150, Springer Japan (2015); L. Susskind and J. Lindesay, *An introduction to black holes, information and the string theory revolution: The holographic universe*, World Scientific (2005).

(63) For a review of loop quantum gravity, see the article by A. Ashtekar, http://www.scholarpedia.org/article/Ashtekar_variables;   A. Ashtekar and J. Lewandowski, Class. Quant. Grav. **21**, R53-R152 (2004); R. Gambini and J. Pullin, *A First Course in Loop Quantum Gravity*, Oxford University Press (2012); C. Rovelli and F. Vidotto, *Covariant loop quantum gravity*, Cambridge University Press (2014).

(64) For noncommutative geometry and gravity, see A. Connes, *Noncommutative geometry*, Academic Press (1994); J. Madore, *An Introduction to Noncommutative Differential Geometry and its Physical Applications*, Cambridge University Press (1995); G. Landi, *An Introduction to Noncommutative Spaces and Their Geometries*, Lecture Notes in Physics Monographs (Book 51), Springer (1997); A. Schenkel, *Noncommutative gravity and quantum field theory on noncommutative curved spacetimes*, arXiv:1210.1115[math-ph]. Among other references relevant to gravity are D. Kastler, Commun. Math. Phys. **166**, 633 (1995); A. Connes, Commun. Math. Phys. **182**, 155 (1996); A.H. Chamseddine and A. Connes, Phys. Rev. Lett. **77**, 4868 (1996); A.H. Chamseddine, Commun. Math. Phys. **186**, 731 (1997).

Index

CPSIA information can be obtained
at www.ICGtesting.com
Printed in the USA
JSHW041131120721
16801JS00001B/63